THINKLERS! 2

MORE Brain Ticklers

Kevin Brougher

ORTING, WASHINGTON USA

THINKLERS!²

MORE Brain Ticklers

Printed in the United States of America
ISBN# 0-9703729-7-3

Note to Teachers:

- Teachers may duplicate pages for classroom use.
- We ask that each individual teacher purchase his or her own copy of the book.
- Schools & teachers may call for group discounts on book purchases.
- Please make reference to the book when using a page with your students.

Thank you!

Other Publications from Missing Piece Press:

Thinklers: A Collection of Brain Ticklers!
State Debate: 50 Unique Playing Cards and 50 Games for Learning about the States!
Number Wonders: A Collection of Amazing Number Facts!
Dreams, Scream, & JellyBeans: Poems for All Ages
The Storybook: A novel for ages 10 on up
Ways to Play with Words: A Collection of Word Games and Activities

Missing Piece Press is publisher of educational books and games. Our goal is produce products that fill the user with a sense of fun, wonder, and intrigue.

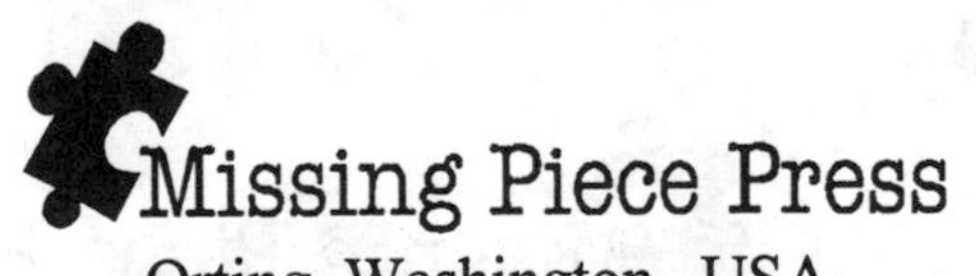

Orting, Washington USA
Toll Free 1-877-56 THINK
MissingPiecePress.com

INTRODUCTION

As with the first Thinklers! book, Thinklers!^{2} is designed to get those brain muscles working in a FUN, and possibly new, way. You will find more Position Puzzles and ***4*** NEW chapters that will keep you, your kids, your classroom, your staff, or your family entertained and challenged for hours on end!

As mentioned in the first Thinklers! book, the mental processes used to figure the puzzles and riddles found in the book have many educational benefits. Though not directly tested on state assessments, developing thinking skills in any form or way directly helps with ANY test or challenge that one may encounter in life.

We sincerely hope that the book is used and enjoyed for years to come.

Missing Piece Press
2006

CONTENTS

POSITION PUZZLES

These types of puzzles have enticed minds for years. You might have come across them as "Wacky Wordies," "Word Rebuses," "Punzzles," or some other name. I have called them POSITION PUZZLES because, for the most part, figuring them out requires that you look at the position of the words. The puzzles are words, letters, numbers, lines, and symbols that represent familiar words, items, places, sayings, movies, etc. For instance:

is the POSITION PUZZLE for "Long Underwear"! Some will come easy. Some will be extremely challenging.

Note: For each of the following pages, the boxes are numbered as follows:

1.	2.	3.
4.	5.	6.
7.	8.	9.
10.	11.	12.

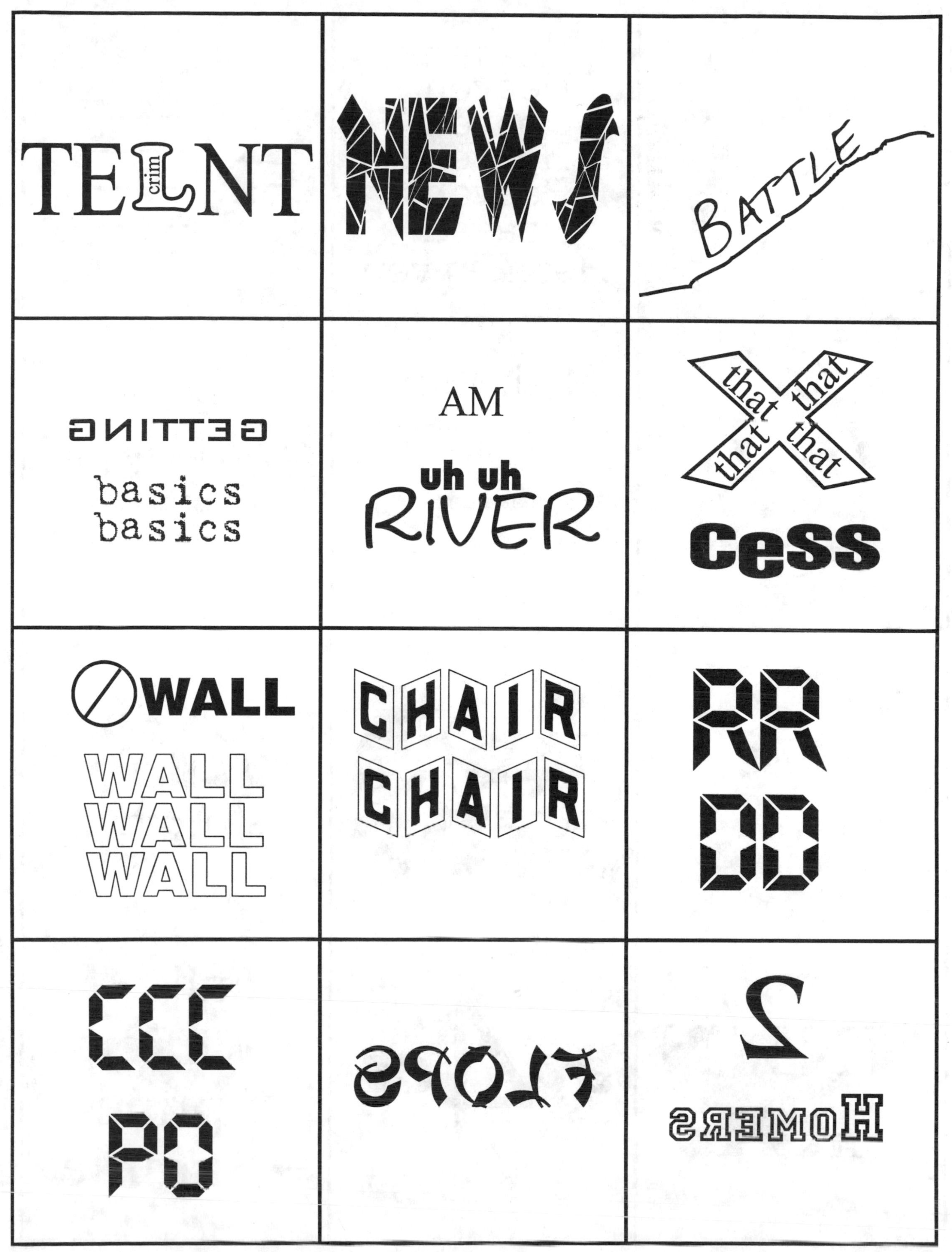
TELNT
crim
NEWS
BATTLE
GETTING
basics
basics
AM
uh uh
RIVER
that
that
that
that
Cess
WALL
WALL
WALL
WALL
CHAIR
CHAIR
RR
DD
CCC
PO
FLOPS
2
HOMERS

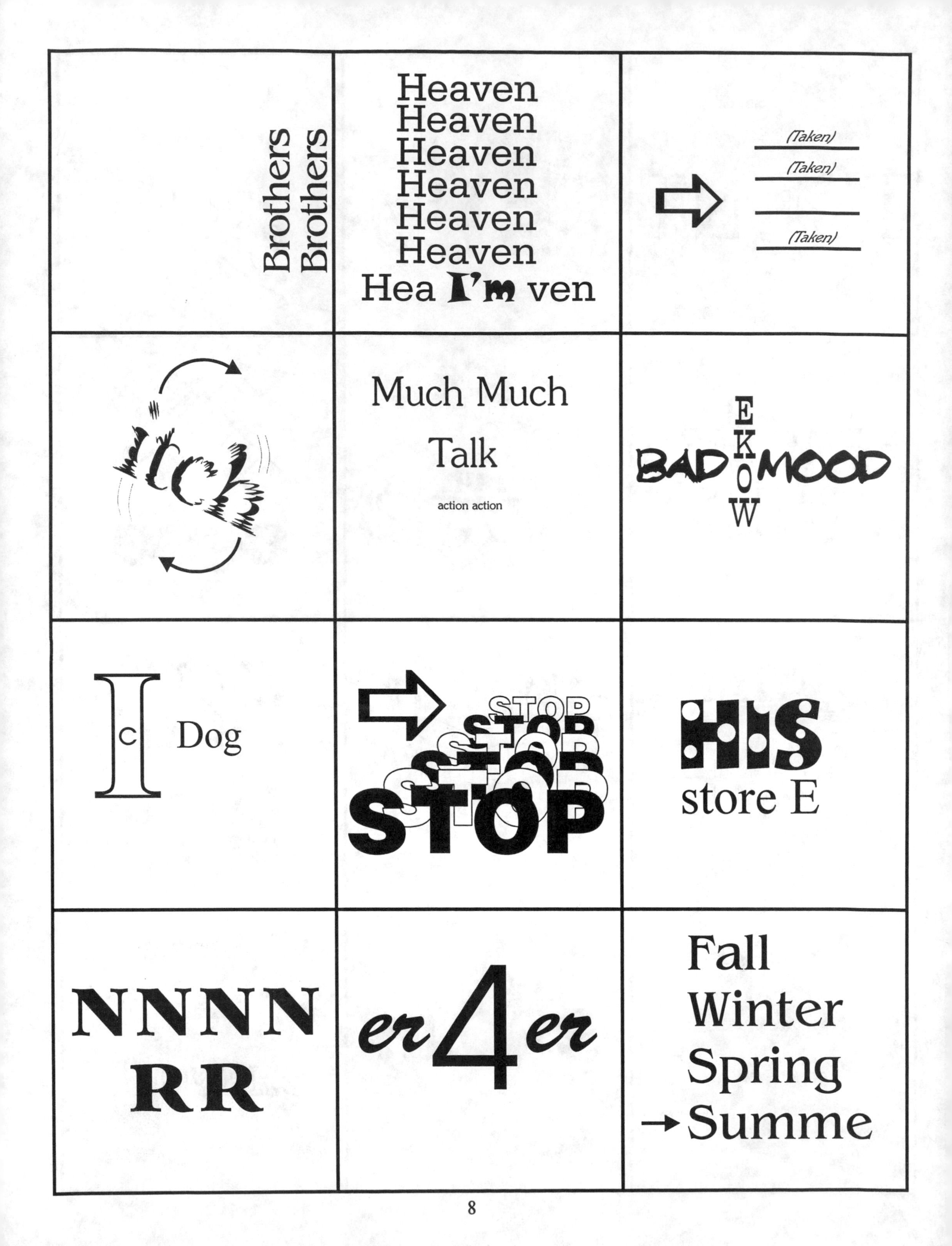

Brothers Brothers
Heaven
Heaven
Heaven
Heaven
Heaven
Heaven
Hea I'm ven
(Taken)
(Taken)
(Taken)
Much Much
Talk
action action
BAD KEEW MOOD
C Dog
STOP
HIS
store E
NNNN
RR
er 4 er
Fall
Winter
Spring
Summe

"ER"
tray
ding
IrollingL
IrollingL
IrollingL
SHA cry ME
Sleeve
Sle eca eve
C
BIS
TR HID AY
SURE
TURN YOUR LIFE
DIN chick NER
PA awalk RK
Splitting
LAUGHTER
LAUGHTER side
strength
R

HOME HOME	1. Home ☞ 2. Home 3. Home	I CAB N the would wood
woodcabinwould	CABINLAKE	BR bost UINS
____ cadet	40	TO RN
TAN ____ ____	ST magazine YLE	M ТТ R State

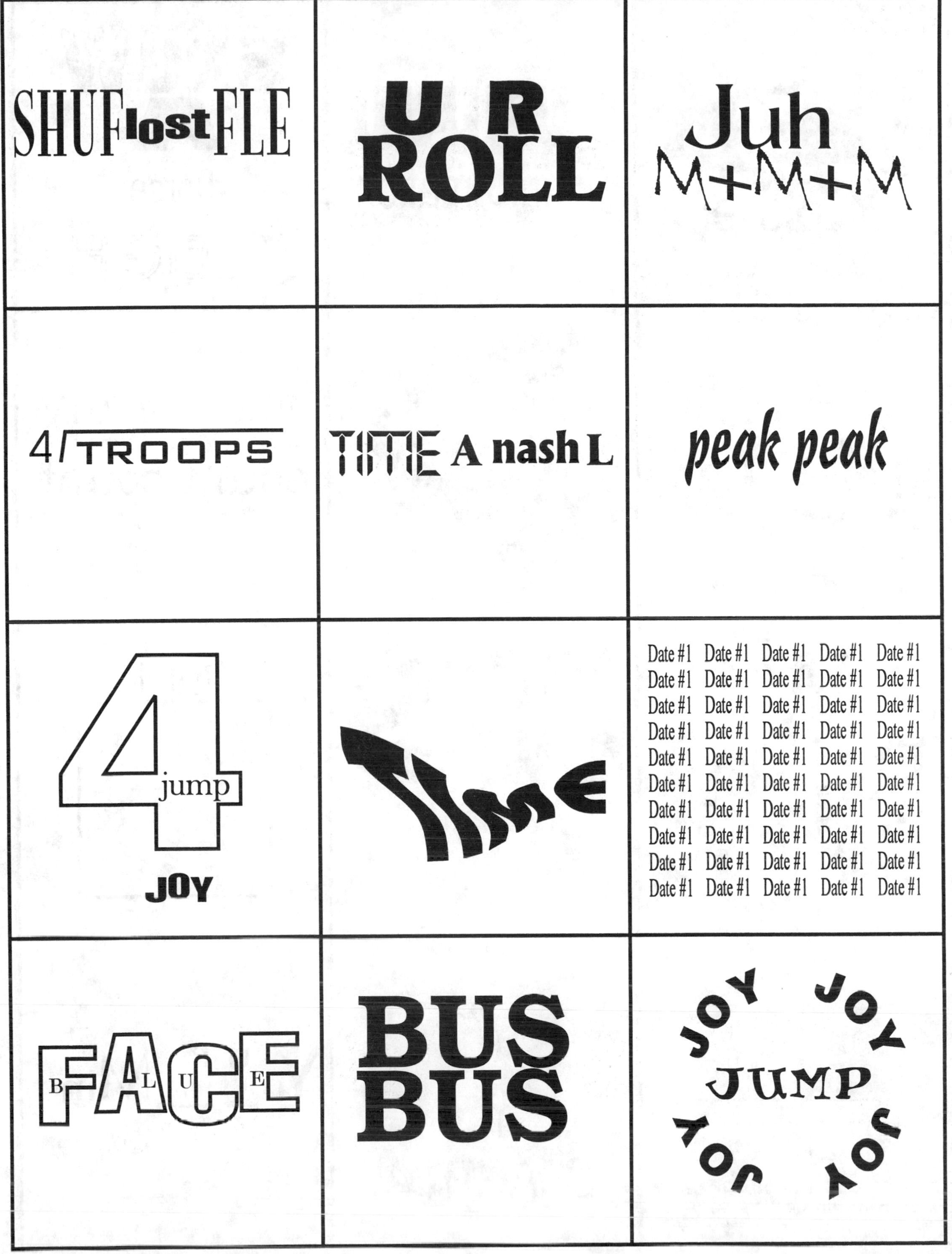
SHUF lost FLE
U R
ROLL
Juh
M+M+M
4/TROOPS
TIME A nash L
peak peak
4 jump
JOY
TIME
Date #1 Date #1 Date #1 Date #1 Date #1
Date #1 Date #1 Date #1 Date #1 Date #1
Date #1 Date #1 Date #1 Date #1 Date #1
Date #1 Date #1 Date #1 Date #1 Date #1
Date #1 Date #1 Date #1 Date #1 Date #1
Date #1 Date #1 Date #1 Date #1 Date #1
Date #1 Date #1 Date #1 Date #1 Date #1
Date #1 Date #1 Date #1 Date #1 Date #1
Date #1 Date #1 Date #1 Date #1 Date #1
Date #1 Date #1 Date #1 Date #1 Date #1
FACE
B L U E
BUS
BUS
JOY JOY JOY JOY
JUMP
JOY JOY

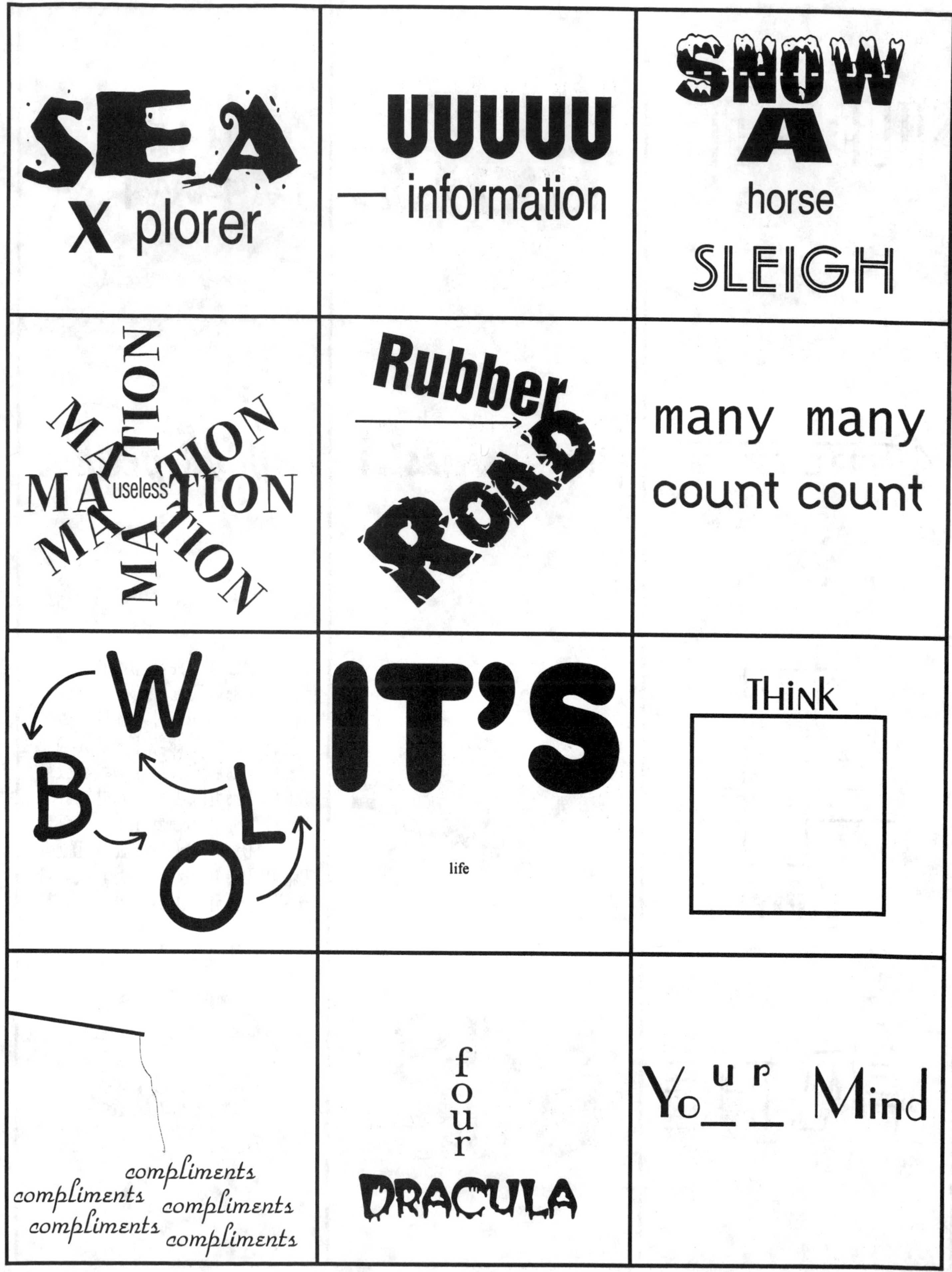
SEA
X plorer
UUUUU
— information
SNOW
A
horse
SLEIGH
MATION
MATION
MA useless TION
MATION
MATION
Rubber
ROAD
many many
count count
W
B
L
O
IT'S
life
THINK
compliments
compliments
compliments
compliments
compliments
four
DRACULA
Yo_ _ Mind
u r

Froy
slDip
UUUUU
COM
¢¢¢
weigh
go go
Searching
Searching
FR
bid
bid
bid
bid
UIT
Mo SET Shun
U
B
me me
-10°
SHOULDER
ECO
+ H
2
O
Places Places
nuhfish
nuhfish

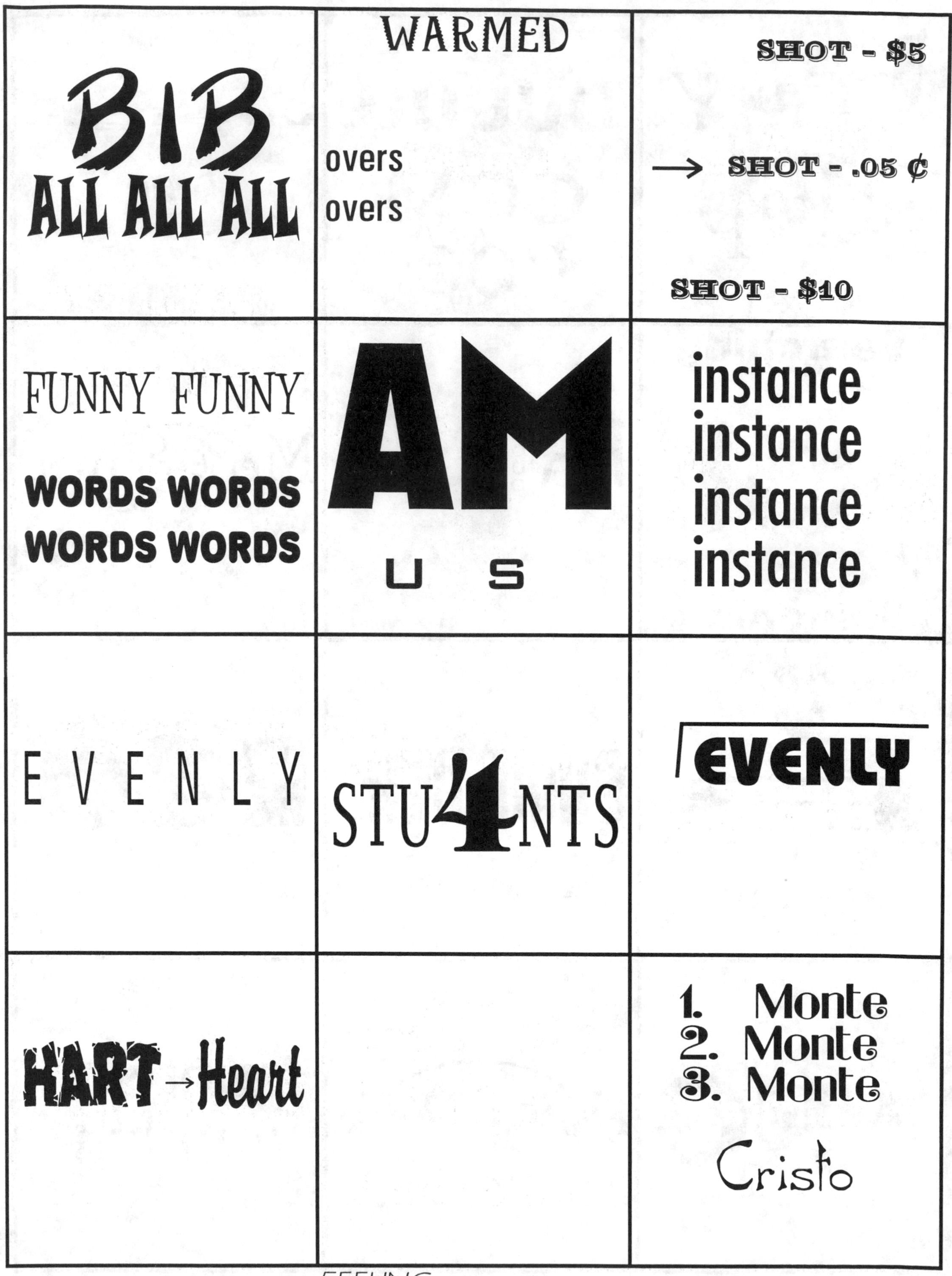
BIB
ALL ALL ALL
WARMED
overs
overs
SHOT - $5
→ SHOT - .05 ¢
SHOT - $10
FUNNY FUNNY
WORDS WORDS
WORDS WORDS
AM
U S
instance
instance
instance
instance
E V E N L Y
STU4NTS
EVENLY
HART → Heart
1. Monte
2. Monte
3. Monte
Cristo

&
GOAL
GO GO
FIRST
✓count
mum
PAYMENT
MARKET
grand grand grand grand grand
grand grand grand grand grand
grand grand grand grand grand
grand grand grand grand grand
C
league
league
many many
C
fish
foot
H ing IS
step
step
FALL
H ing RU | S
footsteps
PUSHED
EDGE
PRICE PRICE
Tie Thai
ERD
Think Think
PRICES

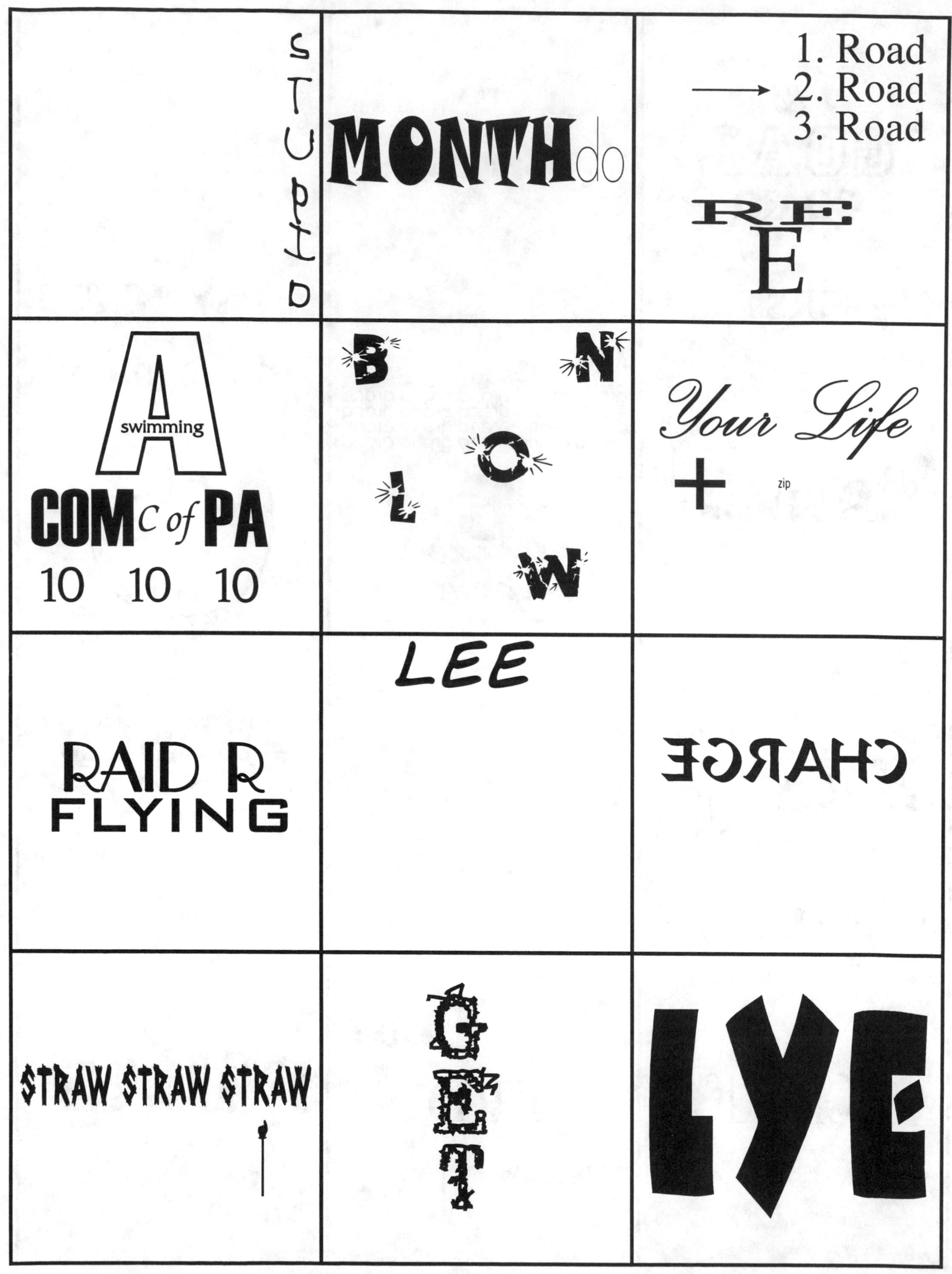
STUPID
MONTHdo
1. Road
2. Road
3. Road
RE
E
A
swimming
COM C of PA
10 10 10
B
N
O
L
W
Your Life
+
zip
RAID R
FLYING
LEE
CHARGE
STRAW STRAW STRAW
G
E
T
LYE

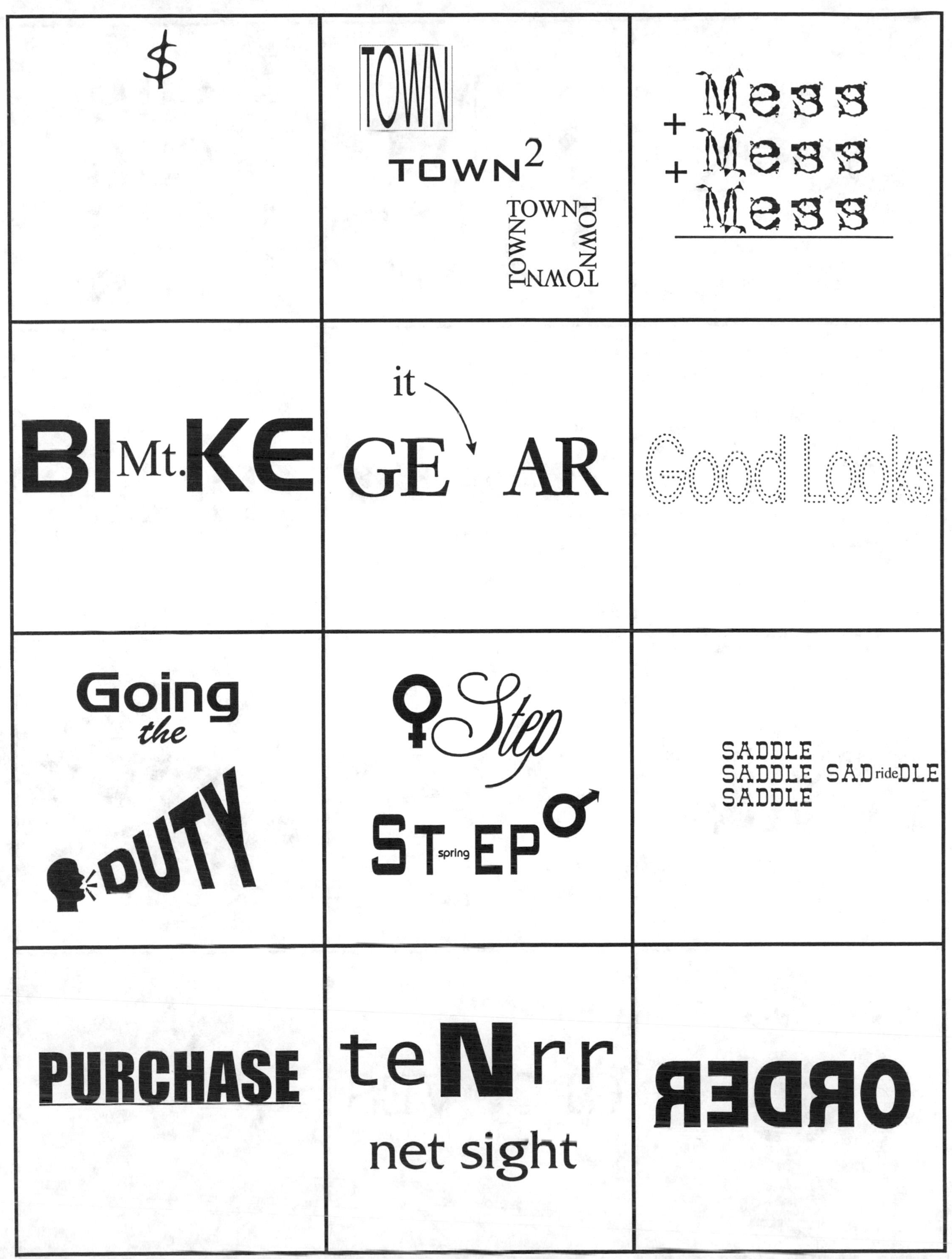
$
TOWN
TOWN2
TOWN TOWN TOWN TOWN
Mess
+ Mess
+ Mess
BI Mt. KE
it
GE AR
Good Looks
Going
the
DUTY
Step
ST spring EP
SADDLE
SADDLE
SADDLE
SADrideDLE
PURCHASE
teNrr
net sight
ORDER

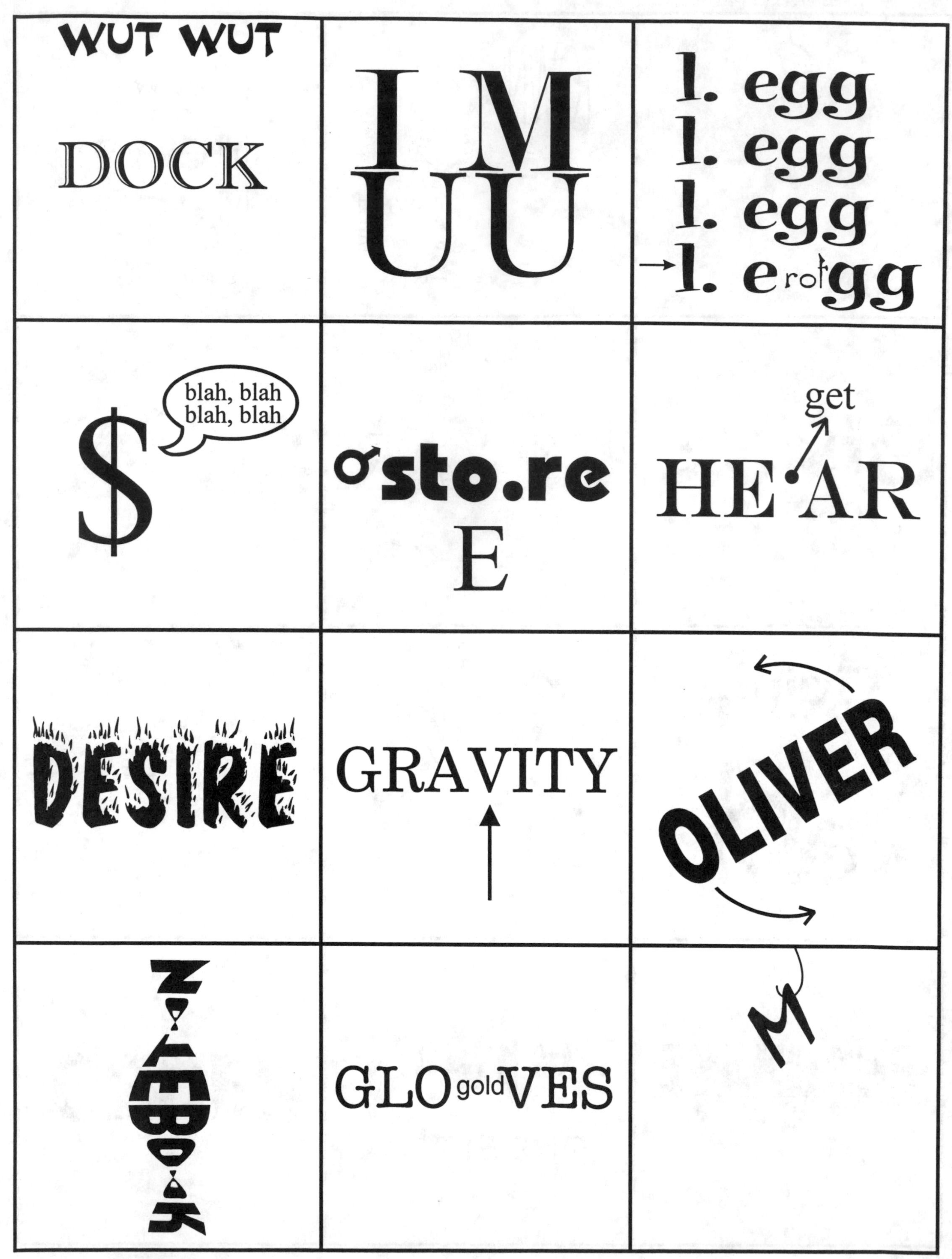
WUT WUT
DOCK
I M
U U
l. egg
l. egg
l. egg
l. e rot gg
blah, blah
blah, blah
$
sto.re
E
get
HEAR
DESIRE
GRAVITY
OLIVER
M
NOTEBOOK
GLO gold VES

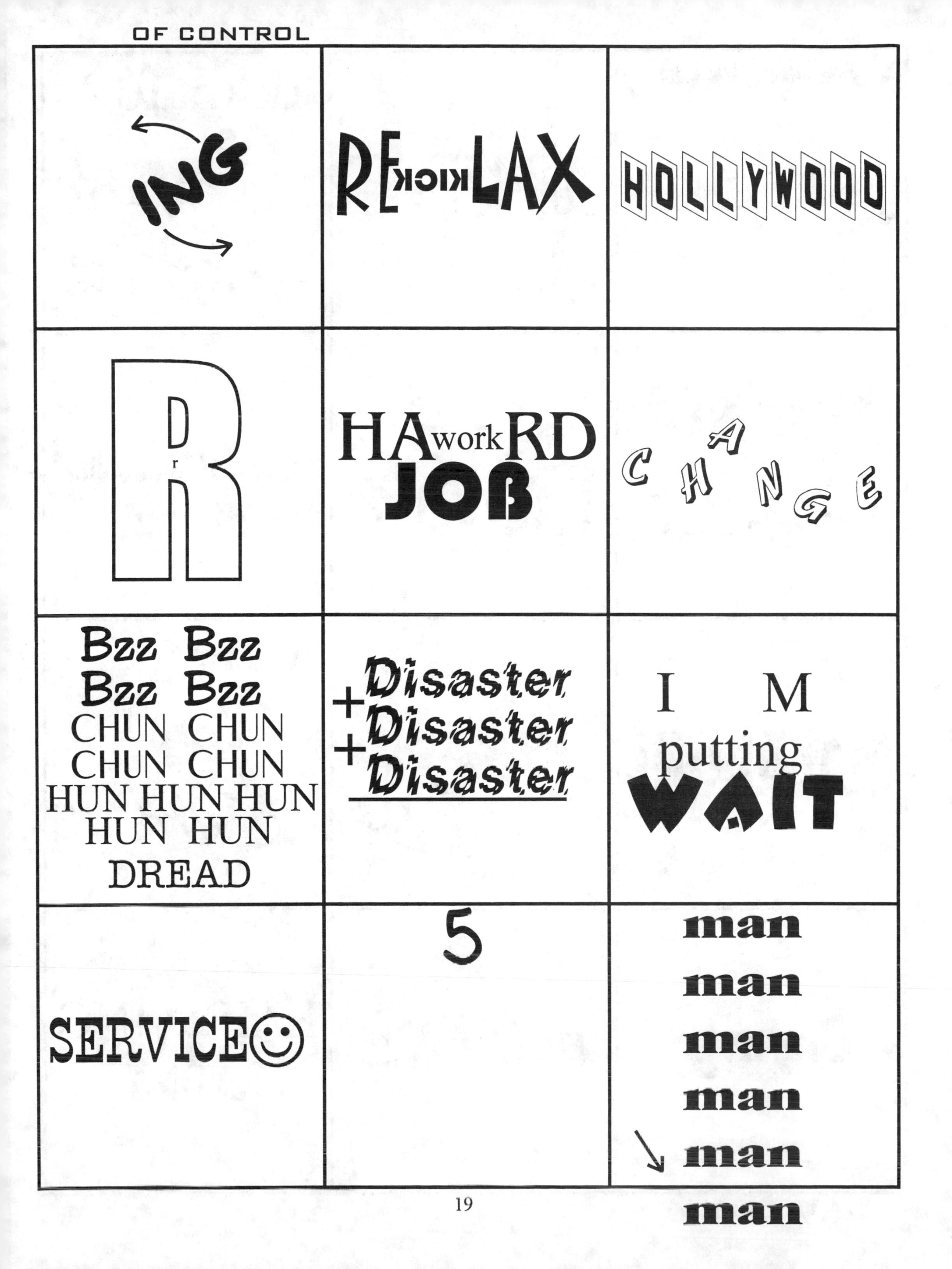
ING
REkickLAX
HOLLYWOOD
R
D
r
HAworkRD
JOB
CHANGE
Bzz Bzz
Bzz Bzz
CHUN CHUN
CHUN CHUN
HUN HUN HUN
HUN HUN
DREAD
Disaster
+Disaster
+Disaster
I M
putting
WAIT
SERVICE☺
5
man
man
man
man
man
man

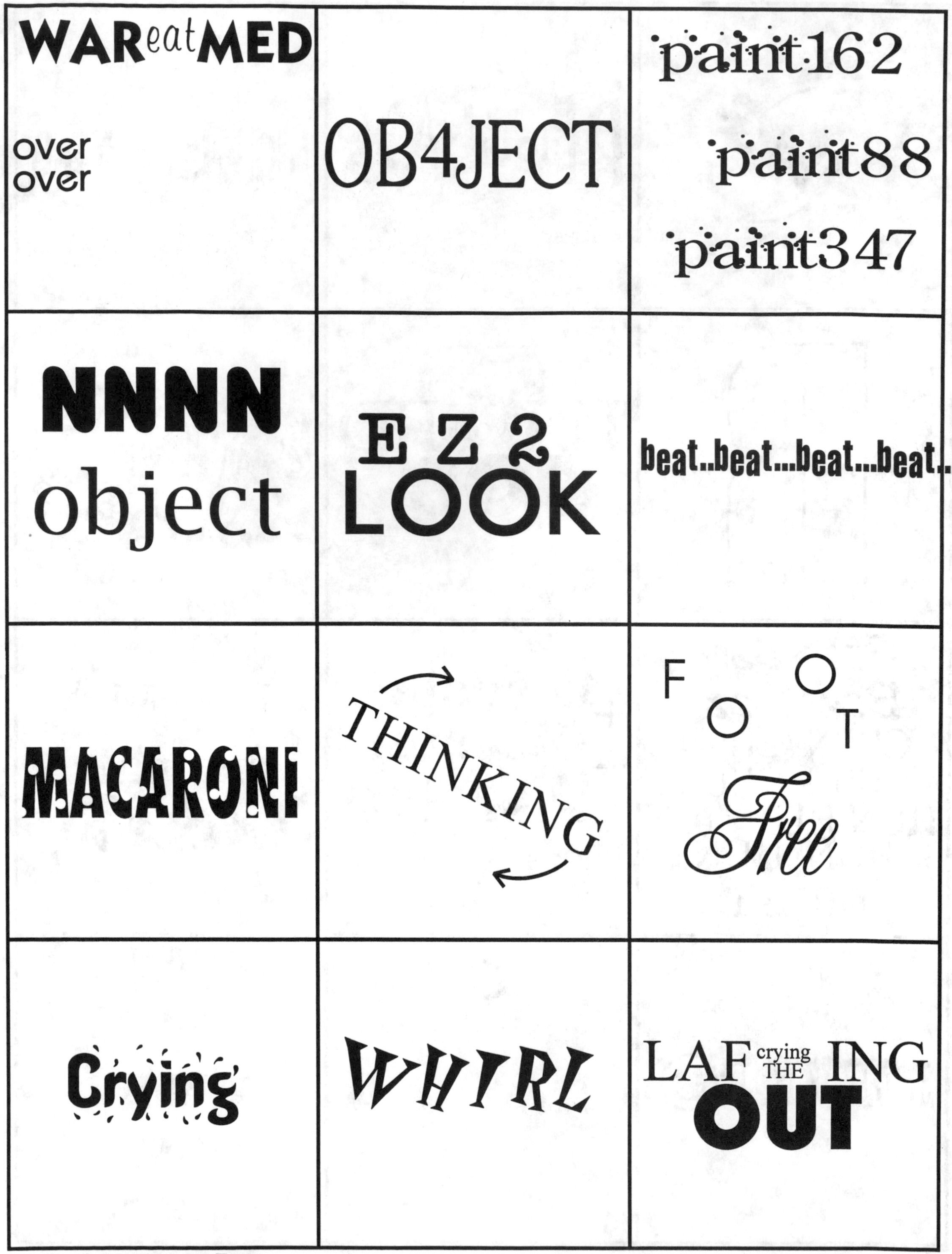
WAR eat MED
over
over
OB4JECT
paint162
paint88
paint347
NNNN
object
EZ2
LOOK
beat..beat...beat...beat...
MACARONI
THINKING
F O O T
Free
Crying
WHIRL
LAF crying THE ING
OUT
LAUGHING

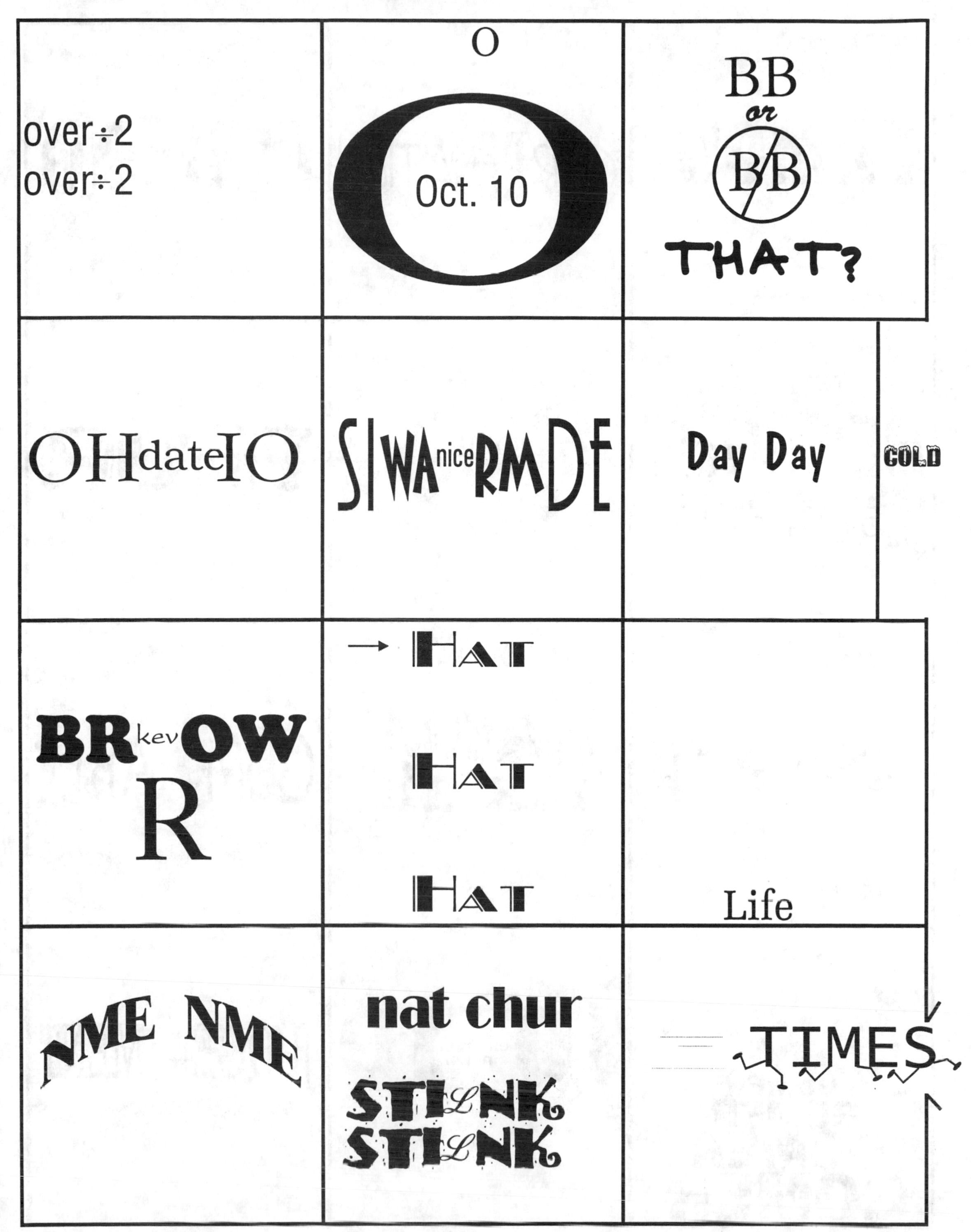
over÷2
over÷2
O
Oct. 10
BB
or
B/B
THAT?
OHdateIO
SIWAniceRMDE
Day Day
GOLD
BRkevOW
R
→ HAT
HAT
HAT
Life
NME NME
nat chur
STILNK
STILNK
TIMES

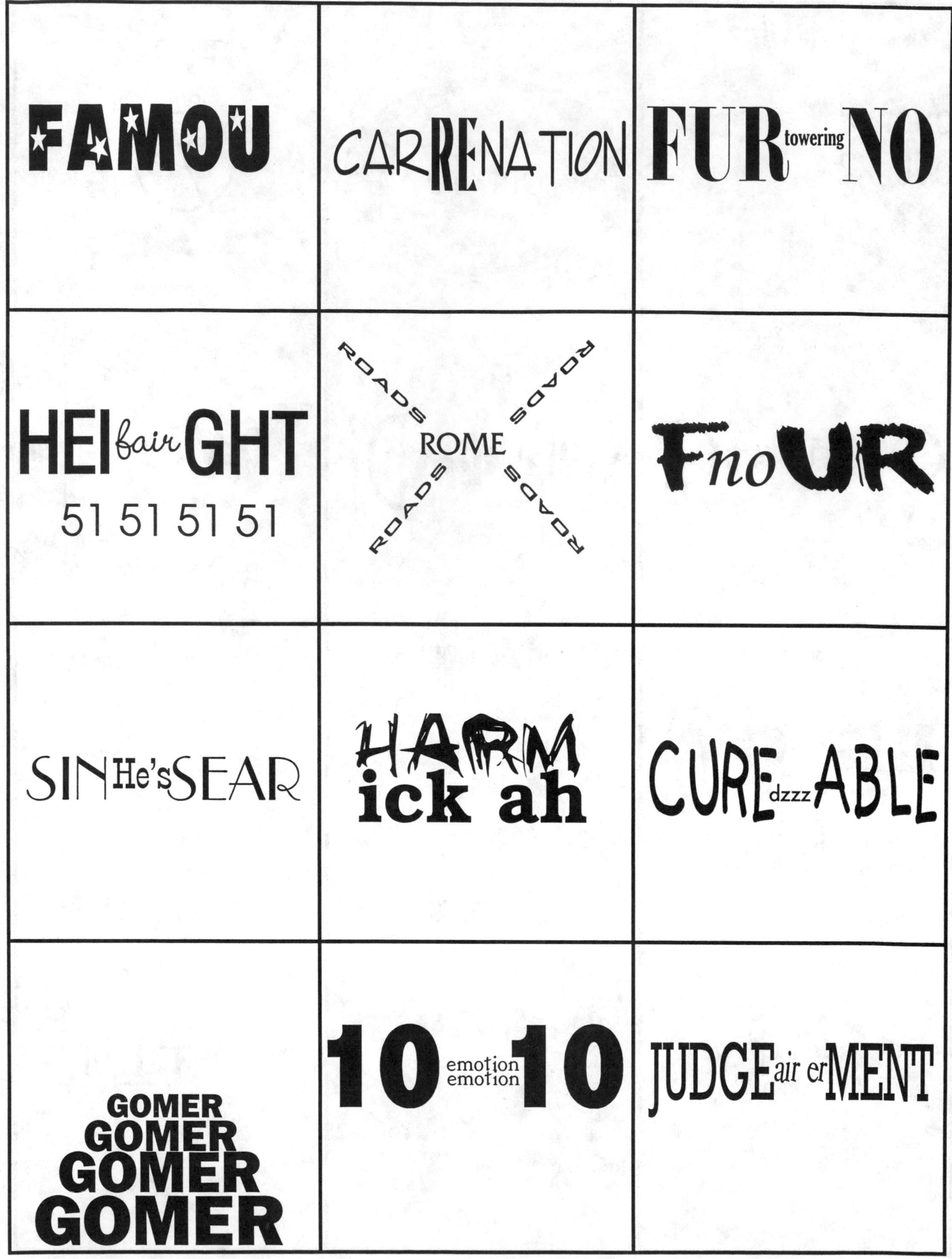
FAMOU
CARRENATION
FUR towering NO
HEI fair GHT
51 51 51 51
ROADS
ROADS
ROME
ROADS
ROADS
F no UR
SIN He's SEAR
HARM
ick ah
CURE dzzz ABLE
GOMER
GOMER
GOMER
GOMER
10 emotion emotion 10
JUDGE air er MENT

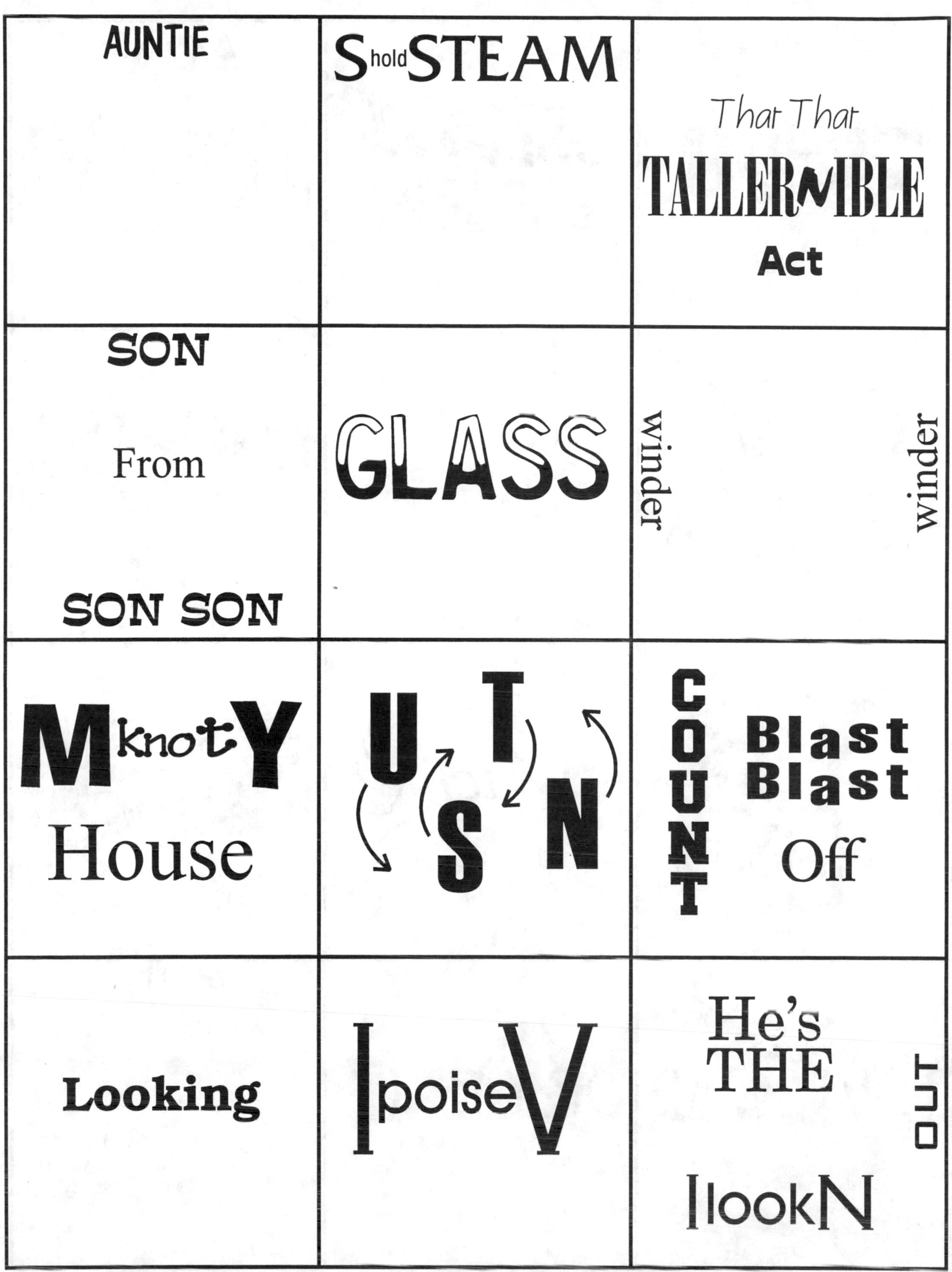

AUNTIE
S hold STEAM
That That
TALLERNIBLE
Act
SON
From
SON SON
GLASS
winder
winder
M knot Y
House
U T S N
COUNT
Blast
Blast
Off
Looking
I poise V
He's
THE
OUT
I look N

HE'S

<table>
<tr><td>STATE
TEtheR
Weigh</td><td>SIGN
BORN</td><td>WHEY
TERTHdriveESTATE</td></tr>
<tr><td>CX
ploration</td><td>SIGH</td><td>COMsteerMIT
E</td></tr>
<tr><td>YR
IN</td><td>→Watch</td><td>FEVER</td></tr>
<tr><td>LOVE WAR</td><td>OR OR O</td><td>GUN</td></tr>
</table>

Part
Part
Part
Part
HARM
E
BARE marry E
HA RM ON Y
Frank Frank
Bean Bean
B D iiiii
SCHOOL Stay URGO Stay
DAGcloakGER
Office
RENT
RENT
RENT
RENT
PEEK
END
UR
LIFE

UH
shun shun shun shun shun
shun shun shun shun shun
skedge
r
U L
FIST
BOARD
BEAR
TH SALE E
CCCCCCC
BALL
ARM
hundred
hundred
hundred
hundred
hundred
TRAVEL
AND
FOURTH
TRUB
dice L dice
KLI kev NE
Look
Look

KCAP	close close comfort comfort comfort comfort	SI DEEP DE
Day Day Day	clean Yourself	Think U speak
DNUORG ✓	uuuuu CEcomNTS	——— probe
PEPPERMINT	XeatingS	IRON

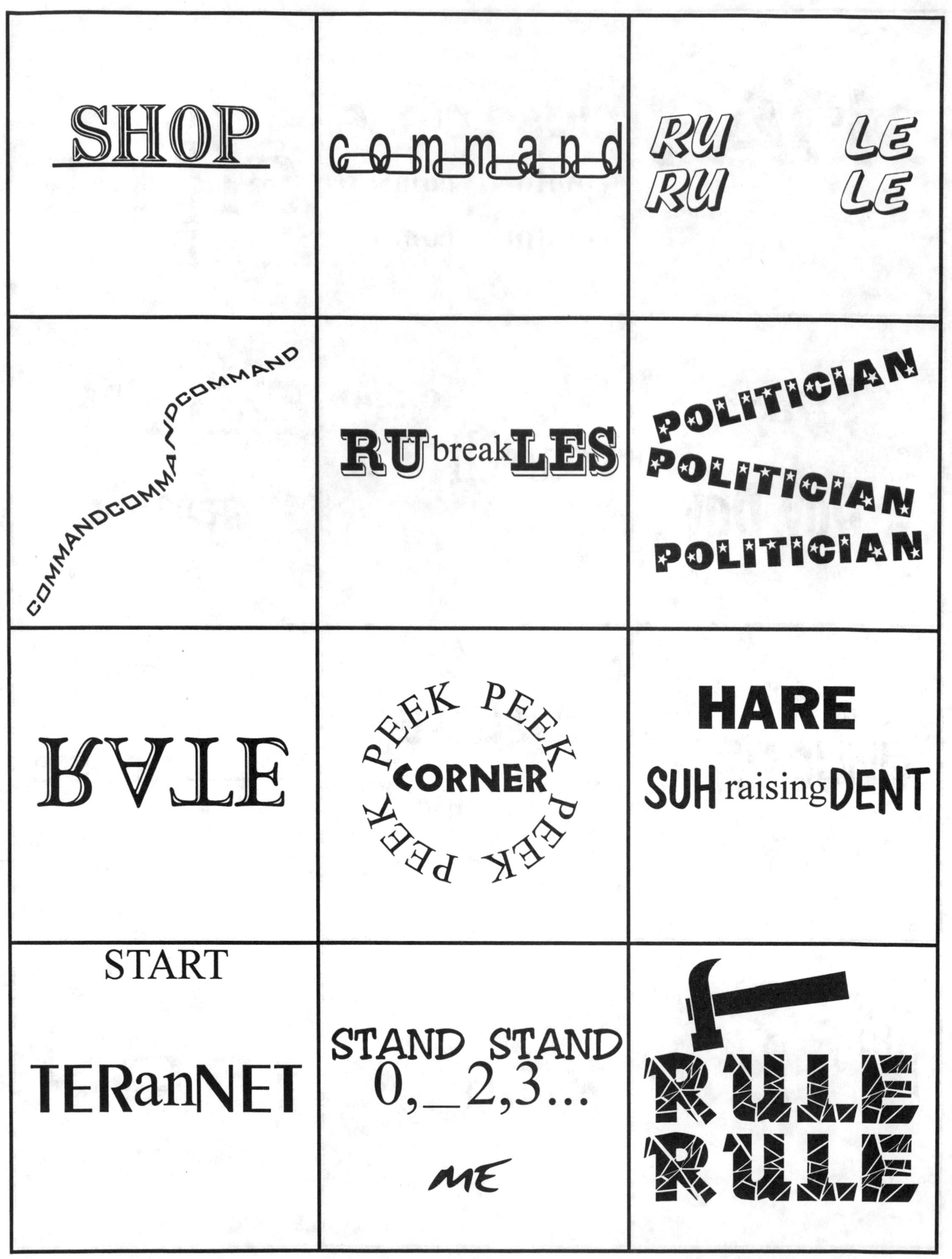

SHOP
command
RU LE
RU LE
COMMANDCOMMANDCOMMAND
RU break LES
POLITICIAN
POLITICIAN
POLITICIAN
PEEK PEEK PEEK PEEK PEEK
CORNER
HARE
SUH raising DENT
START
TERanNET
STAND STAND
0,_2,3...
ME
RULE
RULE

scenery ↓ SCENERY	ROCK CAUGHT HARD PLACE	SEARCH SEARCH
GREAT packTHINGS ages COME GREAT packTHINGS ages COME GREAT packTHINGS ages COME	DEADMANS	GUN GUN
Exposure Exposure	4 MATION LOAD	CRO FACES WD
3ear 5mouth 9leg → 1nose	CHAIMRGE	T.A.B.L.E.

<table>
<tr><td>control
+ control</td><td>Conı'mtrol</td><td>SHUT
&don't talk
SIT</td></tr>
<tr><td>GETGETGETGET</td><td>eyes
Class...
voices</td><td>book
book
page3
page3
plea plea plea</td></tr>
<tr><td>CLA sleeping SS</td><td>WAKE
START
NO take TES</td><td>Your turn Works</td></tr>
<tr><td>minute
minute
minute
minute
minute
TIME</td><td>CARE 1is FULLY</td><td>PAY PENCIL PURR</td></tr>
</table>

GET

AF 4 FAIR AF FAIR	Pull UP the the curb	IN IN IN IN *uh* fair fair
vicious vicious vicious vicious	**over** *Pull* **the curb** **the curb**	☆C ☆C
+ ERY ERY	STRAW THAT ƧJƎMAƆ	GREETINGS GREETINGS
BULL warm PEN	2 0,1,2.......60 ND 2 0,1,2.......60 ND 2 0,1,2.......60 ND	FIRE FIRE FIRE FIRE

2
con
ICEBERG
SHOW
M I L K
MILK
OPEN
OPEN
HURRICANE
MY IM MIND
worry
GAME
thinking I L B thinking I L B
U
WORLD
WORLD
WORLD
I L B
AB think OUT
U

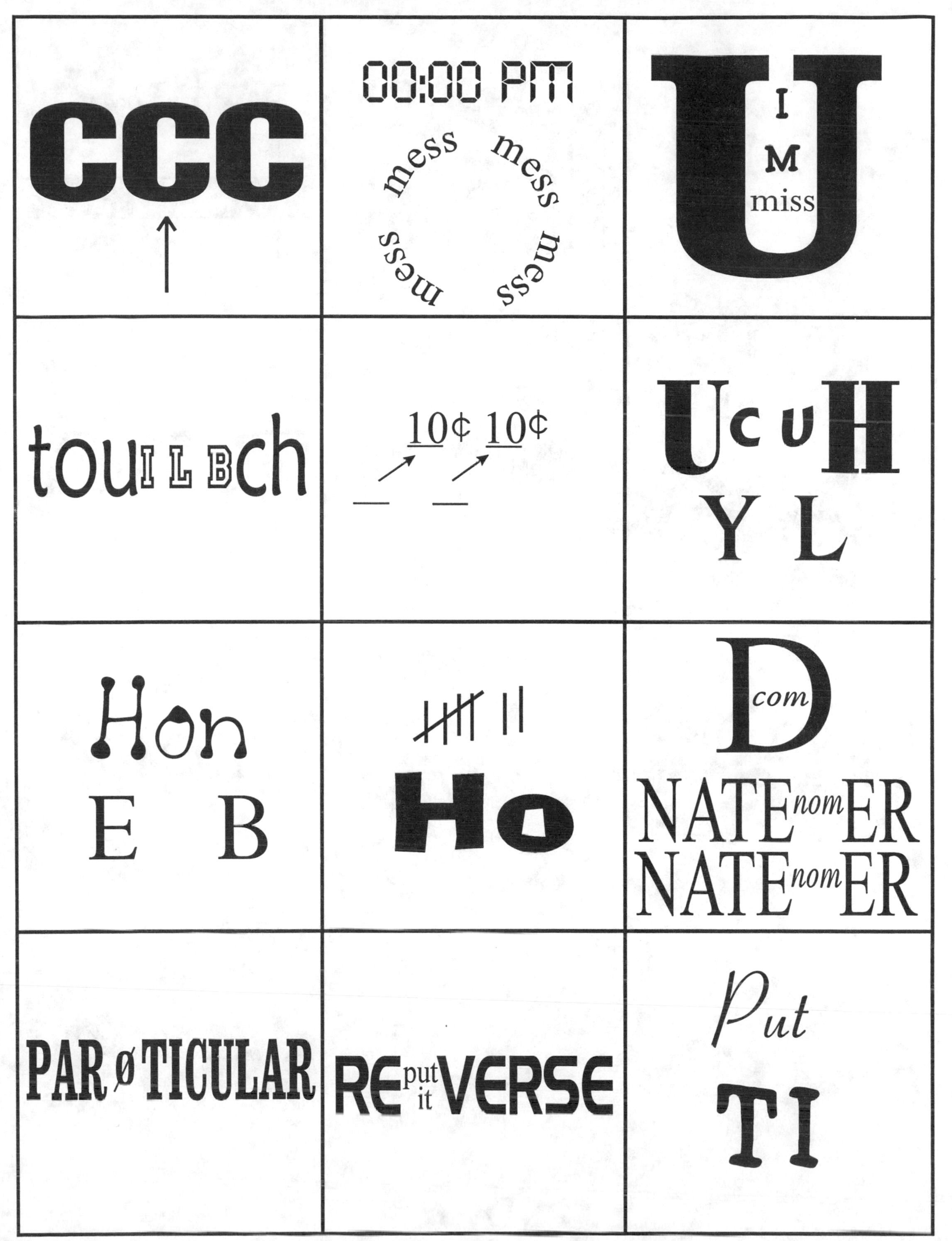
CCC
00:00 PM
mess
mess
mess
mess
U
I
M
miss
touILBch
10¢ 10¢
U c u H
Y L
Hon
E B
Ho
D
com
NATEnomER
NATEnomER
PARøTICULAR
RE put it VERSE
Put
TI

WOwolfOL
MO cry RE
MO RE
MO RE
MO RE
OlivN
DISASTER
U D
zerve
a
BAY
BAY
icARGUMENTic
DAY
winding
LIVING
EDGE
I L GET I L GET
GET I L
it it
Surgery
Ear Ear
dead
SPRING
living
DISASTER

WORD WORD
uu uu
SHOP
Just S
all all all all
D Liv er E
NIGHT
COM PAIL PAR PAIL ISON
MOON
SITTING
SITTING
NI ships ships GHT
SITTING
SIDELINE SIDELINE
CHI editor EF
story
story
story
4 U

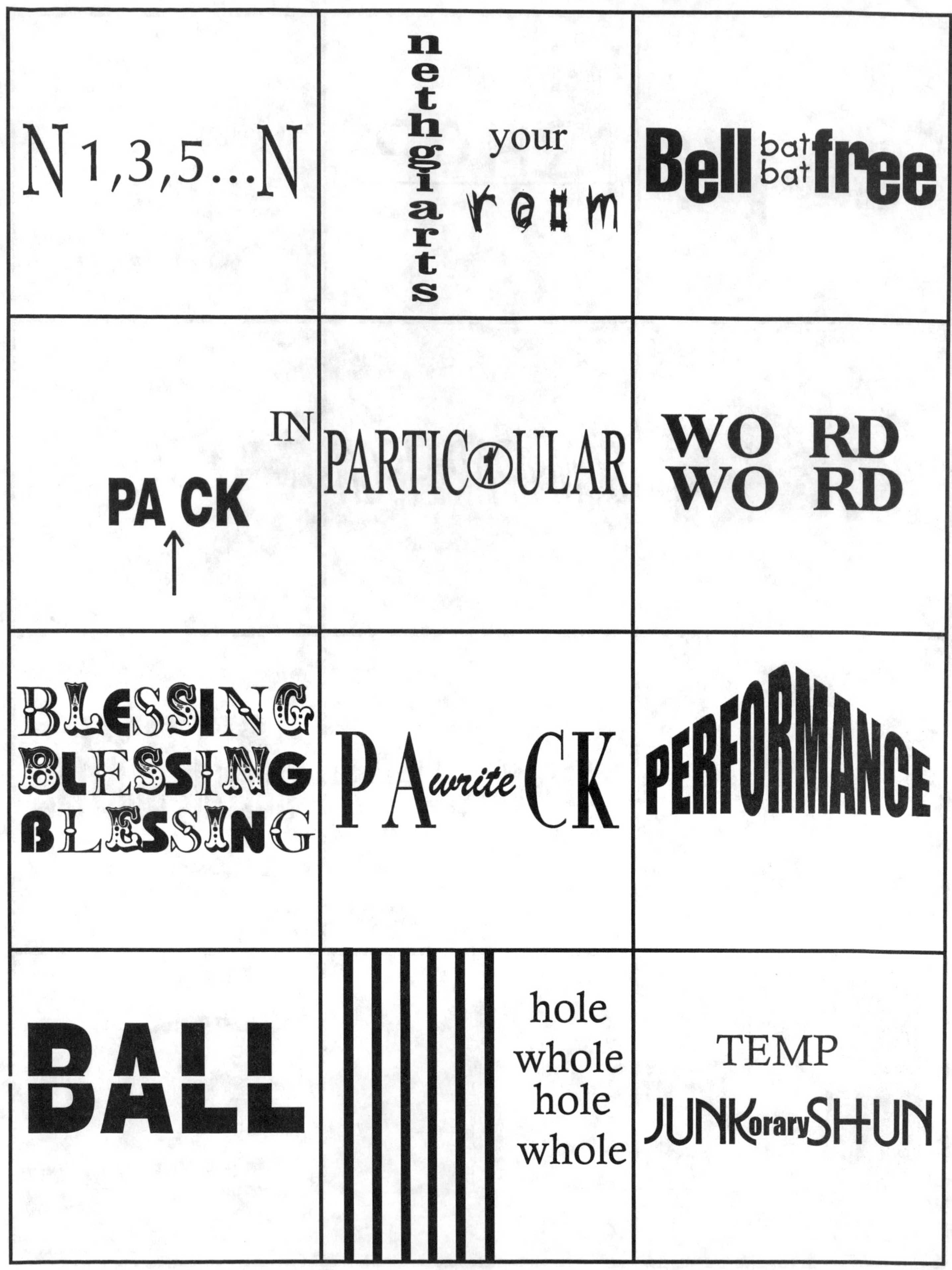
N 1,3,5...N
nethgiarts
your
room
Bell bat bat free
IN
PA CK
PARTICULAR
WO RD
WO RD
BLESSING
BLESSING
BLESSING
PA write CK
PERFORMANCE
BALL
hole
whole
hole
whole
TEMP
JUNKorarySHUN

TAPE
A i+ I i+ R
HE
NOW // RE
GEAR
GEAR
GEAR
plans → PLANS
ORARY
TEMP
STI
CK
Role
BAY
toven
most most most most most
most most most most most
wanted
MENTAL
JOAN
FIE STANDING LD

HE'S

LOOKING
PAST
SAND
SAND
SAND
HOME
WOOD WOOD
GRANDMOTHER GRANDMOTHER
WOOD WOOD
MOUNTAIN
MOUNTAIN
house
GO
BREAT
BUILT
Last Last
THROUGH
the Berry
er
is is is is
is is is is
enough
DRAWN
SCALE SCALE
1,3,5...
WHELMING
BARRIER
BREAKING
BARRIER
YOUR HANDS

COME

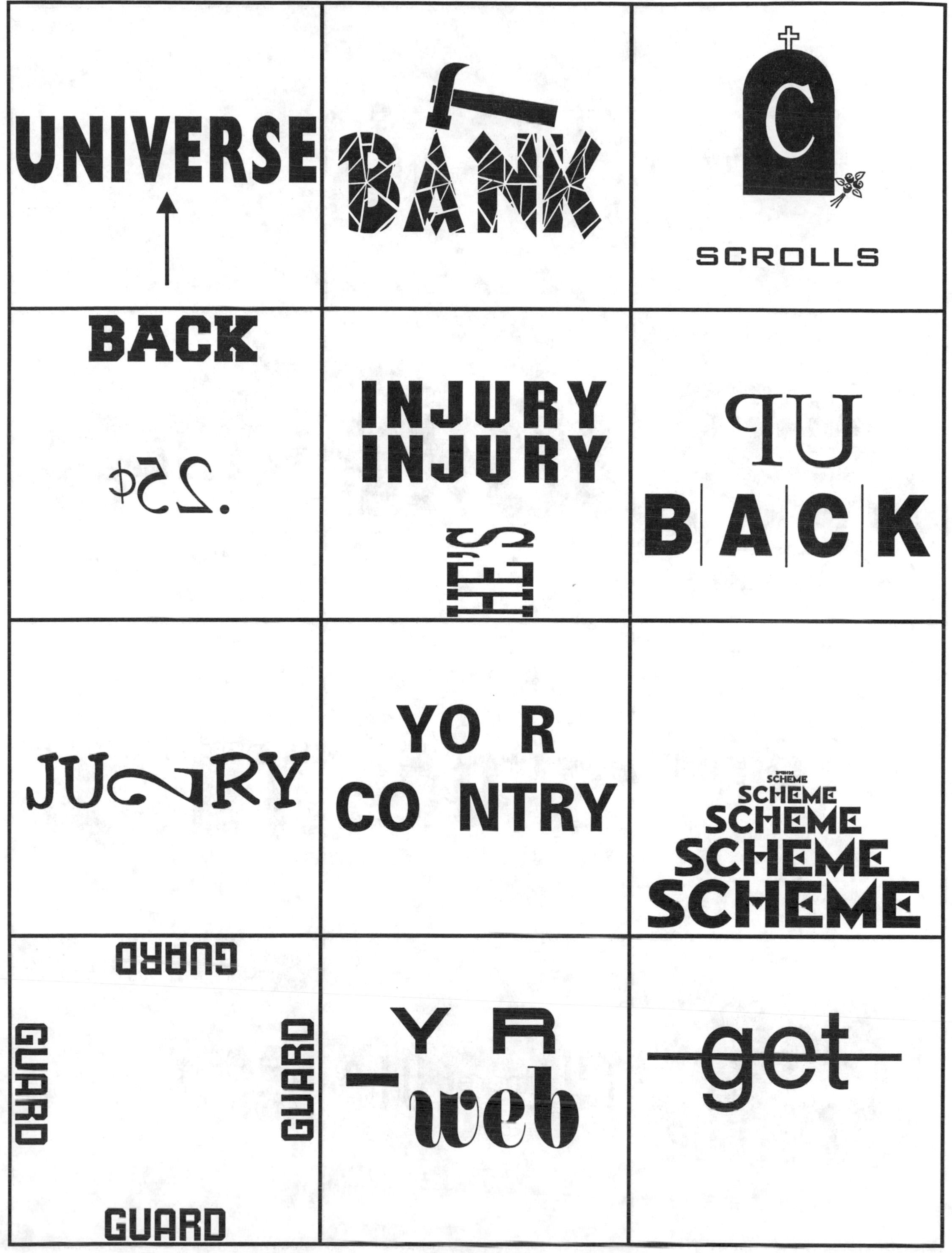

UNIVERSE
BANK
C
SCROLLS
BACK
25¢
INJURY
INJURY
HE'S
UP
BACK
JURY
YO R
CO NTRY
SCHEME
SCHEME
SCHEME
SCHEME
SCHEME
GUARD
GUARD
GUARD
GUARD
Y R
web
get

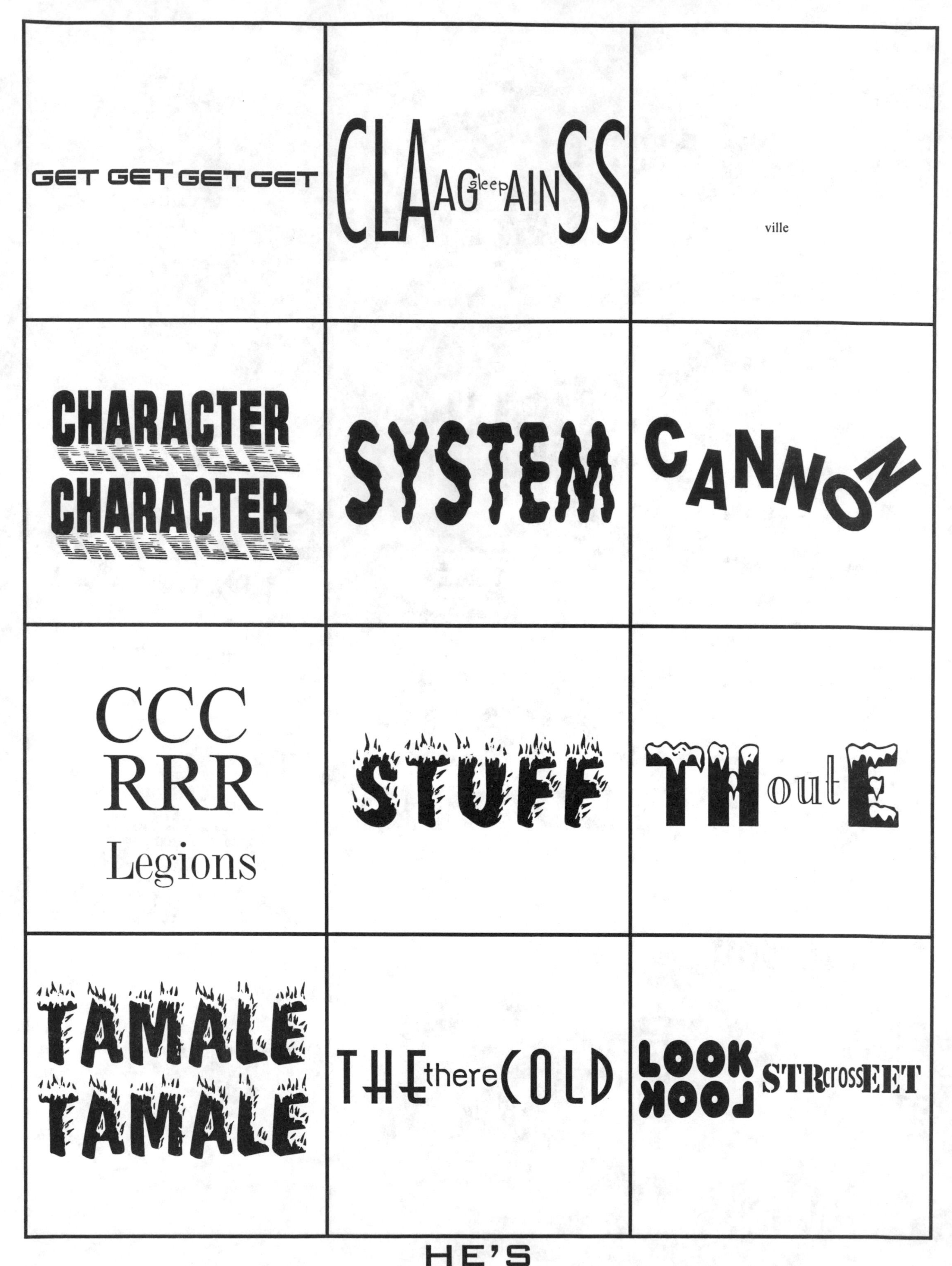
GET GET GET GET
CLA AG sleep AIN SS
ville
CHARACTER
CHARACTER
CHARACTER
CHARACTER
SYSTEM
CANNON
CCC
RRR
Legions
STUFF
TH out E
TAMALE
TAMALE
THE there COLD
LOOK
LOOK
STR cross EET

HE'S

BLA fill NK
BLA fill NK
RISK
+ RISK
+ RISK
DEW
BAD
+ vice
vice
CANDLE
I M T
MY HEAD
A vanished IR
A vanished IR
LOOKING
THINGS R
of your league
Q T
SHE'S

L
E
T
E
my
your
BALL
Roger
routine✓
REST
placed
Purpose
Purpose
U R B A N
I M
O dream F
a
CHRISTMAS
U R
target
Christmas
IM
working
SCENE SCENE

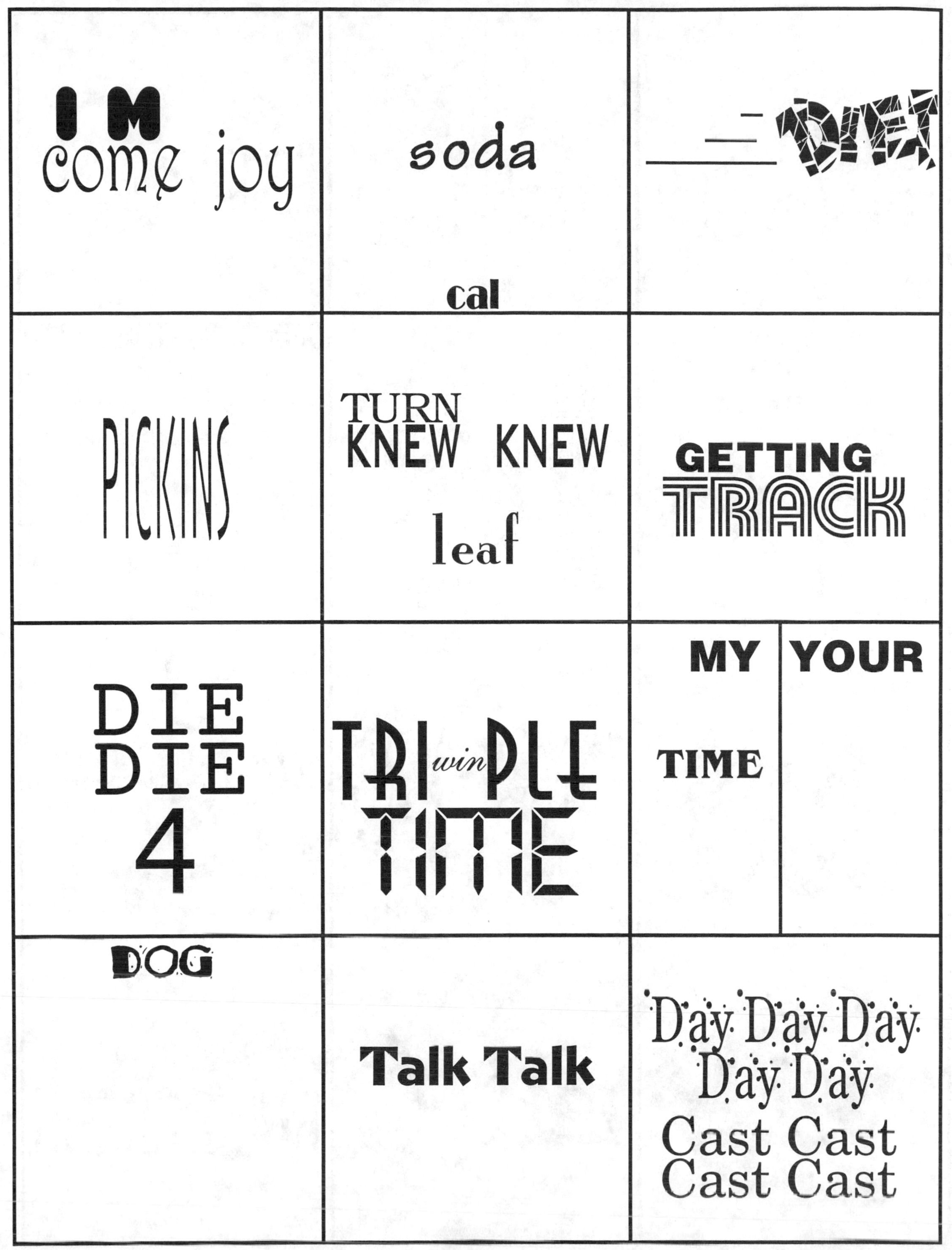
I M
come joy
soda
cal
DIET
PICKINS
TURN
KNEW KNEW
leaf
GETTING
TRACK
DIE
DIE
4
TRI win PLE
TIME
MY
YOUR
TIME
DOG
Talk Talk
Day Day Day
Day Day
Cast Cast
Cast Cast

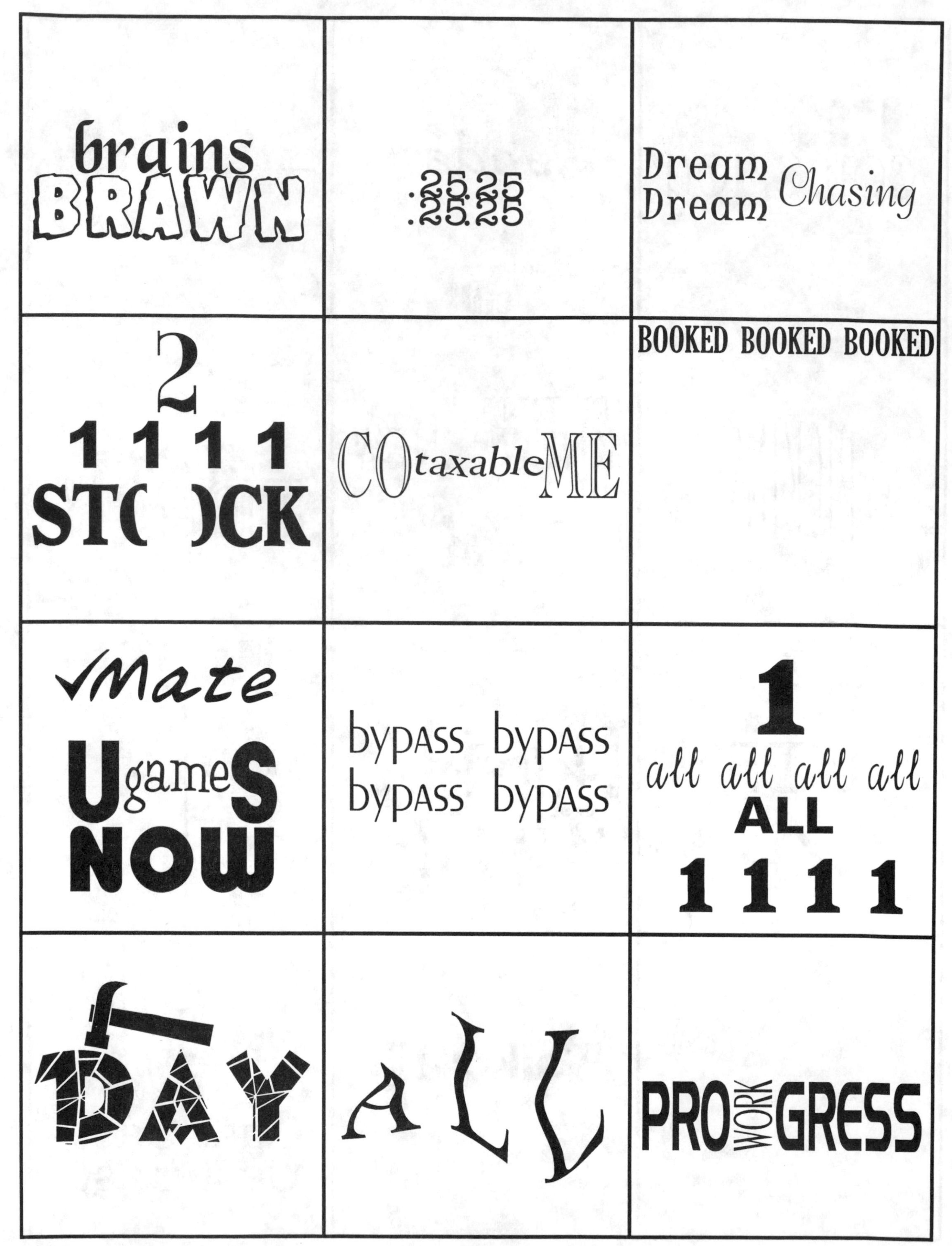
brains
BRAWN
.25.25
.25.25
Dream
Dream
Chasing
2
1 1 1 1
ST( )CK
COtaxableME
BOOKED BOOKED BOOKED
Mate
UgameS
NOW
bypass bypass
bypass bypass
1
all all all all
ALL
1 1 1 1
DAY
ALL
PRO
WORK
GRESS

LABOR
RRR
+ iii
the
graph graph
contin ental
MY SKIN
He's getting
She's getting
MY NERVES
σ BONDING
knowledge = Dangerous
thing
STORY
SHE'LL BE COMING
Mt.
YO feel UR
WEIGH
Labor
I L B
wait
4
uuuu

YOURfeelWAY IT	MORNING	AIspringR
X QQ S X QQ S	RUNNING RUNNING	WELL
WILweepLOW	Neigh VCL	ping WILL
O Lose Lose	Bartlett Bartlett Bartlett Bartlett	IROLLINGLLL

IT
HOPE
2
EVEN
I get T
ALL
gether
gether
A
L
AIRPORT
N
E
P
BARRIER
reef
I getting T
we grow re
E
I get N
it it
TI ME
JOB
STANDING
GROUND
U 1/2 E
PROSPERITY

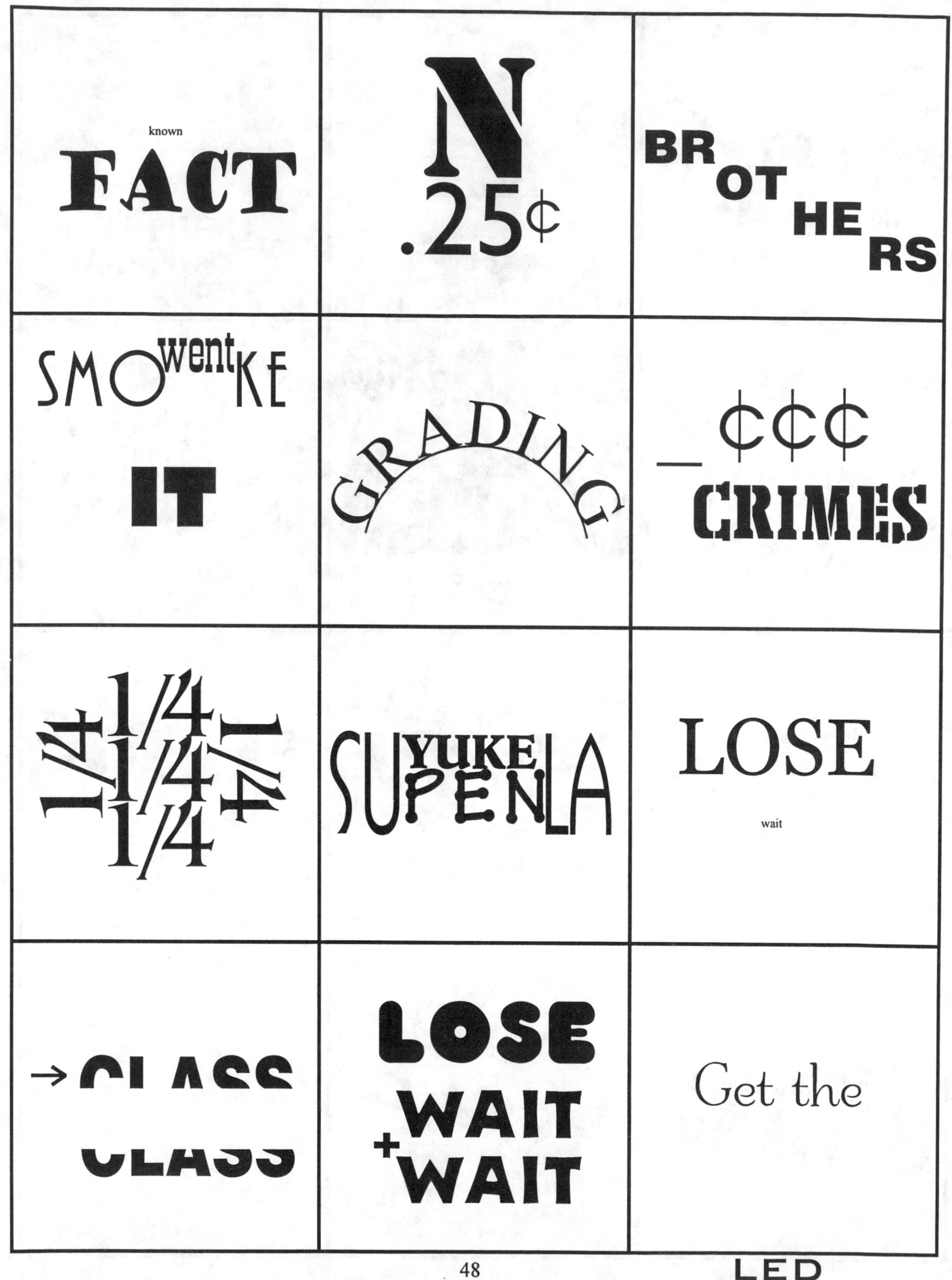
known
FACT
N
.25¢
BR
OT
HE
RS
SMO went KE
IT
GRADING
_ ¢¢¢
CRIMES
1/4
1/4
1/4
1/4
1/4
1/4
SU YUKE PEN LA
LOSE
wait
→ CLASS
CLASS
LOSE
WAIT
+ WAIT
Get the
LED

IT IT
D.E.W.
HOME
PICK IT
HOrobOD
john
U R
Dresser
YEgoldAR
YEgoldAR
LEAVE111
1. Nature
2. Nature
3. Nature
snowflakes
snowflakes
snowflakes
snowflakes
TETHER TETHER TETHER
sweet
zero, zilch, zip

have have
hold hold
I L
BEND
WORD WORD
UUUU
PERISCOPE
U & I
C I
i i
He's
N N N N N N N N
Good
Guy
H 2 dead O
EXPER he he IANCED
DRINK
DRINK
DRINK
DINNER
VIS it it IBLE
FOCUS
– +
FEV cab ER
12th
KNOCK

LOOKING
Thing Thing R
E A G L E
obstacles obstacles
COMING
WEIGH
SCHEDULE
EFFEC that that TIVE
HE HE
SCHEDULE
Apple R
GET GET it GET GET
U CAN
COUNT
ME
Ø
talk
MAP MAP
W E A L T H

FAlowT
U get
CHANCES
CHANCES
FAT
in
SHOT
BOUNCE
BOUNCE
POIkkkNT
ZZ
BOOM
I WHAT
WHAT T
me me
me me
SITE SORE SORE
SORE SORE
iii
DAallZE
WORK
COMThey RPATIBLE

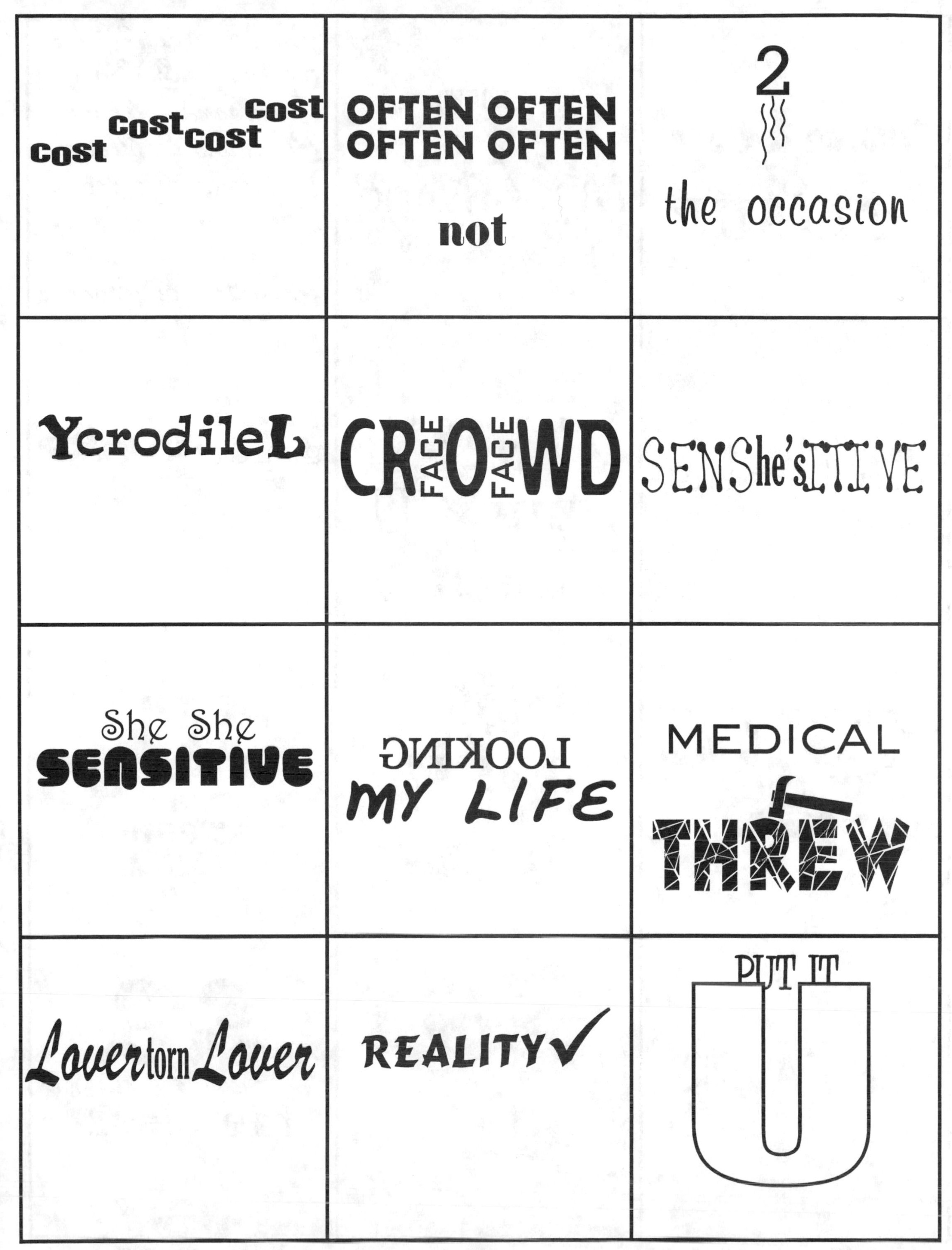
cost cost cost cost
OFTEN OFTEN
OFTEN OFTEN
not
2
the occasion
YcrodileL
CR FACE O FACE WD
SENShe'sITIVE
She She
SENSITIVE
LOOKING
MY LIFE
MEDICAL
THREW
LovertornLover
REALITY
PUT IT
U

Crimson & Clover & AGAIN	BORED My ↗ Mind	Crimson & Clover Crimson & Clover Crimson & Clover Crimson & Clover Crimson & Clover Crimson & Clover Crimson & Clover Crimson & Clover
man base base base	Sum X U **WIN** Sum X U **LOOSE**	guard **GUARD**
FORK **$$$**	it ain't **TILL** ıʇ ıʇ	**111** Gehn
OF FAVOR	**or or** 0	**&&** men ÷ 2

FALL

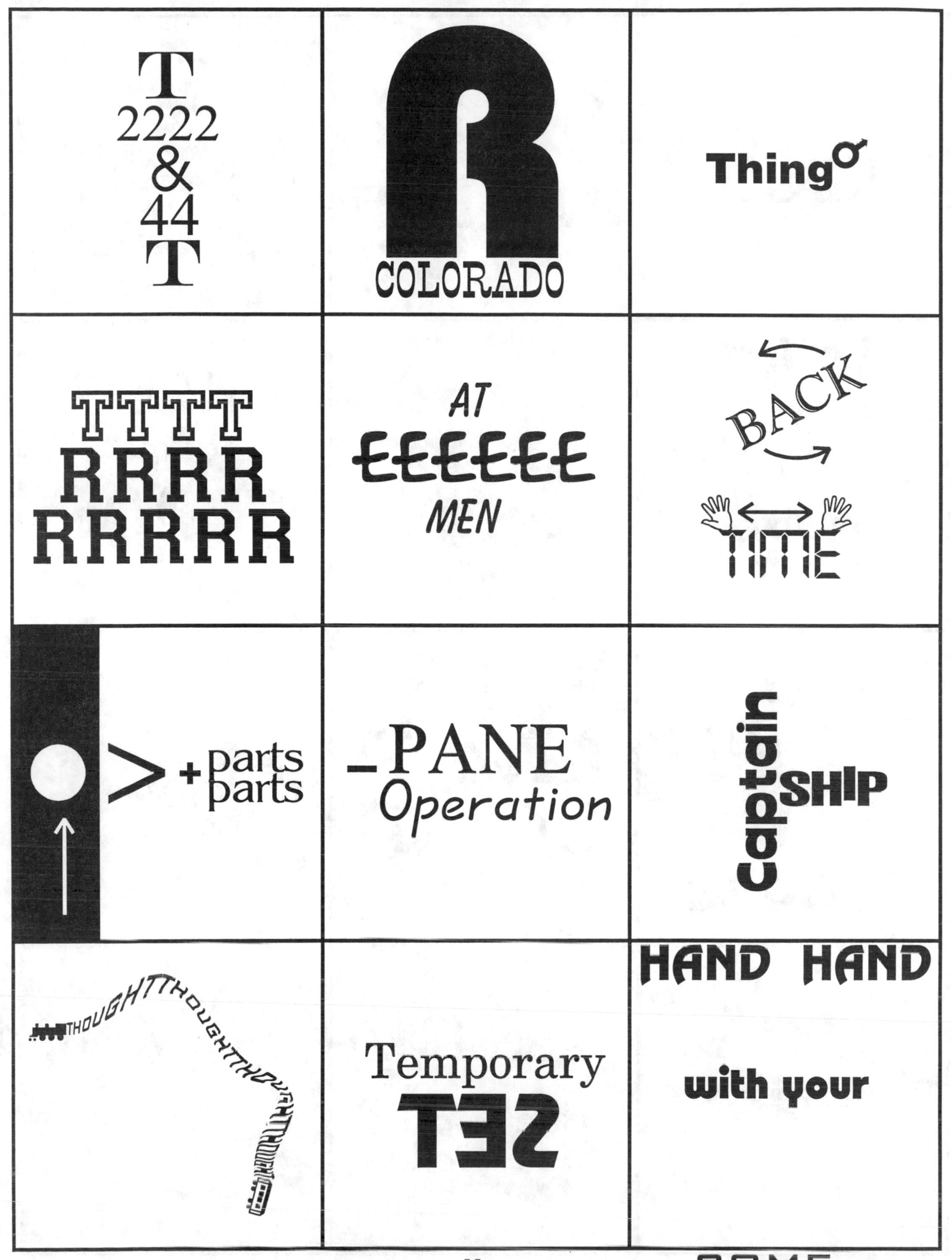

T
2222
&
44
T
COLORADO
Thing
TTTT
RRRR
RRRRR
AT
EEEEEE
MEN
BACK
TIME
parts
parts
PANE
Operation
Captain
SHIP
THOUGHTTHOUGHT
Temporary
HAND HAND
with your
COME

COMIC	1/2 1/2 KNOT KNOT	I M LA work TE night night
Fast Fast & Furious Furious me me me me	by ME	HOW lose lose TEguyN DAZE
+ U win + U loose	LI toe P LI P	start
ESSAY LIFE	Ticket Ticket dice dice dice dice	wound wound

STARE
1. DO DEW
2. DEW DO
3. DO DEW
4. DEW DO
boy blue
CONTRACT
He He
GREAT THINGS
GREAT THINGS
GREAT THINGS
VIT MIN
PAID JOB
TI ME
a bit
cash
vitamin
D fish
C
QUICK
TIME
TURN

_Head Horseman	soda CAL	orseman
coin coin phrase	TROPICAL	MALCOLM
elbow elbow TABLE	1' the other	ELBOWS ELBOWS CHAIR DESK TABLE
	foot foot	WI DE OPEN

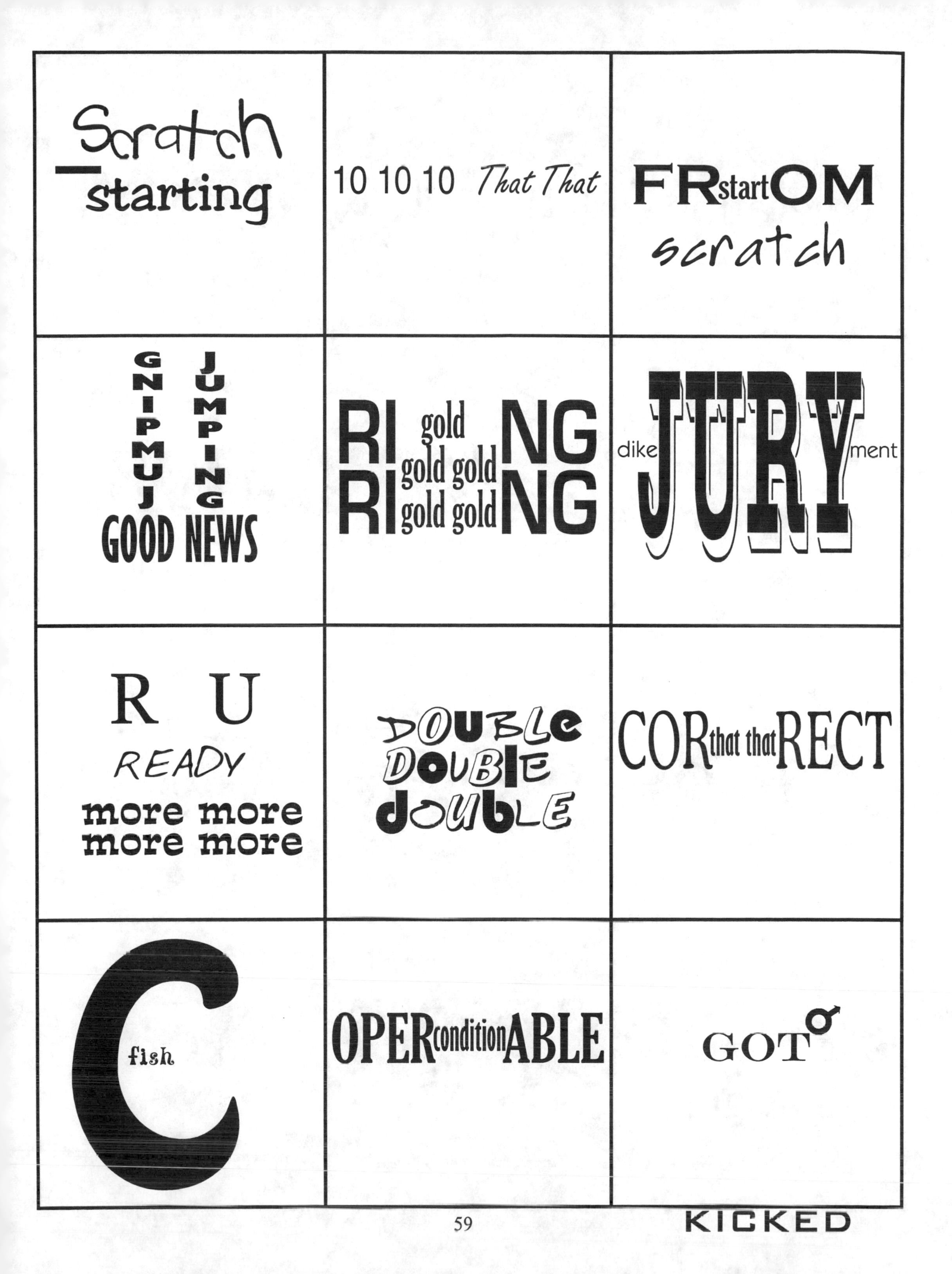
Scratch
starting
10 10 10 That That
FRstartOM
scratch
GNIPMUJ
JUMPING
GOOD NEWS
RI gold NG
gold gold
RI gold gold NG
gold gold
dike JURY ment
R U
READY
more more
more more
DOUBLE
DOUBLE
DOUBLE
CORthat thatRECT
C fish
OPERconditionABLE
GOT♂
KICKED

FALSE PRE 10 10
operating
I L
DNATS
uuuu
standME
Good x R
coming
Eternity
Eternity
Eternity
Eternity
ROLL
get
HE RE
VEGETABLE
VEGETABLE
VEGETABLE
EEEE
it
T
HAplayRD
get get
SPIRIT
of here

GET

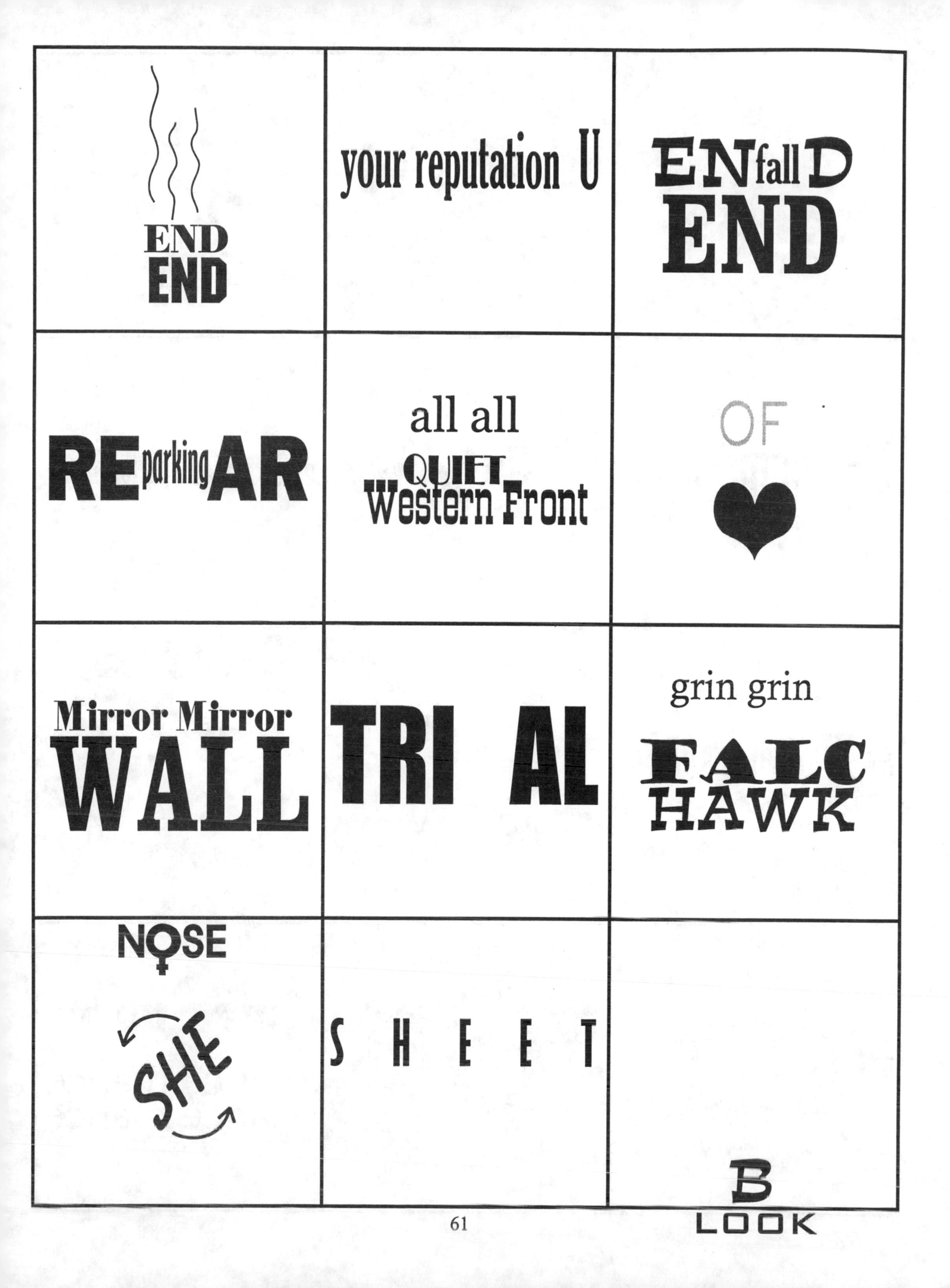

END
END
your reputation U
ENfallD
END
REparkingAR
all all
QUIET
Western Front
OF
Mirror Mirror
WALL
TRI AL
grin grin
FALC
HAWK
NOSE
SHE
S H E E T
B
LOOK

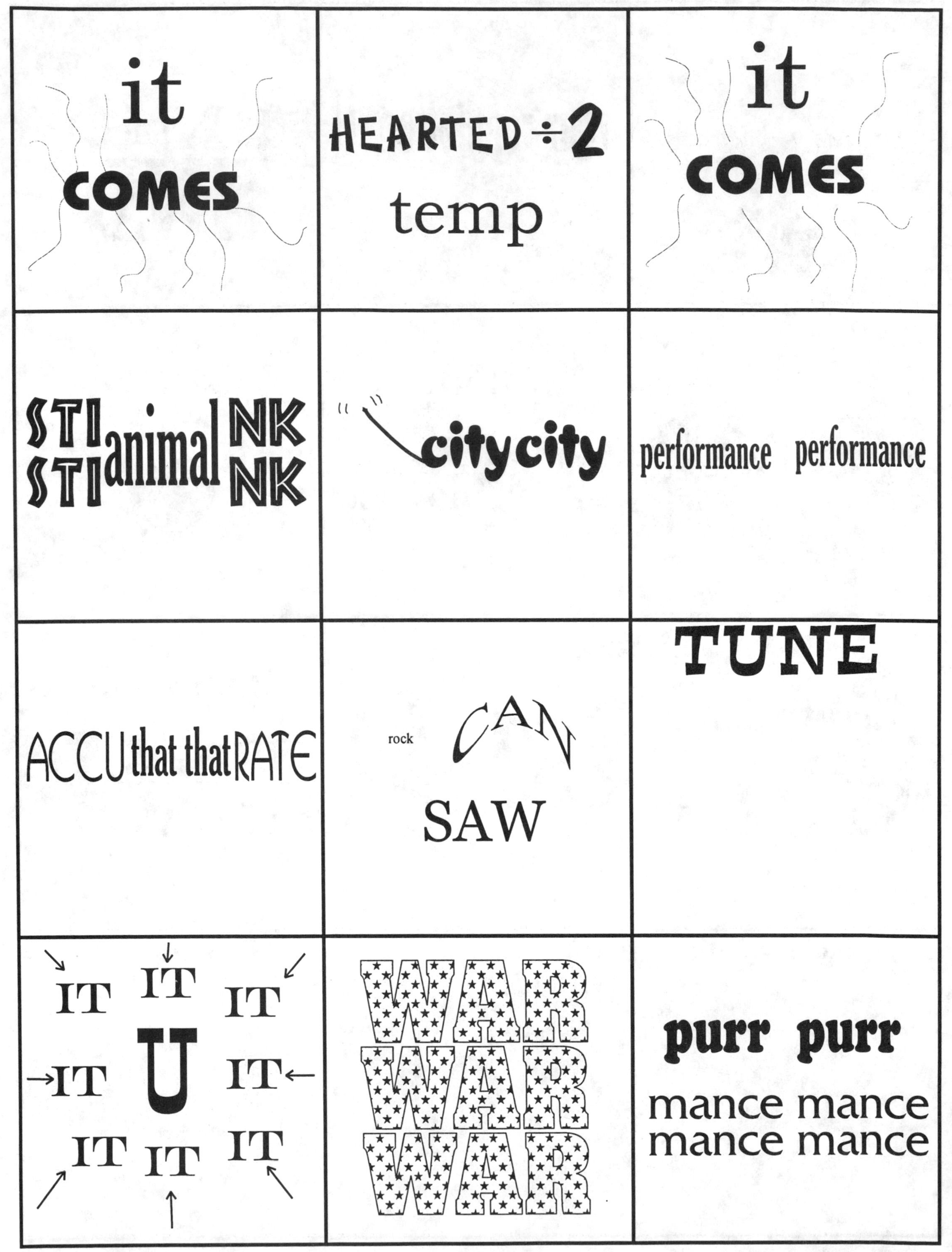
it
COMES
HEARTED ÷ 2
temp
it
COMES
STI STI animal NK NK
city city
performance performance
ACCU that that RATE
rock
CAN
SAW
TUNE
IT IT IT
IT U IT
IT IT IT
WAR
WAR
WAR
purr purr
mance mance
mance mance

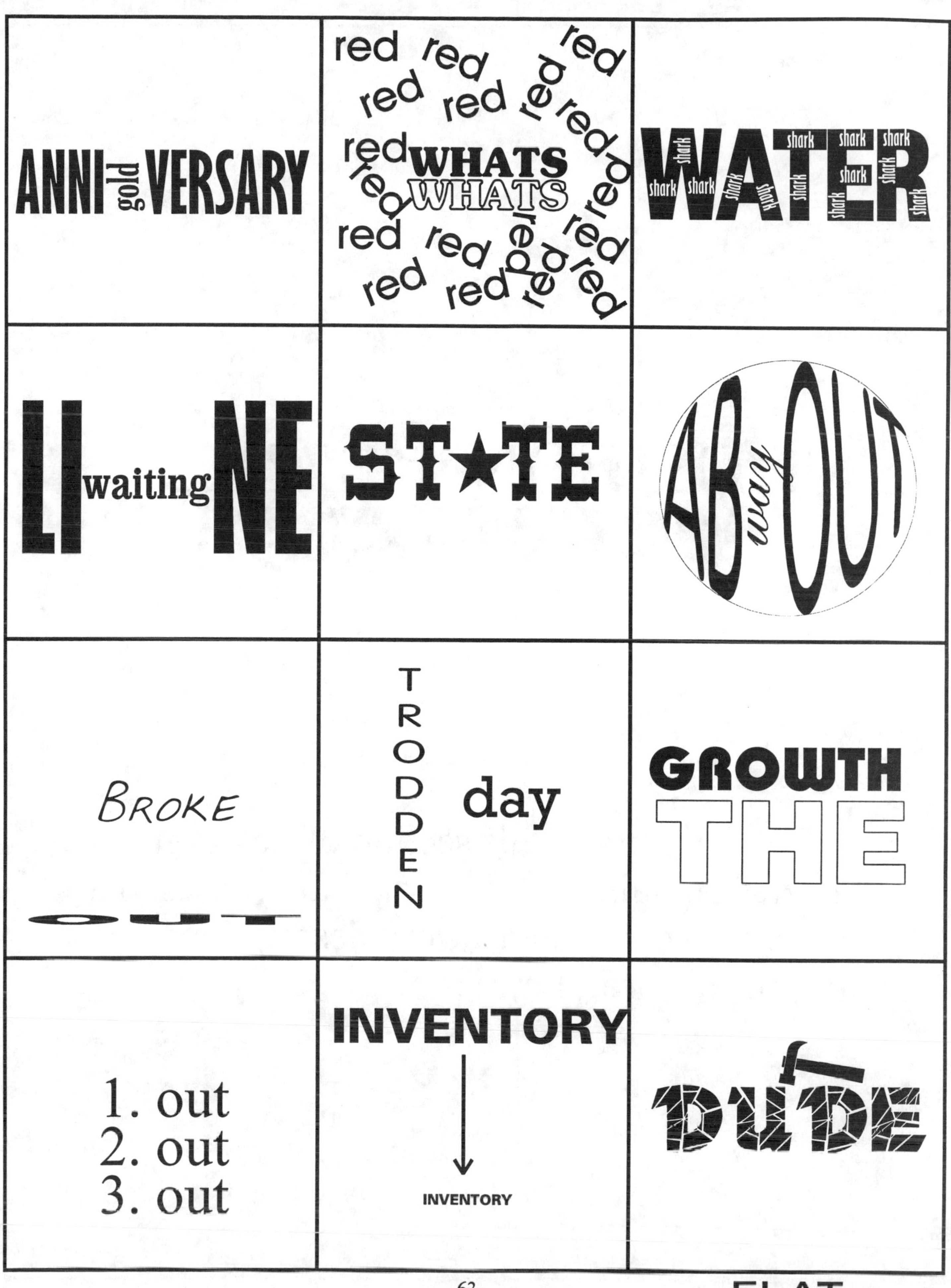
ANNI gold VERSARY
red red red red red red red red red red red red red red red red red red red red
WHATS
WHATS
WATER
shark shark shark shark shark shark shark shark shark shark shark shark
LI waiting NE
ST★TE
AB way OUT
BROKE
OUT
TRODDEN
day
GROWTH
THE
1. out
2. out
3. out
INVENTORY
INVENTORY
DUDE
FLAT

Position Puzzles
WORDS ONLY

The answers to this section of Position Puzzles contain only 1 word. No phrases. No sayings. No 2 or more word descriptions. Just ONE word. Enjoy!

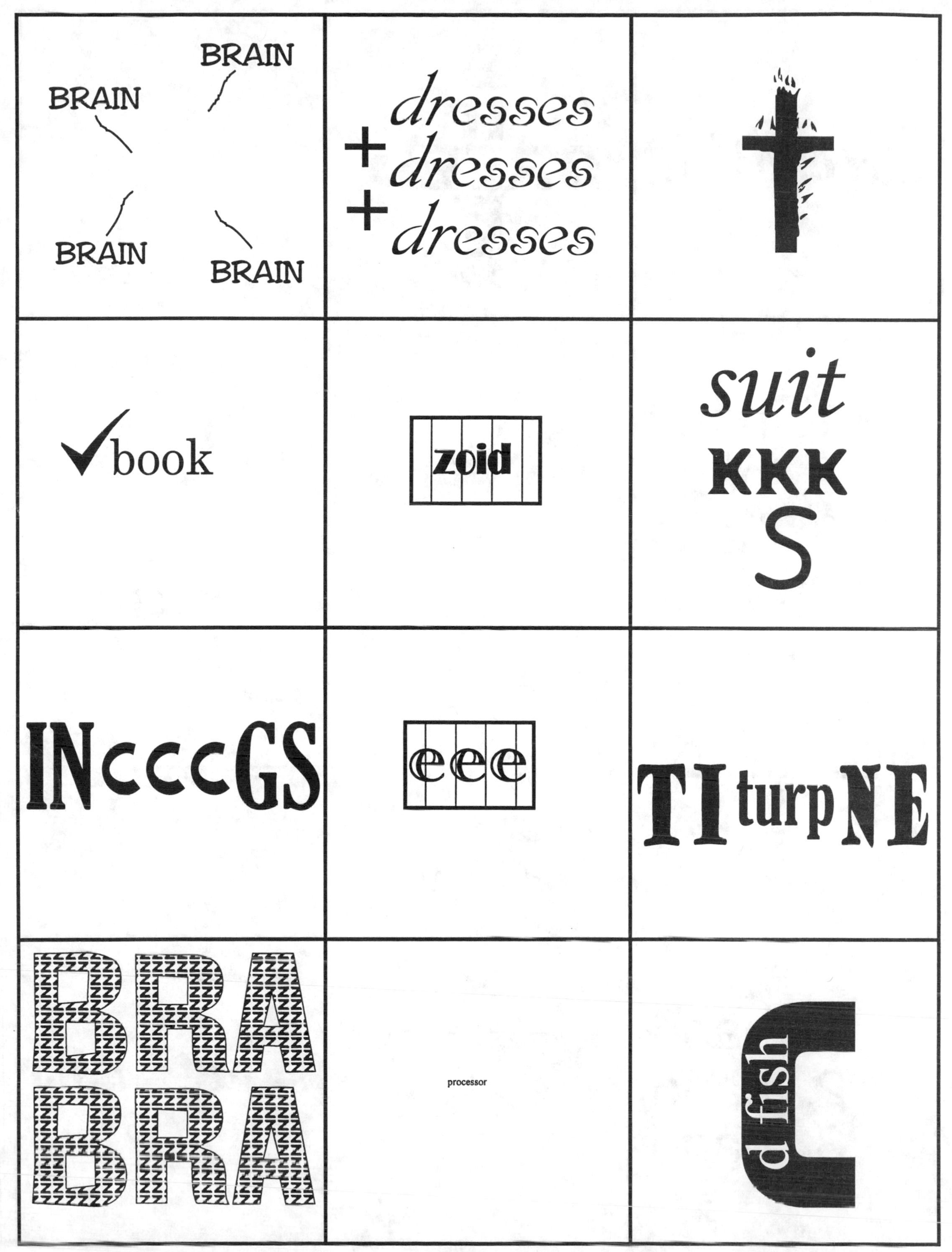
BRAIN
BRAIN
BRAIN
BRAIN
dresses
+ dresses
+ dresses
✓book
zoid
suit
KKK
S
INccccGS
eee
TI turp NE
BRA
BRA
processor
d fish

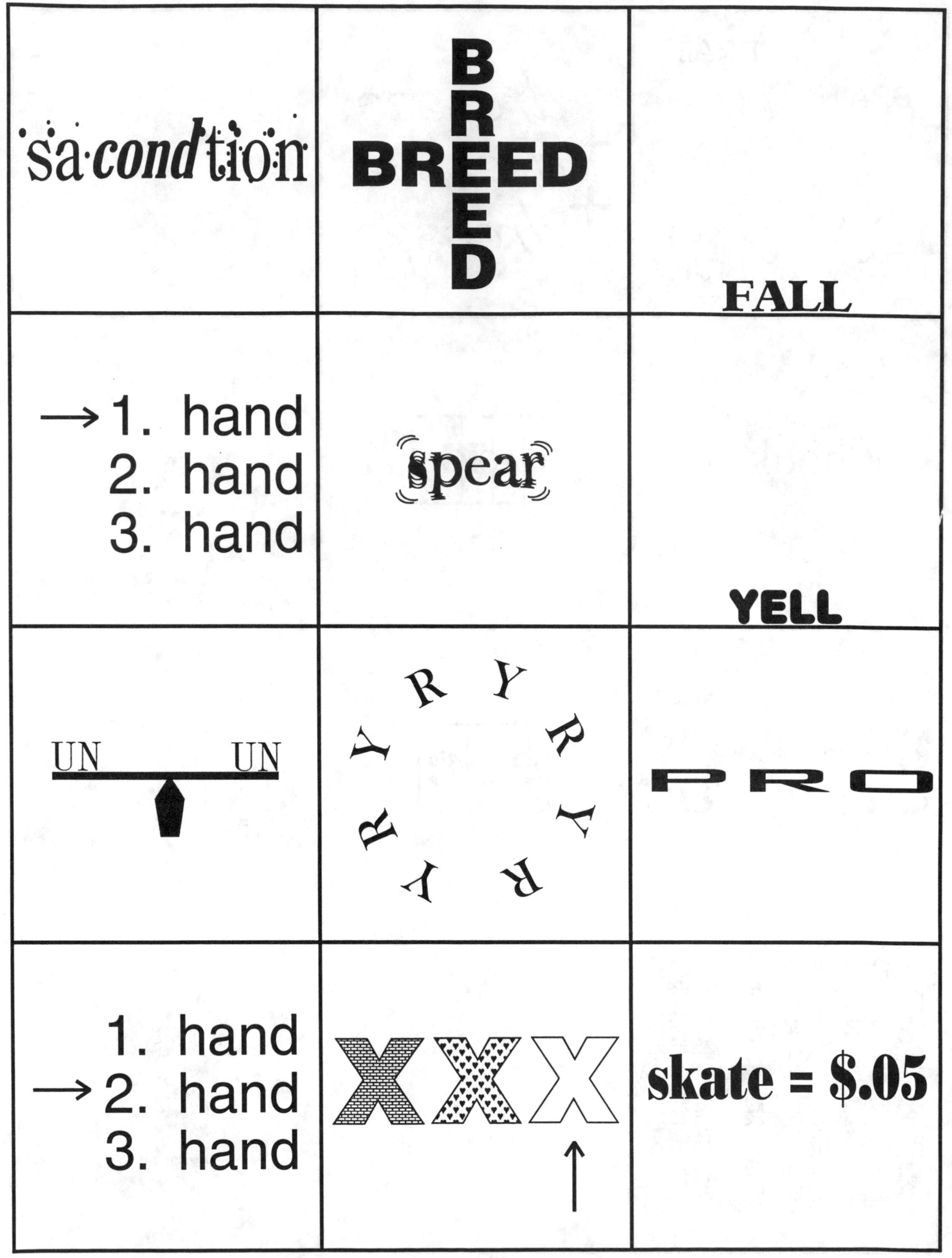
sa·cond·tion
BREED
BREED
FALL
→ 1. hand
2. hand
3. hand
spear
YELL
UN UN
R Y R Y R Y R Y
PRO
1. hand
→ 2. hand
3. hand
XXX
skate = $.05

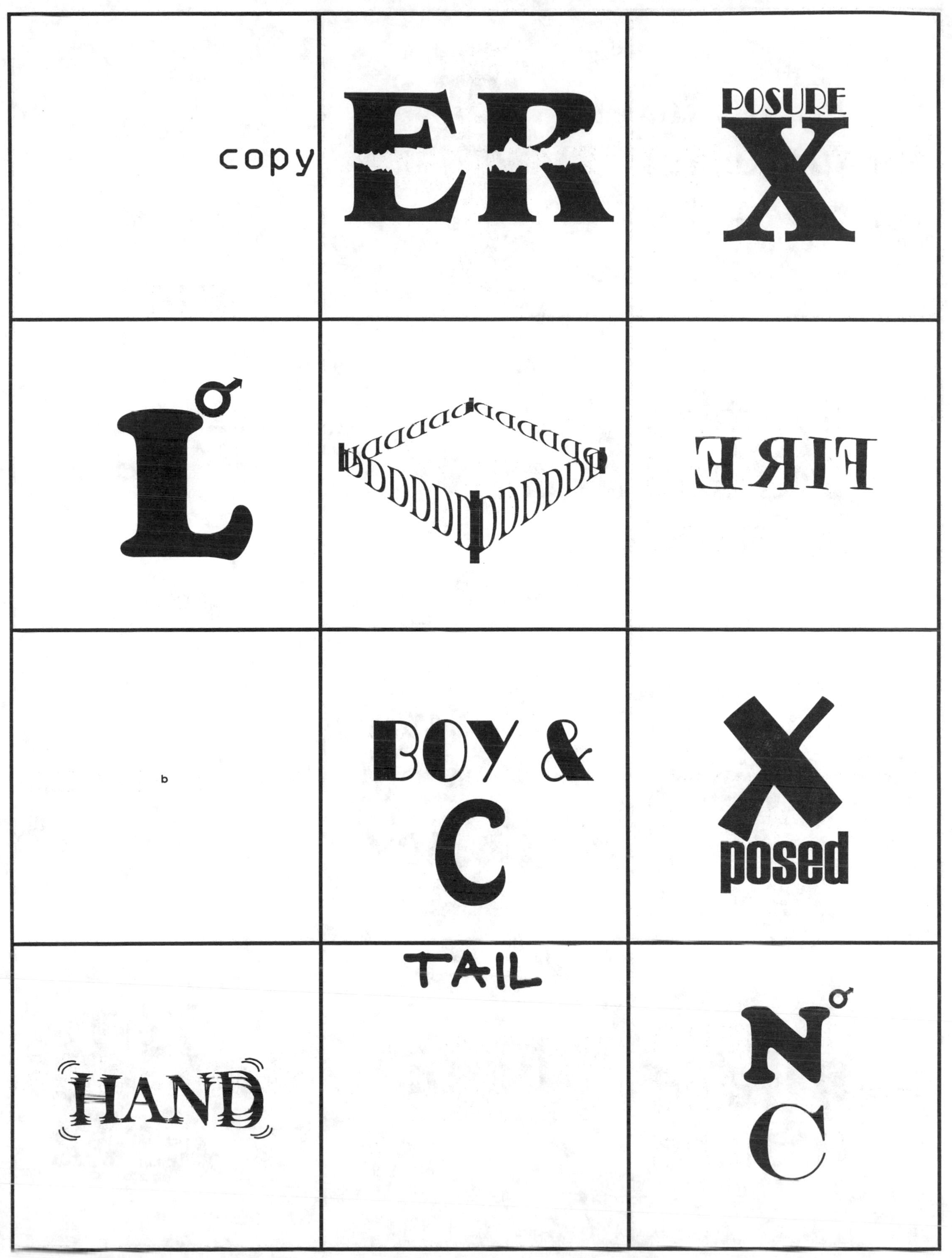
copy
ER
POSURE
X
L
FIRE
b
BOY &
C
X
posed
TAIL
HAND
N
C

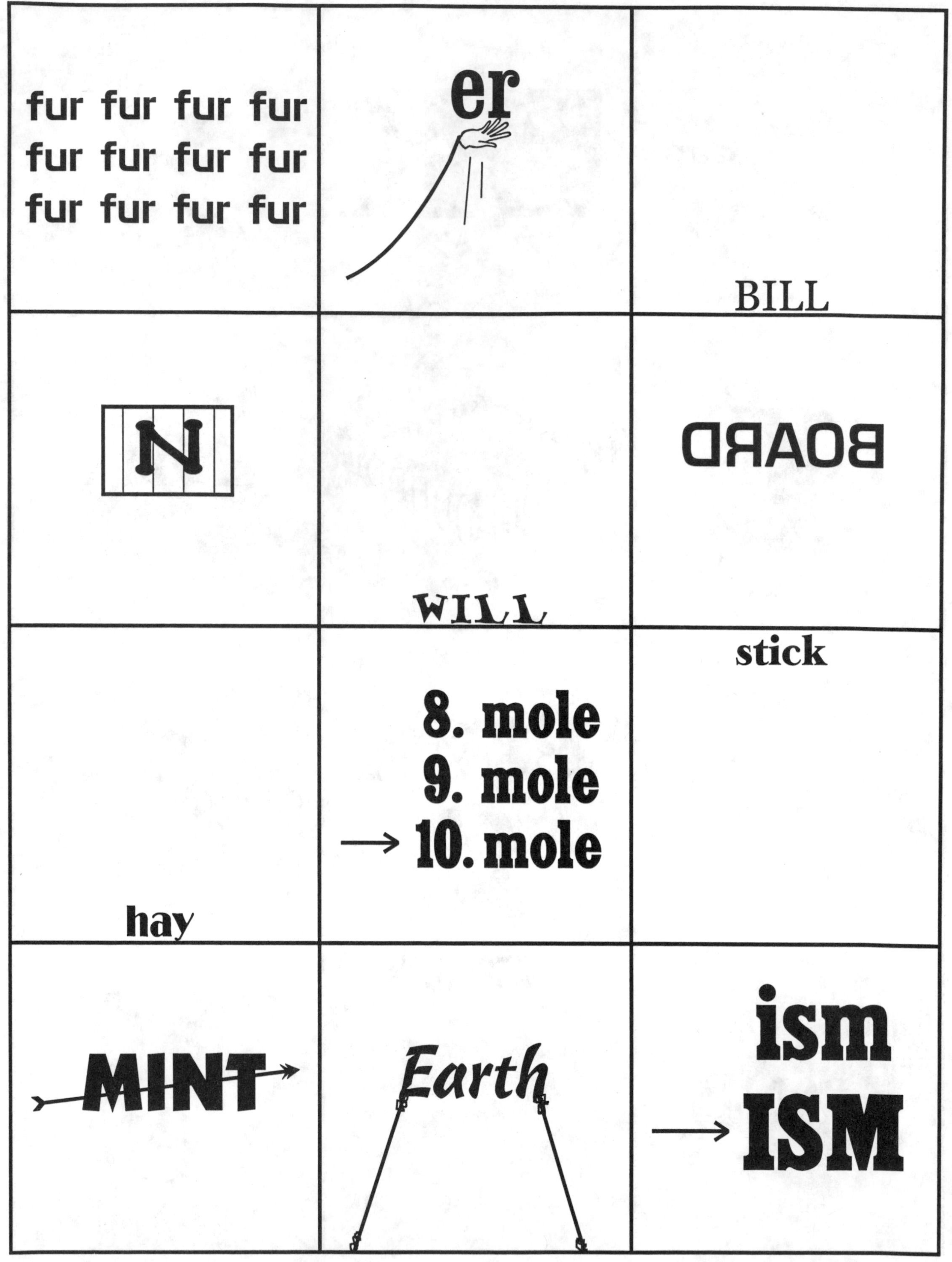
fur fur fur fur
fur fur fur fur
fur fur fur fur
er
BILL
N
BOARD
WILL
stick
hay
8. mole
9. mole
10. mole
MINT
Earth
ism
ISM

Joe
BRID
BEAT
WARD
CAN
PIN
Nail
E
den den den den den
den den den den den
C
Ber BOY BOY ry
Ber BOY BOY ry
SHUN

SIR
AM
US
BACK÷2
GAL
HALF
N N N N N N N N N N N
Catch
CASE
Kate
NIP
i i i i i i i i i i i i i
FUR

Round
bear bear
bear bear
wave
CHUN CHUN
CHUN CHUN
N
LOCK
D
GO
V
TOP
TOP
TOP

BOARD

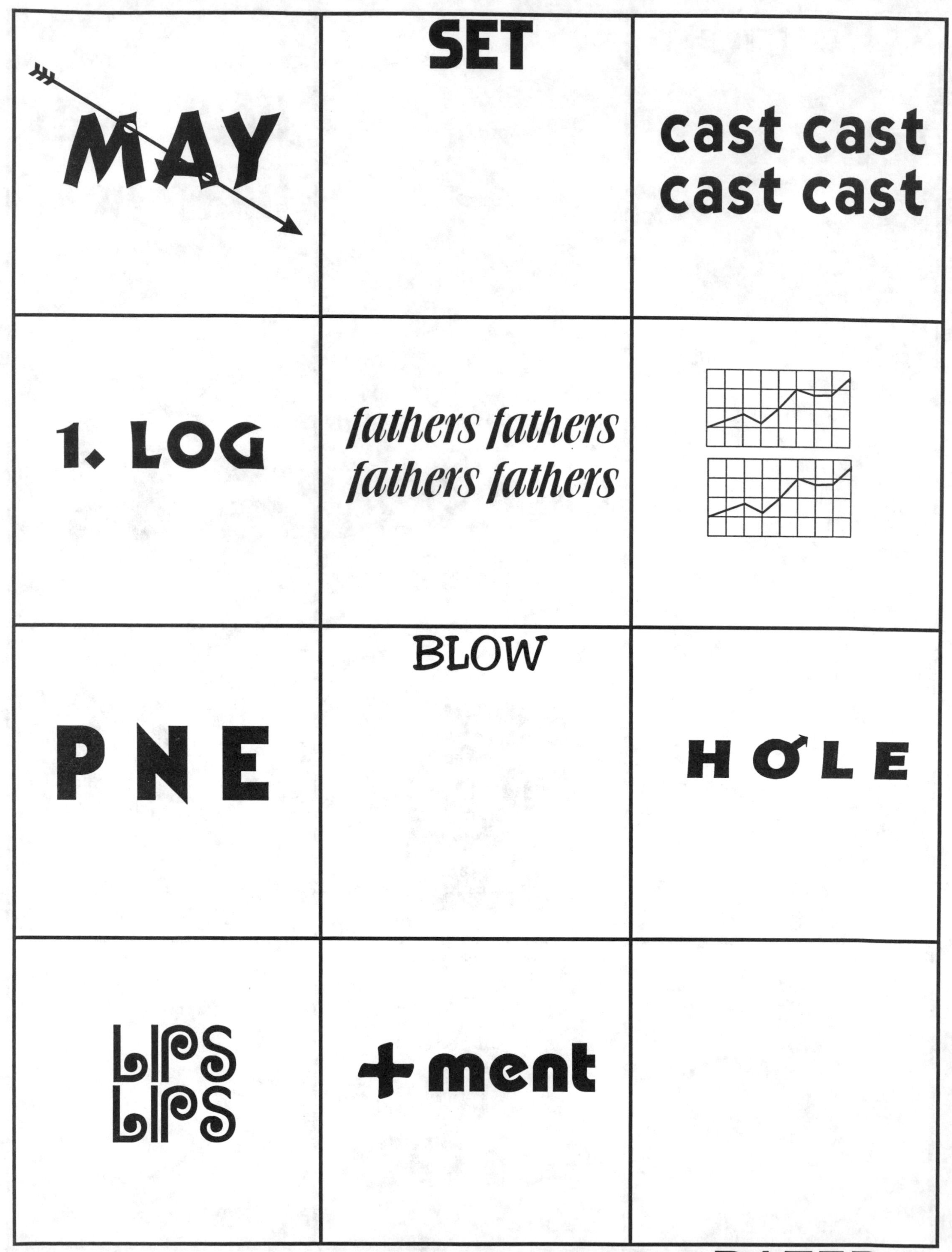
MAY
SET
cast cast
cast cast
1. LOG
fathers fathers
fathers fathers
BLOW
PNE
HOLE
LIPS
LIPS
+ ment

DATED

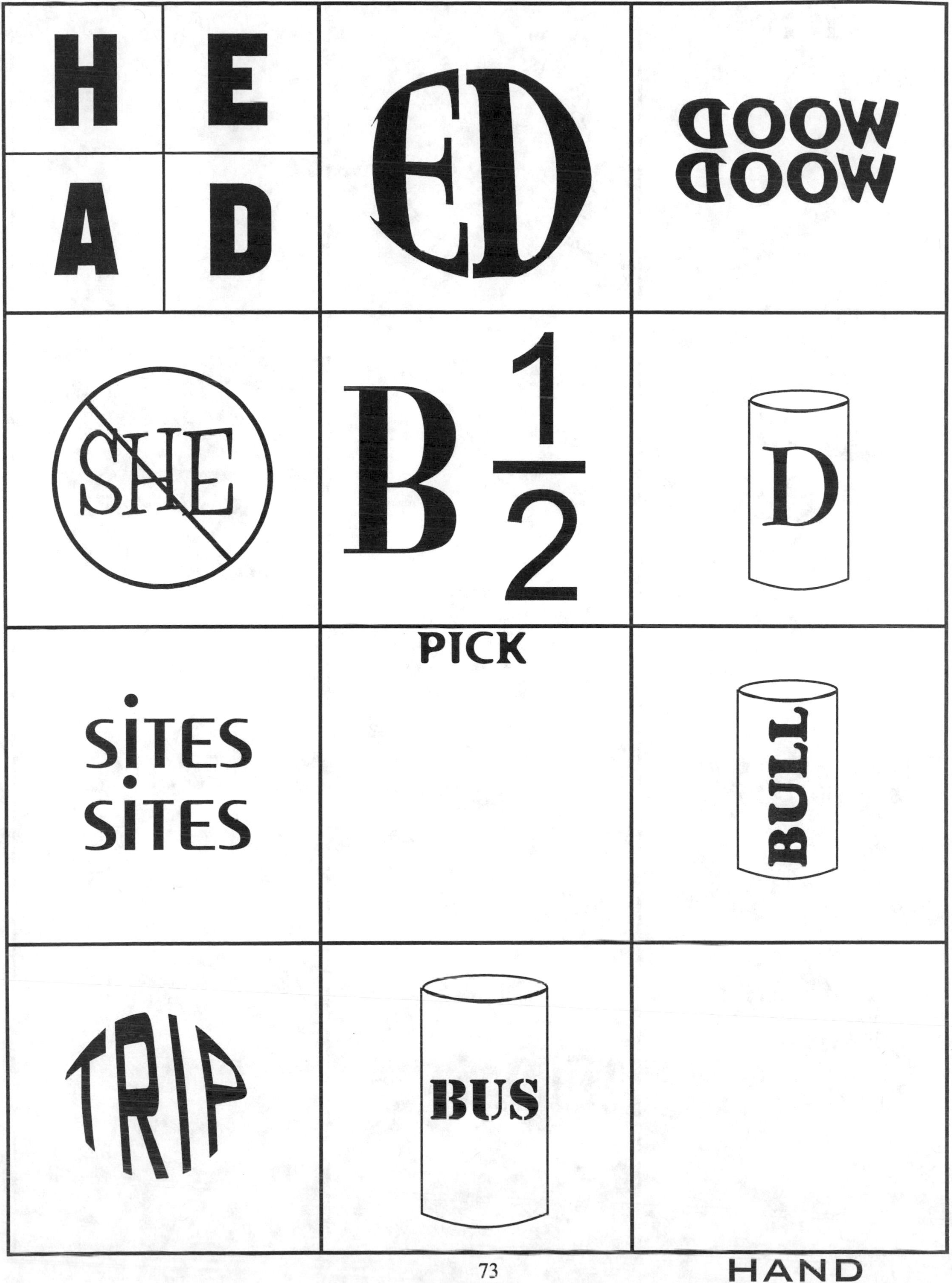
H E
A D
ED
WOOD
WOOD
SHE
B 1/2
D
PICK
SITES
SITES
BULL
TRIP
BUS
HAND

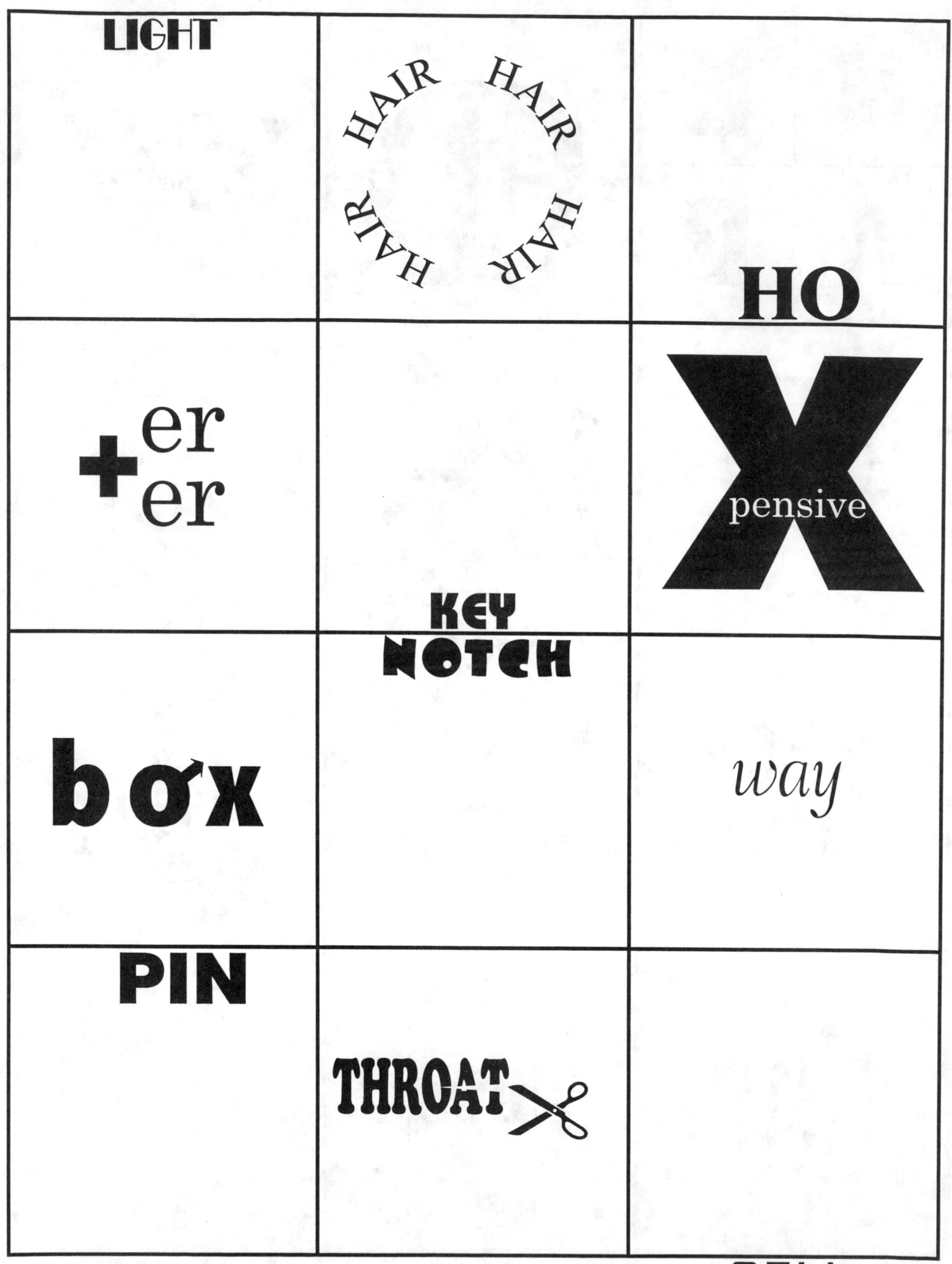
LIGHT
HAIR
HAIR
HAIR
HAIR
HO
er
er
X
pensive
KEY
NOTCH
box
way
PIN
THROAT
SELL

8
X term
dead
earPIEear
weigh
way
it
END
SIGH SIGH
sigh sigh
SIGH SIGH
NNNN
sick
SIGH
TOUCH
ER ER
MAT MAT
MAT MAT

POSITION PUZZLE

ANSWERS

Position Puzzle ANSWERS

Page 7

1. Criminal Intent
2. Breaking News
3. Uphill Battle
4. Getting Back to Basics
5. Amazon River
6. That's in Excess
7. Whitewalls
8. Folding Chairs
9. R2 D2
10. C3 PO
11. Flip Flops
12. Back to Back Homers

Page 8

1. Wright Brothers
2. I'm in 7th Heaven
3. This Space Available
4. Spinach
5. Too Much Talk, Too Little Action
6. Woke Up in a Bad Mood
7. Seein' Eye Dog
8. Back Stop
9. Holes in His Story
10. Foreign Tour
11. Foreign Tour
12. Endless Summer

Page 9

1. Insider Trading
2. Rolling in the Aisles
3. Cryin' Shame
4. Ace Up His Sleeve
5. Sea Biscuit
6. Hidden Treasure
7. Turn Your Life Around
8. Chicken Dinner
9. A Walk in the Park
10. Side Splitting Laughter
11. Side Splitting Laughter
12. Inner Strength

Page 10

1. Home Away from Home
2. Second Home
3. Cabin in the Woods
4. Cabin in the Woods
5. Cabin by the Lake
6. Boston Bruins
7. Space Cadet
8. Top 40
9. Torn Apart, Torn in 2, or Torn in half
10. Tan Lines
11. InStyle Magazine
12. Empire State

Page 11

1. Lost in the Shuffle
2. You Are on a Roll
3. John Adams
4. (A) Division of Troops
5. National Pastime
6. Twin Peaks
7. Jumpin' For Joy
8. Time Warp
9. 50 1st Dates
10. Blue in the Face
11. Double Decker Bus
12. Jumpin' For Joy

Page 13

1. Undersea Explorer
2. Useless information
3. Dashing Through the Snow on a One Horse Open Sleigh
4. Useless Information
5. Where the Rubber Meets the Road
6. Too Many Too Count
7. Mixing Bowl
8. It's Larger Than Life
9. Think Outside the Box
10. Fishing For Compliments
11. Down for the Count
12. You Are Out of Your Mind

Page 13

1. Freudian Slip
2. Use Commons Sense
3. Long Way to Go
4. Searching High and Low
5. Forbidden Fruit
6. Set in Motion
7. You Belong to Me
8. Cold Shoulder
9. Inflated Ego
10. Just Add Water
11. Trading Places
12. Tuna Fish

Page 14

1. Bib Overalls
2. Warmed Up Leftovers
3. Cheap Shot
4. Too Funny For Words
5. Ambiguous
6. For instance
7. Evenly Divided
8. For instance
9. Evenly Divided
10. Change of Heart
11. Feeling Left Out
12. Count of Monte Cristo

Page 15

1. First Down and Goal to Go
2. Checking Account
3. Minimum Down Payment
4. Slump in the Market
5. 20,000 Leagues Under the Sea
6. Too Many Fish in the Sea
7. Following in His Footsteps
8. Are You Following in His Footsteps
9. Pushed Over the Edge
10. A Spike in Prices
11. Too Tired Too Think
12. A Spike in Prices

Page 16

1. Down Right Stupid
2. Due at the End of the Month
3. Road to Recovery
4. Swimming in a Sea of Incompetence
5. Blown Apart
6. Add a little Zip to Your Life
7. Flying Under the Radar
8. (It's) Lonely on Top
9. Reverse the Charge
10. (The) Last Straw
11. Get Down and Dirty
12. Big Fat Lie

Page 17

1. Top Dollar
2. Town Squares
3. Total Mess
4. Mountain Bike
5. Put it in Gear
6. Dashing Good Looks
7. Going Above the Call of Duty
8. Spring in His Step
9. Ridin' Sidesaddle
10. Online Purchase
11. Internet Site
12. Back Order

Page 18

1. What's Up, Doc?
2. I Am On To You
3. Last One's a Rotten Egg
4. Money Talks
5. A Period in History
6. Get Out of Here
7. Burning Desire
8. Center of Gravity
9. Oliver Twist
10. Spiral Notebook
11. Golden Gloves
12. Hang 'em High

Page 19

1. Spinning Out of Control
2. Kick Back and Relax
3. Hollywood Squares
4. A Little R & R
5. Workin' Hard on the Job
6. Loose Change
7. Forbes Fortune 500
8. Total Disaster
9. I'm Putting on Weight
10. Service with a Smile
11. High Five
12. Last Man Out

Page 20

1. Eatin' Warmed-Up Left-Overs
2. Foreign Object
3. Paint by the Numbers
4. Foreign Object
5. Easy to Overlook
6. And the Beat Goes on
7. Holy Macaroni
8. Twisted Thinking
9. Footloose and Fancy Free
10. Crying on the Inside, Laughing on the Out
11. Tilt-a-Whirl
12. Cryin' on the Inside, Laughin' on the Out

Page 21

1. Having Left-Overs
2. Dayton, Ohio
3. To Be or Not To be, That …is the Question
4. Dayton, Ohio
5. (It's) Nice and Warm Inside
6. (It's) Cold Outside
7. Kevin Brougher
8. Top Hat
9. Lowlife
10. Arch Enemies
11. Natural Instincts
12. Time is Running Out

Page 22

1. Almost Famous
2. Reincarnation
3. Towering Inferno
4. Fahrenheit 451
5. All Roads Lead to Rome
6. Inferno
7. He's Insincere
8. Harmonica
9. Incurable Disease
10. Gomer Pyle
11. Intense (ten's) Emotions
12. Error in Judgment

Page 23

1. Ante Up
2. Hold In High Esteem
3. That's an Intolerable Act
4. From Sun Up to Sundown
5. (The) Glass is Half Full (Empty)
6. Sidewinders
7. Not in My House
8. Mixed Nuts
9. Countdown to Blastoff
10. He's On the Outside Looking in
11. Poison Ivy
12. He's on the Outside Looking in

Page 24

1. The Interstate Highway
2. Born Under a Bad Sign
3. Drivin' the Interstate Highway
4. Undersea Exploration
5. (A) Silo
6. Steerin' Committee
7. In Under the Wire
8. Stop Watch
9. Spotted Fever
10. There's a Fine Line Between Love and War
11. Double or Nothing
12. Top Gun

Page 25

1. Four-Part Harmony
2. Marion Berry
3. Four-Part Harmony
4. Franks & Beans
5. Beady Eyes
6. You are going to Stay After School
7. Cloak 'n Dagger
8. Office Space for Rent
9. Pecan Pie
10. Dead End
11. Happy Hour
12. (A) Slice of Life

Page 26

1. Center of Attention
2. We Are on Schedule
3. Fistful of Dollars
4. Bet Across the Board
5. Sailin' the Seven Seas
6. Sidearm Curveball
7. Indy 500
8. Space Travel
9. 4th Down and Long
10. Trouble in Paradise
11. Kevin Kline
12. Better Look Out

Page 27

1. Back Pack
2. Too Close for Comfort
3. Deep Down Inside
4. Day to Day
5. Clean up After Yourself
6. Think Before You Speak
7. Background Check
8. Use Common Sense
9. Space Probe
10. Peppermint Twist
11. Eating in Excess
12. Curling Iron

Page 28

1. Shop Online
2. Chain of Command
3. Breakin' the Rule
4. Chain of Command
5. Breakin' the Rule
6. Crooked Politicians
7. Turn Over Rate
8. Peek Around the Corner
9. Hair Raising Incident
10. An Internet Startup
11. No One Understands Me
12. Breaking the Rules

Page 29

1. Change of Scenery
2. Caught Between a Rock and a Hard Place
3. Search High and Low
4. Great Things Come in Small Packages
5. Deadman's Curve
6. Smoking Guns
7. Double Exposure
8. Information Overload
9. Faces in the Crowd
10. Won by a Nose
11. I Am in Charge
12. Periodic Table

Page 30

1. Total Control
2. I'm in Control
3. Sit Down, Shut Up, (and) Don't Talk Back
4. Get in Line
5. Class, Voices Down, Eyes Up
6. Open Books to Page 3 Please
7. Sleepin' in Class
8. Wake Up, Start Takin' Notes
9. Turn in Your Work
10. Five-Minute Break Time
11. Listen Carefully
12. Get Out Pencil 'n Paper

Page 31

1. Foreign Affairs
2. Pull Over Up to the Curb
3. Foreign Affairs
4. Vicious Circle
5. Pull Over Up to the Curb
6. Seein' Stars
7. Summary
8. (The) Straw that Broke the Camels Back
9. Season Greetings
10. Warm-up in the Bull-pen
11. (From) 0 to 60 in 3 seconds
12. Ring of Fire

Page 32

1. Condescending
2. Up to a Point
3. Tip of the Iceberg
4. Sideshow
5. Condensed Milk
6. Twist to Open
7. Eye of the Hurricane
8. I Am Half Out of My Mind with Worry
9. All Star Game
10. I'll Be Thinking About You
11. Third World
12. I'll Be Thinkin' About You

Page 33

1. Middle C
2. No Time For Messing Around, Now
3. I Am Missin' You
4. I'll Be in Touch
5. Paradigm Shift
6. See You in Awhile
7. Honey Bee
8. Tally Ho
9. Common Denominators
10. Nothing in Particular
11. Put it in Reverse
12. Put it in Reverse or Put it Back

Page 34

1. Wolf in Sheep's Clothing
2. Cryin' for More
3. Living on the Edge of Disaster
4. You Deserve a Break Today
5. I See Both Sides of the Argument
6. Winding Down After a Long day
7. Living On the Edge
8. I'll Get Around To It
9. Back Surgery
10. Nothing Between the Ears
11. Spring Loaded
12. Living On the Edge of Disaster

Page 35

1. I Bent Over Backwards for You
2. Shop Online
3. Justice for All
4. Pales in Comparison
5. Overnight Delivery
6. Dark Side of the Moon
7. Sitting on the Sidelines
8. Two Ships Passing in the Night
9. Sitting on the Sidelines
10. Editor in Chief
11. A Collection of Short Stories
12. I Bent Over Backwards for You

Page 36

1. Odds 'n Ends
2. Straighten Up Your Messy Room
3. Bats in the Belfry
4. Right in the Middle of the Pack
5. No One in Particular
6. Parting Words
7. Mixed Blessings
8. Right in the Middle of the Pack
9. Peak Performance
10. Having a Ball
11. No Holes Barred
12. Temporary Injunction

Page 37

1. Roll of Tape
2. It's Up in the Air
3. He Came Out of Nowhere
4. Shifting Gears
5. Change of Plans
6. Temporary Set-Back
7. (The) Short End of the Stick
8. Roll Over Beethoven
9. Top 10 Most Wanted
10. Mental Block
11. Joan of Arc
12. He's Outstanding in His Field

Page 38

1. Looking Back Over the Past
2. Shifting Sands
3. Dashing Home
4. Over the Mountains and Through the Woods To Grandmother's House We Go
5. Short of Breath
6. Built to Last
7. Breaking Through the Barrier
8. Eight is Enough
9. Drawn to Scale
10. (The) Odds are Overwhelming
11. Breaking Through the Barrier
12. Come Out with Your Hands Up

Page 39

1. Center of the Universe
2. Break the Bank
3. Dead Sea Scrolls
4. Back Up Quarterback
5. He's Prone to Injury
6. Back Up Quarterback
7. Prone to Injury
8. Your Country Needs You
9. Pyramid Scheme
10. Border Guards
11. Wireless Web
12. Get in a Line

Page 40

1. Get in Line
2. Sleepin,' Again, in Class
3. Smallville
4. Shady Characters
5. Nervous System
6. Loose Cannon
7. Caesar's Legions
8. Hot Stuff
9. Out in the Cold
10. Hot Tamales
11. He's Out There in the Cold
12. Look Both Ways Before Crossin' the Street

Page 41

1. Twisting the Truth
2. Quarter Back
3. Fill in the Blanks
4. Calculated Risk or Total Risk
5. It's Long Overdue
6. Bad Advice
7. Burning the Candle at Both Ends
8. I Am in it Over My Head
9. Vanished Into Thin Air
10. Things are Looking Up
11. She's Out of Your League
12. Cutie Pie

Page 42

1. Circle of Life
2. The Ball is in Your Court
3. Roger Over & Out
4. Routine Check Up
5. Icy Slopes
6. Placed Under Arrest
7. Duel Purpose
8. Urban Sprawl
9. I Am Dreamin' of a White Christmas
10. You are Right on Target
11. I Am Dreaming of a White Christmas
12. Workin' Behind the Scenes

Page 43

1. I Am Overcome with Joy
2. LowCal Soda
3. Crash Diet
4. Slim Pickin's
5. Turn Over a New Leaf
6. Getting on Track
7. To Die For
8. Win in Triple Overtime
9. Time is on My Side
10. Top Dog
11. Double Talk
12. Five Day Forecast

Page 44

1. Brains Over Brawn
2. Close Quarters
3. Chasing After a Dream
4. Two For One Stock-Split
5. Taxable Income
6. All Booked Up
7. Checkmate, Game Between Us is Over Now
8. Quadruple Bypass
9. One for All and All for One
10. Daybreak
11. All Bent Out of Shape
12. Work in Progress

Page 45

1. Division of Labor
2. Summarize the Paragraphs
3. Continental Divide
4. He's Getting Under my Skin
5. She's Getting On my Nerves
6. Male Bonding
7. A Little Knowledge is a Dangerous Thing
8. (The) Top Story
9. She'll Be Coming Around the Mountain
10. Feelin' Your Way Around
11. Division of Labor
12. I'll be Waitin' for You Outside

Page 46

1. Feelin' Your Way Around It
2. Morning Has Broken
3. Spring is in the Air
4. Excuses, Excuses
5. Running Down the Sidelines
6. Well Rounded
7. Weepin' Willow
8. Navy Seal
9. Weeping Willow
10. Nothing Left to Lose
11. Bartlett Pairs
12. Rolling in the Aisles

Page 47

1. Check it Twice
2. Hopin' to Break Even
3. Getting' it All Together
4. (The) Plane is Circling the Airport
5. Great Barrier Reef
6. Getting Into It
7. Growing Weary
8. Getting Into It
9. Part Time Job
10. Standing on Shaky Ground
11. You Have E-mail
12. Prosperity is Right Around the Corner

Page 48

1. Little Known Fact
2. Blown to Bits
3. Step Brothers
4. It Went Up in Smoke
5. Grading On a Curve
6. Senseless Crimes
7. Close Quarters
8. Yukon Penninsula
9. Lose a Little Weight
10. Top Half of the Class
11. Lose Some Weight
12. Get the Lead Out

Page 49

1. It's Long Overdue
2. Home Alone
3. Crazy Eights
4. Pick it Up a Step
5. Robin Hood and Little John
6. You Are a Fancy Dresser
7. Golden Years
8. Leave at Once
9. Second Nature
10. No Two Snowflakes are Alike
11. Tether Ball
12. Sweet Nothings

Page 50

1. To Have and To Hold
2. I'll Bend Over Backwards for You
3. Up Periscope
4. You and I See Eye to Eye
5. He' 'n All Around Good Guy
6. Dead in the Water
7. He's Inexperienced
8. Mixed Drinks Before Dinner
9. It's Invisible
10. Focus on the Positive
11. Cabin Fever
12. 12th Round Knockout

Page 51

1. Things Are Looking Up
2. Spread Eagle
3. Overcoming the Obstacles
4. Way Behind Schedule
5. That's Ineffective
6. He's Way Behind Schedule
7. Apple Cider
8. Forget About It
9. You Can Count on Me
10. No Backtalk
11. Contour Map
12. Spread a Little Wealth

Page 52

1. Low in Fat
2. You Get Two Chances
3. Low in Fat
4. Shot in the Dark
5. Bounce Up and Down
6. Case in Point
7. ZZ Top
8. Lowering the Boom
9. What's In It For Me?
10. Sight For Sore Eyes
11. All in a Day's Work
12. They Are Incompatible

Page 53

1. Staggering Costs
2. More Often Than Not
3. Rising to the Occasion
4. In Awhile Crocodile
5. Faces in the Crowd
6. He's Insensitive
7. She's Oversensitive
8. Looking Back on My Life
9. Medical Breakthrough
10. Torn Between Two Lovers
11. Reality Check
12. Put it Behind You

Page 54

1. Crimson & Clover, Over and Over Again
2. Bored Out of My Mind
3. Crimson & Clover, Over and Over Again
4. Man on 1st Base
5. Some Times You Win, Some Times You Loose
6. Changing of the Guard
7. Fork Over the Money
8. It Ain't Over Till It's Over
9. Once and Again
10. Fall Out of Favor
11. Double or Nothing
12. Two and a Half Men

Page 55

1. Tea for Two and Two for Tea
2. Boulder, Colorado
3. (It's a) Guy Thing
4. 49'ers
5. At Ease Men
6. Turn Back the Hands of Time
7. Whole is Greater Than the Sum of the Parts
8. Painless Operation
9. (The) Captain Goes Down with The Ship
10. Train of Thought
11. Temporary Set Back
12. Come Out with Your Hands Up

Page 56

1. Comic Relief
2. The Haves and Have Not's
3. I Am Workin' Late Tonight
4. Two Fast and Furious For Me
5. Fine by Me
6. How to Lose a Guy in 10 Days
7. You Win Some, You Loose Some
8. Tip-Toe Through the Tulips
9. Staggered Start
10. A Long Essay on Life
11. Two Tickets to Paradise
12. Exit Wounds

Page 57

1. Blank Stare
2. Sea Biscuit
3. Little Boy Blue
4. Running Backwards
5. Contract Extension
6. He's Runnin' Backwards
7. Great Things Come in Small Packages
8. Vitamin A Deficiency
9. Part Time Under-Paid Job
10. A Bit Short on Cash
11. Vitamin Deficiency
12. Quick Turn Around Time

Page 58

1. Headless Horseman
2. LowCal Soda
3. Headless Horseman
4. To Coin a Phrase
5. Tropical Depression
6. Malcolm in the Middle
7. Elbows on the Table
8. One Foot in Front of the Other
9. No Elbows on the Table
10. Split Wide Open
11. One Foot In Front of the Other
12. Split Wide Open

Page 59

1. Starting From Scratch
2. That's Past Tense
3. Startin' From Scratch
4. Jumping Up and Down Over Good News
5. 5 Golden Rings
6. Grand Jury Indictment
7. Are You Ready For More?
8. Mixed Doubles
9. That's Incorrect
10. (The) Fish in the Sea
11. Inoperable Condition
12. He Got Kicked Out

Page 60

1. Operating under False Pretenses
2. I'll Stand Up For You
3. Stand by Me
4. Good Times Are Coming
5. For Eternity
6. Roll Back or Roll Reversal
7. Get Out of Here
8. Mixed Vegetables
9. For Eternity
10. Playin' Hard to Get
11. Holy Spirit
12. Get Out of Here

Page 61

1. Falling End Over End
2. Your Reputation Precedes You
3. Fallin' End Over End
4. Parking in (the) Rear
5. All's Quiet On the Western Front
6. Faint of Heart
7. Mirror Mirror on the Wall
8. Trial Separation
9. Peregrine Falcon Hawk
10. She Turned Her Nose Up
11. Spread Sheet
12. Look Out Below

Page 62

1. It Comes with Strings Attached
2. Half-Hearted Attempt
3. It Comes with No Strings Attached
4. Animal Instincts
5. Tale of Two Cities
6. Repeat Performance
7. That's Inaccurate
8. Little Rock, Arkansas
9. Tune Up
10. It's coming at You from All Directions
11. Star Wars Trilogy
12. Repeat Performance

Page 63

1. Golden Anniversary
2. What's Black & White and Red All Over
3. Shark Infested Water
4. Waiting in Line
5. Lone Star State
6. In Around-About Way
7. Flat Out Broke
8. Downtrodden Day
9. Clear the Undergrowth
10. We Are Outnumbered
11. Downsize the Inventory
12. Flat Out Broke, Dude

Position Puzzle - *Words Only* ANSWERS

Page 65

1. Scatterbrain
2. Addresses
3. Crossfire
4. Checkbook
5. Trapezoid
6. Suitcases
7. Seasonings
8. Trapeze
9. Turpentine
10. Zebras
11. Microprocessor
12. Deficiency

Page 66

1. Condensation
2. Crossbreed
3. Follow
4. Firsthand
5. Shakespeare
6. Yellow
7. Unbalanced
8. Wiring
9. Prolong
10. Secondhand
11. Explain
12. Cheapskate

Page 67

1. Copyright
2. Terror
3. Overexposure
4. Boil
5. Defense
6. Backfire
7. Belittle
8. Buoyancy
9. Underexposed
10. Handshake
11. Hightail
12. Buoyancy

Page 68

1. Furrows
2. Razor
3. Billow
4. Entrap
5. Willow
6. Backboard
7. Halo
8. Molten
9. Stickup
10. Spearmint
11. Earthbound
12. Capitalism

Page 69

1. Banjo
2. Backlog
3. Hybrid
4. Deadbeat
5. Drawback
6. Cannonball
7. Terrapin
8. Hangnail
9. Lefty
10. Tendency
11. Boysenberries
12. Lotion

Page 70

1. Syrup
2. Ambiguous
3. Halfback
4. Gallup
5. Halfback
6. Encircle
7. Ketchup
8. Locate
9. Lower Case
10. Turnip
11. Eyeball
12. Loafer

Page 71

1. Round-up
2. Partially
3. Forebear
4. Microwave
5. Fortune
6. Beaten
7. Logo
8. Deadlock
9. Details
10. Gravy
11. Blacktop
12. Outboard

Page 72

1. Gourmet
2. Setup
3. Forecast
4. Monologue
5. Forefathers
6. Paragraphs
7. Peony
8. Blowup
9. Manhole
10. Tulips
11. Adamant
12. Outdated

Page 73

1. Headquarters
2. Rounded
3. Backwoods
4. Banshee
5. Behalf
6. Candy
7. Parasites
8. Pickup
9. Cannibal
10. Roundtrip
11. Cannabis
12. Handout

Page 74

1. Highlights
2. Herring
3. Hoe-down
4. Summer
5. Low-key
6. Inexpensive
7. Mailbox
8. Topnotch
9. One-way
10. Pinup
11. Cutthroat
12. Sellout

Page 75

1. Exterminate
2. Loaded
3. Pioneers
4. Sideways
5. Spirit
6. Dead-end
7. Cyclones
8. Silo
9. Forensic
10. Touchdown
11. Tour
12. Format

What's the Word?

These fun little puzzles have readers trying to figure out the **ONE** word that the other words are describing. Think hard – have fun!

Example 1:
Not a high laugh

Answer:
A low "ha" Wait a minute….that's ALOHA!

Example 2:
5th letter with a green light

Answer:
"E" Go Oh…that's EGO!

*Hints: Words or letters in quotation marks are the actual used words or sounds in the WORD. Example: Double "buh" Answer: Two "buh" = Tuba

What's the Word?

	CLUE	*Literal Answer*	*ANSWER*
1.	4th letter, placard	"D" Sign	Design
2.	Stumble…close to the ground	Fall – Low	Follow
3.	Before the second, foot cousin	1st Hand	Firsthand
4.	Tavern ringer	Bar Bell	Barbell
5.	An upset flea-type bug	A Cross Tick	Acrostic
6.	An extra "agus"	A Spare "Agus"	Asparagus
7.	Rattle the javelin	Shake Spear	Shakespeare
8.	Height challenged wedding dessert	Short Cake	Shortcake
9.	Electrocute "ING"	Shock "ing"	Shocking
10.	Double "BUH"	Two "buh"	Tuba
11.	Two dishonest remarks	Pair of Lies	Paralyze
12.	Shares of the RE corporation	RE Stock	Restock
13.	Choose the 12th letter	Pick "L"	Pickle
14.	Street jogger	Road Runner	Roadrunner
15.	Scream close to the ground	Yell Low	Yellow
16.	"UN" in equilibrium	"Un" Balanced	Unbalanced
17.	Copper string wedding band	Wire Ring	Wiring
18.	Not for the short issue	Pro Long	Prolong
19.	Hit the 5th letter	Punch "E"	Punchy
20.	#2 leg cousin	2nd Hand	Secondhand
21.	Fast 5th letter	Quick "E"	Quickie
22.	25th letter, Nothing fancy	"X" Plain	Explain
23.	Uncooked "CAM"	"CAM" Raw	Camera
24.	4th letter smell	"D" Scent	Descent
25.	Automobiles animal	Car Pet	Carpet
26.	Bovine, tongue movement	Cow Lick	Cowlick
27.	Area of nothing	A Void	Avoid

CLUE	Literal Answer	ANSWER
28. Honey-maker, on the way	Bee Coming	Becoming
29. Margarine maggot	Butter Fly	Butterfly
30. Stupid ringers	Dumb Bells	Dumbbell
31. 25th letter's harbor	"X" Port	Export
32. Display the animal hair	Show Fur	Chauffeur
33. 5th letter with green light	"E" Go	Ego
34. Sketch the Golden Gate	Draw Bridge	Drawbridge
35. Extra 4th letter	"D" Spare	Despair
36. Inexpensive roller blade	Cheap Skate	Cheapskate
37. Done and past, the revealing	Over Exposure	Overexposure
38. Wedding band director	Ring Leader	Ringleader
39. Poverty stricken "SHUN"	Poor "SHUN"	Portion
40. "Left On" opposite	Right Off	Write off
41. Lawn limb	Yard Stick	Yardstick
42. Xerox the other left	Copy Right	Copyright
43. Uncooked cookie, smell	Dough Scent	Docent
44. Jar "UH" Urine	Can "UH" Pee	Canopy
45. Not a high laugh	A Low "Ha"	Aloha
46. Trip onto my patella	Fell on Knee	Felony
47. Jab the 5th letter	Poke "E"	Pokey
48. A dog foot and…another dog foot	Paw Paw	Papa
49. Rip "ERR" in half	Tear "Err"	Terror
50. "RE", hunt	"RE" Search	Research
51. Marijuana hook	Pot Latch	Potlatch
52. Eggshell colored paneling	White Wall	Whitewall
53. Beneath the appendage	Under Hand	Underhand
54. Tool for squeezing and holding "DEL"	A "DEL" Vice	Edelweiss
55. Honey-makers buddy	Bee Friend	Befriend
56. Pectoral, hard-shelled legume	Chest Nut	Chestnut
57. Charge for "TRO's"	"TRO" Fee	Trophy
58. Stupid discovered	Dumb Found	Dumbfound
59. Beat the burger with a stick	Club Sandwich	Club Sandwich
60. Guys working for the "ABDO" Corp.	"ABDO" Men	Abdomen

	CLUE	***Literal Answer***	***ANSWER***
61.	Triple 4th letter	Three D	3-D
62.	Made-to-order sight organs	Custom Eyes	Customize
63.	Metal encase the gentleman	Can Sir	Cancer
64.	Take a hatchet to the letter "S"	Ax "S"	Access
65.	Young male, 12th letter	Boy "L"	Boil
66.	Chain link to keep the 4th letter out	"D" Fence	Defense
67.	No money for me & you	Poor Us	Porous
68.	Quiz the 5th letter	Test "E"	Testy
69.	15th letters area	"O" Zone	Ozone
70.	Gently swing baby "ET"	Rock "et"	Rocket
71.	Walk over the stream of light	Cross Beam	Crossbeam
72.	Gate jelly	Door Jam	Doorjamb
73.	Not the front flame	Back Fire	Backfire
74.	2nd letter …small	"B" Little	Belittle
75.	Not the front of the bun	Roll Back	Rollback
76.	Electrocute "ING"	Shock "ING"	Shocking
77.	Split the 5th letter	Part "E"	Party
78.	Two "KEETS"	Pair of "KEETS"	Parakeets
79.	Lacking a ringer	No Bell	Noble
80.	Take on yellow metal as life partner	Marry Gold	Marigold
81.	4th letter's essay	"D" Composition	Decomposition
82.	Young man in an ocean	Boy in Sea	Buoyancy
83.	Toes short letter	Foot Note	Footnote
84.	4th letter sightseeing expedition	"D" Tour	Detour
85.	House hinged entry way	A Door	Adore
86.	Mother or father	A Parent	Apparent
87.	Beneath….revealed	Under Exposed	Underexposed
88.	4th letters cover	"I" Lid	Eyelid
89.	Sum up the skirts	Add Dresses	Addresses
90.	Get introduced to Pooh' donkey	Meet Eeyore	Meteor
91.	All fingers, rattle	Hand Shake	Handshake
92.	Garden mound-builder's butts	Mole Asses	Molasses
93.	Slimy mallard	Gooey Duck	Geoduck
94.	15th letter guy	"O" Men	Omen

CLUE		Literal Answer	ANSWER
95.	Hello, folk story	High Tail	Hightail
96.	Sick bald bird	Ill Eagle	Illegal
97.	Emerald vertebrae	Green Back	Greenback
98.	Tomorrow is when to get a major sunburn	Fry Day	Friday
99.	Child's patella	Kid Knee	Kidney
100.	Not-dead shares of a corp.	Live Stock	Livestock
101.	Female pest	Lady Bug	Ladybug
102.	Got to have the 12th letter	Need "L"	Needle
103.	Bailed grass, telephone line	Hay Wire	Haywire
104.	15th letter's harbor	"O" Bay	Obey
105.	Transfer the 5th letter	Move "E"	Movie
106.	2 + 2, leg cousin	4 Arm	Forearm
107.	Longing for the English drink	Miss Tea	Misty
108.	Queen's stupid husband	King Dumb	Kingdom
109.	Off opposite, piece of lumber	On Board	Onboard
110.	Snooze bag	Nap Sack	Knapsack
111.	Little dog bite at the 12th letter	Nip "L"	Nipple
112.	Pet hair, columns cousin	Fur Rows	Furrows
113.	Massage the girl	Rub Her	Rubber
114.	Money-less, serving platter	Poor Tray	Portray
115.	Protected Saltine	Safe Cracker	Safecracker
116.	Naked 5th letter	Bare "E"	Berry
117.	Lumber oven	Wood Stove	Woodstove
118.	Fermented grape juice, leg joint	Wine Knee	Whiny
119.	Put the 5th letter in a sack	Bag "E"	Baggy
120.	Lift up the girl	Raise Her	Razor
121.	William not high	Bill (or Will) Low	Billow or Willow
122.	The wave behind a boat	A Wake	Awake
123.	14th letter, snare	N Trap	Entrap
124.	Decommission the adult maggot	Fire Fly	Firefly
125.	Money-less, young male	Poor Boy	Poor-boy
126.	15th letter, tied ribbon	"O" Bow	Oboe
127.	English mom, 5th letter	Mum "E"	Mummy

	CLUE	***Literal Answer***	***ANSWER***
128.	Group, emerald color	Gang Green	Gangrene
129.	Golf ball holder, Urine	Tee, Pee	Teepee
130.	Punch on a keyboard, throw a fishing line	Type Cast	Typecast
131.	Ouch assassin	Pain Killer	Painkiller
132.	Happy cat sound, men's 3-piece	Purr Suit	Pursuit
133.	"RE", not many, 12th letter	Re Few "L"	Refuel
134.	Female, check mass	Broad Weigh	Broadway
135.	Vertebrae, piece of lumber	Back Board	Backboard
136.	4th Letter, music score	"D" Composition	Decomposition
137.	Got introduced to 2+2	Met a "4"	Metaphor
138.	Horse food, not high	Hay, Low	Halo
139.	Arm cousin, job	Leg, Work	Legwork
140.	"Less women" opposite	More Men	Mormon
141.	"Hee" cousin, splinter from a rose bush	Haw Thorn	Hawthorn
142.	Mound building garden pest, after 9	Mole Ten	Molten
143.	Experience scent of the 5th letter	Smell "E"	Smelly
144.	Green light, pet hair	Go Fur	Gopher
145.	Above neck, skirt	Head Dress	Headdress
146.	Cardiac nation	Heart Land	Heartland
147.	"RE", plant embryo	"RE" Seed	Reseed
148.	Limb, mug	Stick Cup	Stickup
149.	Javelin, Coin production plant	Spear Mint	Spearmint
150.	Our planet's leap	Earth Bound	Earthbound
151.	Opposite lowercase "ISM"	Capital "ISM"	Capitalism
152.	Bake the 5th letters	Cook "E"	Cookies
153.	After middle C	"D" Note	Denote
154.	Prohibit Joseph	Ban Joe	Banjo
155.	Not the front, fallen tree	Back Log	Backlog
156.	Above the neck, illumination	Head Light	Headlight
157.	Hello, sourdough	Hi! Bread	Hybrid
158.	Try the flavor of a golf ball holder	Taste Tee	Tasty
159.	No longer living, purplish vegetable	Dead Beet	Deadbeat
160.	14th letter won the lotto	"N" Rich	Enrich
161.	Sketch the vertebrae	Draw Back	Drawback

	CLUE	Literal Answer	ANSWER
162.	Soup container up upon a sphere	Can on Ball	Cannonball
163.	Ax "ER"	Chop "ER"	Chopper
164.	Ocular charge	Eye Rate	Irate
165.	Open up and say this, 17th letter, Cake cousin	Ahh, Q, Pie	Occupy
166.	15th letter's buddy	"O" Pal	Opal
167.	Female thumb	Lady Finger	Ladyfinger
168.	Scour the 5th letter	Scrub "E"	Scrubby
169.	Destroyed, 45°	Wrecked Angle	Rectangle
170.	Bottom, not many	Rear Few	Review
171.	Rip a ballpoint marker	Tear a Pen	Terrapin
172.	A couple of Doctors	Pair of Doc.'s	Paradox
173.	"RE" umbilical	"RE" cord	Record
174.	Shelled embryo abuser	Egg Beater	Eggbeater
175.	Ax the twigs	Chop Sticks	Chopsticks
176.	Douglas fir, 13th letter	A tree, "M"	Atrium
177.	Push pin	A Tack	Attack
178.	Put a noose around the 16-Penny	Hang Nail	Hangnail
179.	Longing for the 12th letter	Miss "L"	Missile
180.	Didn't bring the 5th letter home	Left "E"	Lefty
181.	Steam press the 5th letter	Iron "E"	Irony
182.	"Give-on" opposite	Take Off	Take-off
183.	Golf ball holder, mug	Tee Cup	Teacup
184.	After 9, Bear home, 3rd letter	10, Den "C"	Tendency
185.	12th letter, tied ribbon	"L" Bow	Elbow
186.	Adult maggot next to the man in shining armor	Fly by Knight	Fly-by-night
187.	24th letter, grape squeezer	"X" Press	Express
188.	Knock out the concave in the car	Deck a Dent	Decadent
189.	4th letter quiz	"D" Test	Detest
190.	Light "ER" on fire	Burn "ER"	Burner
191.	Take $ for 1 "BRATE"	Sell a "BRATE"	Celebrate
192.	Chair for the 4th letter	"D" Seat	Deceit
193.	Put the adolescents in metal jars	Can Teens	Canteens

	CLUE	Literal Answer	ANSWER
194.	Young men in a brier patch	Boys in Berries	Boysenberries
195.	Tied ribbon, what grapes grow on	Bow Vines	Bovines
196.	18th letter, I	"R" Me	Army
197.	Leg cousin, 5th letter	Arm "E"	Army
198.	Pig cleaning	Hog Wash	Hogwash
199.	Not high, "SHUN"	Low "SHUN"	Lotion
200.	Display rifle	Show Gun	Shogun
201.	Flesh, Leg joint	Skin Knee	Skinny
202.	Knighted Englishman, down opposite	Sir Up	Syrup
203.	PM opposite, large, America abbreviation	AM Big U.S.	Ambiguous
204.	Seriously date the boat	Court Ship	Courtship
205.	Cardiac fire	Heart Burn	Heartburn
206.	Split in two, front opposite	Half Back	Halfback
207.	Mouth rim, wash basin	Lips Sink	Lip-synch
208.	Lacking the 12th letter	No "L"	Noel
209.	Missing the "little piggies"	Lack Toes	Lactose
210.	"Guy-down" opposite	Gal Up	Gallup
211.	14th letter in the round	"N" circle	Encircle
212.	Sketch the small rope	Draw String	Drawstring
213.	Car, angel instrument	Auto Harp	Autoharp
214.	Take money for 1 "BRATE"	Sell a "BRATE"	Celebrate
215.	"Drop (the ball) - down" opposite	Catch Up	Ketchup
216.	Not high, Katherine	Low Kate	Locate
217.	Spear the 5th letter	Gore "E"	Gory
218.	Reduce the height of a 24 pack	Lower Case	Lowercase
219.	Color the roadside vegetation	Paint Brush	Paintbrush
220.	Startle the 5th letter	Scare "E"	Scary
221.	Change direction, light dog bite	Turn Nip	Turnip
222.	Classify the 5th letter	Sort "E"	Sortie
223.	Knighted, use profanity	Sir Cuss	Circus
224.	9th letter, sphere	"I" Ball	Eyeball
225.	Coming up to hit the ball is the player after player "D"	Batter "E"	Battery
226.	4th letter illumination	"D" light	Delight

	CLUE	*Literal Answer*	*ANSWER*
227.	14th letter head first into the water	"N" Dive	Endive
228.	Margarine phalanges	Butter Fingers	Butterfingers
229.	The plane after plane "D"	Jet "E"	Jetty
230.	Not high, animals hair	Low Fur	Loafer
231.	Ballistic device, foot phalange	Missile Toe	Mistletoe
232.	Crazy, movement	Loco Motion	Locomotion
233.	Cut tree, jelly	Log Jam	Logjam
234.	Not smooth home	Rough House	Roughhouse
235.	Marijuana hook	Pot Latch	Potlatch
236.	Sewing line, anxiety	Seam Stress	Seamstress
237.	"Square-down" opposite	Round Up	Round-up
238.	Parchment mass	Paper Weight	Paper weight
239.	Not all of the 5th letter	Partial "E"	Partially
240.	Viewed the floating dirt	Saw Dust	Sawdust
241.	2+2, grizzly	4 Bear	Forebear
242.	Above neck, straight mark	Head Line	Headline
243.	House, throw-up	Home Sick	Homesick
244.	Small Tsunami	Micro Wave	Microwave
245.	"Foot sit" opposite	Hand Stand	Hand Stand
246.	2+2, lowest part of the face	4 Chin	Fortune
247.	Dog do when hot, 5th letters	Pant "E's"	Panties
248.	Snip, lumber	Clip Board	Clipboard
249.	Cool down the 5th letter	Chill "E"	Chili
250.	Linked metal rope, fire by-product	Chain Smoke	Chain-smoke
251.	Hack up the 5th letter	Cough "E"	Coffee
252.	Frigid, deltoid muscle	Cold Shoulder	Cold shoulder
253.	14th letter somersault	"N" Roll	Enroll
254.	Above neck, musical group	Head Band	Headband
255.	Mouth rim, limb	Lip Stick	Lipstick
256.	Speed it up, walking stick	Hurry Cane	Hurricane
257.	Beach dirt, broom pilots	Sand Witches	Sandwiches
258.	3rd letter, we would contraction	"C" We'd	Seaweed
259.	Turn around & around, scratch an ___	Spin Itch	Spinach
260.	Ax the 5th letter	Chop "E"	Choppy

	CLUE	Literal Answer	ANSWER
261.	Victory over the 14th letter	Beat "N"	Beaten
262.	Automobile country	Car Nation	Carnation
263.	Hat, Are you positive?	Cap Sure?	Capture
264.	"High-stop" opposite	Low Go	Logo
265.	In opposite, piece of lumber	Out Board	Outboard
266.	Put one "DUH " in a tin jar	Can a "duh"	Canada
267.	Throw away the 12th letter	Chuck "L"	Chuckle
268.	Tell the sphere he is out of a job	Fire Ball	Fireball
269.	Embryo, put seeds in the ground	Egg Plant	Eggplant
270.	Not living, dead-bolt	Dead Lock	Deadlock
271.	Lady, hop	Broad Jump	Broad-jump
272.	Throw away Redflyer	Chuck Wagon	Chuck-wagon
273.	Foot cousin, sphere	Hand Ball	Handball
274.	Out opposite, "A" penny	In a Cent	Innocent
275.	Ocean cousin, wood cut tool	Sea Saw	Seesaw
276.	Start tennis with a…, picnic pest	Serve Ant	Servant
277.	14th letter, to do notes	"N" List	Enlist
278.	Inexpensive writing tool	Cheap Pen	Cheapen
279.	Girl edge	Broad Side	Broadside
280.	Grizzlies Vertebrae	Bear Back	Bareback
281.	4th letter, what wags	"D" Tails	Details
282.	Ash colored, 22nd letter	Gray "V"	Gravy
283.	Wrestling winning move, "A", golf call	Pin "A" Fore	Pinafore
284.	Give the briers a bad time	Raz Berries	Raspberries
285.	____on the straw, plant embryo	Suck Seed	Succeed
286.	"Crooked-leg" opposite	Straight Arm	Straight-arm
287.	Automobile, green light	Car Go	Cargo
288.	"White-bottom" opposite	Black Top	Blacktop
289.	Spear the 5th month	Gore May	Gourmet
290.	Under opposite, 24th letter, do it for pictures, confident	Over "X" Pose Sure	Overexposure
291.	6 games in tennis, down opposite	Set Up	Setup
292.	Viewed equine	Saw Horse	Sawhorse

	CLUE	Literal Answer	ANSWER
293.	2 bangs	Pair of Shoots	Parachutes
294.	A survey, bank's safe	Poll, Vault	Pole-vault
295.	2+2, throw the fishing line	4, Cast	Forecast
296.	Smeller, head first into water	Nose Dive	Nosedive
297.	This ___ That, rifle	Or Gun	Organ
298.	Opens a door, nothing to do	Key Bored	Keyboard
299.	On opposite, coil	Off Spring	Offspring
300.	"Female – woman" opposite	Male Man	Mailman
301.	9th then 15th letter, eat out	I O Dine	Iodine
302.	No money, characteristic	Poor Trait	Portrait
303.	Weakest chess piece, working garage	Pawn Shop	Pawnshop
304.	Spook, raven	Scare Crow	Scarecrow
305.	Undercover surveillance, Ocean cousin	Spy Sea	Spicy
306.	_____on the straw, sewage _____pool	Suck Cess	Success
307.	Green opposite, 5th letter	Red "E"	Ready
308.	Child, snooze	Kid Nap	Kidnap
309.	"In-sitting" opposite	Out Standing	Outstanding
310.	Unlocks door, yes opposite	Key No	Keno
311.	Isn't the 5th letter	Not "E"	Naughty
312.	Youth kissing disease, cut tree	Mono Log	Monologue
313.	"Mr. Water" opposite	Miss Fire	Misfire
314.	10th then 12th letter, feathered friend	"J" "L" Bird	Jailbird
315.	2+2, dads	4 Fathers	Forefathers
316.	In opposite, windows cousins	Out Doors	Outdoors
317.	Kissing disease, Raymond, 12th letter	Mono Ray "L"	Monorail
318.	Quickly pull the 5th letter	Jerk "E"	Jerky
319.	"Foot-in" opposite	Hand Out	Handout
320.	2 dice	Pair of dice	Paradise
321.	Needle and thread, close to the ground	Sew Low	Solo
322.	Tear umbilical	Rip Cord	Ripcord
323.	Friend or ___, pull a car, Policeman, 5th letter	For Tow Cop "E"	Photocopy

	CLUE	*Literal Answer*	*ANSWER*
324.	Undercover surveillance, window material	Spy Glass	Spyglass
325.	Make the 14th letter stumble	Trip "L"	Triple
326.	Wash basin, 4/4	Sink Whole	Sinkhole
327.	A couple of business graphs	Pair of Graphs	Paragraphs
328.	16th letter, off opposite, leg joint	"P" On Knee	Peony
329.	____on a banana peel, under____ cop	Slip Cover	Slipcover
330.	Also, crease	Too Fold	Twofold
331.	Honey maker, chain____fence	Bee Link	Blink
332.	Suck down opposite	Blow Up	Blowup
333.	Woman opposite, complete	Man Whole	Manhole
334.	Murder happiness	Kill Joy	Killjoy
335.	Right opposite, plane appendage	Left Wing	Left-wing
336.	In opposite, pop	Out Burst	Outburst
337.	Basic life unit, him opposite	Cell Her	Cellar or Seller
338.	Also, surrounds the mouth	Too Lips	Tulips
339.	"RE", pet hair	"RE" fur	Refer
340.	Wrestling winning more, sphere	Pin Ball	Pinball
341.	"SUH", wash basin	"SUH" Sink	Succinct
342.	10th letter, next after crawling	"J" Walking	Jaywalking
343.	"Pull-under" opposite	Push Over	Pushover
344.	Honey-baked, string	Ham String	Hamstring
345.	Middle of earth, 12th letter	Core "L"	Corral
346.	Eve's partner, picnic pest	Adam Ant	Adamant
347.	Honey-maker, light thump on the head	Bee Bop	Be-bop
348.	Division of a hospital	A Ward	Award
349.	5th letter, past tense ride	"E" Rode	Erode
350.	"Wet –dirt" opposite	Dry Clean	Dry-clean
351.	Metal jar, do past tense	Can Did	Candid
352.	School vehicle, young man	Bus Boy	Busboy
353.	Noose use, down opposite	Hang Up	Hang-up
354.	5th letter, Harbor	"E" Bay	E-bay
355.	In opposite, went out as a couple	Out Dated	Outdated
356.	Took a match to the 12th letter	Lit "L"	Little

	CLUE	*Literal Answer*	*ANSWER*
357.	Foot cousin, coils	Hand Springs	Handsprings
358.	Above the neck, $.25 pieces	Head Quarters	Headquarters
359.	Square opposite, Edward	Round Ed	Rounded
360.	Cannabis, 4/4	Pot Hole	Pothole
361.	"AT", afraid of roof growth	"AT" Moss Fear	Atmosphere
362.	Front opposite, could's cousin	Back Would's	Backwoods
363.	Sack the plumbing	Bag Pipes	Bagpipes
364.	Prohibit her	Ban She	Banshee
365.	13th letter's knee support	"M" Brace	Embrace
366.	5th letters, 12th letter	"E's" "L"	Easel
367.	Barbie_____, fish appendage	Doll Fin	Dolphin
368.	Honey-maker, weapon	Bee Gun	Begun
369.	"Buy-him" opposite	Sell Her	Cellar or Seller
370.	Deed to a gold mine	A Claim	Acclaim
371.	2nd letter, leg joint	"B" Knee	Beanie
372.	Similar to smash, empty opposite	Bash Full	Bashful
373.	Honey-maker, purpose	Bee Cause	Because
374.	4th letter, "eyes, nose, mouth…"	"D" Face	Deface
375.	Pull the fish scooper	Drag Net	Dragnet
376.	Not hot, holiday meat	Cold Turkey	Cold-turkey
377.	Beat the ham-on-rye with a stick	Club Sandwich	Club Sandwich
378.	½ of a honey-maker	Bee Half	Behalf
379.	Metal jar, 4th letter	Can "D"	Candy
380.	Put a school vehicle in a metal jar	Can a Bus	Cannabis
381.	Put a male cow in a metal jar	Can a Bull	Cannibal
382.	Wagon, Tire	Cart Wheel	Cartwheel
383.	Tear production, girl sibling abbreviation	Cry Sis	Crisis
384.	Slice the vertebrae	Cut Back	Cutback
385.	Couple of medical personnel	Pair of Medics	Paramedics
386.	Sight sight	Pair of Sights	Parasites
387.	Choose, down opposite	Pick Up	Pickup
388.	16th letter, push opposite	"P" Pull	People
389.	Square opposite, stumble	Round Trip	Roundtrip
390.	Exchange for money, in opposite	Sell Out	Sellout

	CLUE	*Literal Answer*	*ANSWER*
391.	Loan out the 5th letter	Share "E"	Sherry
392.	Ringer, young man	Bell Boy	Bellboy
393.	Feline, what cookies cool on	Cat A Rack	Cataract
394.	24th letter, do for a photograph	"X" Pose	Expose
395.	4th letter, cryptic combination	"D" Code	Decode
396.	19th letter, raven cousin	"S" Crow	Escrow
397.	Single woman title, fire starter stick	Miss Match	Mismatch
398.	"Low-heavy" opposite	High Light	Highlight
399.	Fur, wedding band	Hair Ring	Herring
400.	High slow hit in tennis, 2nd letter	Lob "B"	Lobby
401.	1/3 of Santa's laugh, up opposite	Ho Down	Hoe-down
402.	High opposite, car starter	Low Key	Low-key
403.	L,M,N,___, oozes from a sore	O, Pus	Opus
404.	Cake cousin, J,K,___, off opposite	Pile "L" On	Pylon
405.	New opposite, hour glass	Old Timer	Old-timer
406.	Ethnicity, Curds & ______	Race Whey	Raceway
407.	Fish scoop, play opposite	Net Work	Network
408.	Quiz, C,D,____	Test "E"	Testy
409.	Answer to addition, him opposite	Sum Her	Summer
410.	Medieval battering ____, ___airplane	Ram Jet	Ramjet
411.	L,M,___, Hypnotic state	"N" Trance	Entrance
412.	Policeman, E,E,E,E,….	Cop "E's"	Copies
413.	4th letter, short	"D" Brief	Debrief
414.	Honey-maker, tree droppings	Bee Leaves	Believes / Belief
415.	B,C,___, score in school	"D" Grade	Degrade
416.	Out opposite, 24th letter, thoughtful mood	In "X" Pensive	Inexpensive
417.	Lemon cousin, heavy opposite	Lime Light	Limelight
418.	Perfect pair = perfect _____, novel	Match Book	Matchbook
419.	Female opposite, punch with gloves	Male Box	Mailbox
420.	Groovy, 5th letter	Hip "E"	Hippy
421.	Bottom opposite, wood nick	Top Notch	Topnotch
422.	Street, 5th & 15th letters	Road "E" "O"	Rodeo
423.	Grocery ____, C,D,___	Store "E"	Story
424.	Bake the novel	Cook Book	Cookbook

	CLUE	*Literal Answer*	*ANSWER*
425.	Metal jar, rope's tied in a ____	Can Knot	Cannot
426.	Wood patio, what 100cm equals	Deck A Meter	Decameter
427.	Grasp the ball out of the air, down opposite	Catch Up	Ketchup
428.	Crimp, unlocks door	Kink Key	Kinky
429.	Grown up boys, first sound of a doorbell	Men Ding	Mending
430.	Not whole, sage, rosemary & _____	Part Thyme	Part-time
431.	L,M,N,___, baseball glove	"O" Mitt	Omit
432.	"Old-sit" opposite	New Stand	Newsstand
433.	Dogsled call, area in a house	Mush Room	Mushroom
434.	Use needle & thread, use needle & thread	Sew Sew	So-so
435.	Animal appendage, not heavy	Tail Light	Taillight
436.	Knighted title, award	Sir Prize	Surprise
437.	Brush the floor, cuts of beef	Sweep Steaks	Sweepstakes
438.	_____in the fish, Q,R,____, ____of the Union	Reel, "S", State	Real-estate
439.	Retail place, living on the ____	Store Edge	Storage
440.	Leg joint, "off-heavy" opposite	Knee, On Light	Neon light
441.	"Push-under" opposite	Pull Over	Pullover
442.	Past-tense win, curds & ___	Won Whey	One-way
443.	___, Y, Z, rope tightness	"X" Tension	Extension
444.	Tack cousin, down opposite	Pin Up	Pinup
445.	Church bench, leg joint	Pew Knee	Puny
446.	Metal jar, sleepiness indicator	Can Yawn	Canyon
447.	Slice the thorax	Cut Throat	Cutthroat
448.	Automobile barf	Car Sick	Carsick
449.	24th letter, semester, out opposite, eat past-tense	"X" Term In Ate	Exterminate
450.	Honey-maker, beer foam	Bee Head	Behead
451.	Rub-a-dub-___, ___M,N, naked, J,K,___	Dub "L" Bare "L"	Double Barrel
452.	Feline, said when thinking, brush cousin	Cat Uh Comb	Catacomb
453.	✓ = a check _____, car starter	Mark Key	Marquee
454.	24th letter, civil wrong or pastry type	"X" Tort	Extort
455.	Indoor walkway, smudge___	Hall Mark	Hallmark
456.	"High-alive" opposite	Low Dead	Loaded

	CLUE	*Literal Answer*	*ANSWER*
457.	¼ gallon, "ER", front opposite	Quart "ER" Back	Quarterback
458.	Chip 12th letter	Nick "L"	Nickel
459.	"Get on " the horse, L,M,___ hearing appendage	Mount "N" Ear	Mountaineer
460.	___up the tires, family's next of___	Pump Kin	Pumpkin
461.	"OB", on stage display	"Ob" Scene	Obscene
462.	Work the bread dough, 5th letter	Need "E"	Needy
463.	"Push-front" opposite	Pull Back	Pullback
464.	On opposite, yard barrier	Off Fence	Offense
465.	Cake cousin, out opposite, hearing orifice	Pie In Ears	Pioneers
466.	Shop cloth, rosemary & ____	Rag Thyme	Ragtime
467.	Edge, she ____125 lbs.	Side Weighs	Sideways
468.	Capture the 5th letters	Trap "E's"	Trapeze
469.	Bank vault, coffee or ___	Safe Tea	Safety
470.	Javelin "that thing"	Spear It	Spirit
471.	Show & ____, ___,B,C, chart	Tell "A" Graph	Telegraph
472.	___the boat, older boy	Row Man	Roman
473.	Low opposite, curds and ____	High Whey	Highway
474.	"Live-beginning" opposite	Dead End	Dead-end
475.	Tear your pants, push opposite	Rip Pull	Ripple
476.	Pan cousin, ringer, c,d,___	Pot Bell "E"	Potbelly
477.	Secretly watched someone, him opposite	Spied Her	Spider
478.	Don't ____the boat, c,d,___	Rock "E"	Rocky
479.	Medieval battering____, turn the ___in the book	Ram Page	Rampage
480.	__, Y, Z, printing___, use needle and thread	"X" Press Sew	Espresso
481.	Hearing appendage, ✓ check____	Ear Mark	Earmark
482.	Honey-maker, ___down the law	Bee Lay	Belay
483.	4'x4'x8' of cut wood	A Cord	Accord
484.	Policeman, 5th letter, feline	Cop "E" Cat	Copycat
485.	Relief sound, genetic duplicates	Sigh Clones	Cyclones
486.	Ringer, tops opposite	Bell Bottoms	Bellbottoms
487.	Metal jar, sleepy sign	Can Yawn	Canyon
488.	Automobile, adjust the guitar	Car Tune	Cartoon

	CLUE	*Literal Answer*	*ANSWER*
489.	Noah's boat, metal jar, cuts wood	Ark Can Saw	Arkansas
490.	4th letter, water dwellers, out opposite, ocean cousin	"D" Fish In Sea	Deficiency
491.	___'em or fold 'em, down opposite	Hold Up	Holdup
492.	Off opposite, bird home	On Nest	Honest
493.	Out opposite, pet hair, yes opposite	In Fur No	Inferno
494.	They're a perfect____, punch with gloves	Match Box	Matchbox
495.	Tack cousin, tire part	Pin Wheel	Pinwheel
496.	Less opposite, auction offer	More Bid	Morbid
497.	L,M,N,___, Hello, ___, P, Q	"O" Hi "O"	Ohio
498.	Past tense say, #2 playing card	Said Deuce	Seduce
499.	Go opposite, view something	Stop Watch	Stopwatch
500.	Song, where "what" goes	Tune Up	Tune-up
501.	Animal appendage, What Sherlock puts in his mouth	Tail Pipe	Tailpipe
502.	Turn around and around, on opposite	Spin Off	Spin-off
503.	_____of relief, high opposite	Sigh Low	Silo
504.	One way to tell a dog to get away, honk the ___	Shoo Horn	Shoehorn
505.	Put a blanket over the credit card transaction	Cover Charge	Cover charge

What's the Word?

PEOPLE, PLACES, PRODUCTS

Same thing as the regular "***What's the Word***" puzzles, but with a twist. All the words are well-known people, cities, states, nations, businesses, products, or animals. Good luck!

CLUE	***Literal Answer***	***ANSWER***
1. Young man's 5th letter	Boy's "E"	Boise
2. Out opposite, 4th letter, without the Red Delicous	In "D" and apple-less	Indianapolis
3. "ANNA" surrounded by the 4th letter	In "D" …"ANNA"	Indiana
4. 18th lette, is able to cut wood	"R" Can Saw	Arkansas
5. Mr. Sippy's wife	Mrs. Sippy	Mississippi
6. 2 wrongs against God while visiting the 5th letter	Sin Sin at "E"	Cincinnati
7. The 15th & 18th letters left	"O", "R" Gone	Oregon
8. Cleaning 2000 pounds	Washing Ton	Washington
9. Throw it over the boat, Goes up on birthdays	Anchor Age	Anchorage

CLUE	Literal Answer	ANSWER
10. Next after supervisor nine	Boss Ten	Boston
11. Even score, give $ for a bill	Tie Pay	Taipei
12. Mr. Ho Ho Ho, drive around	Santa Cruise	Santa Cruz
13. $ charge, between shoulders and heads	Fee Necks	Phoenix
14. Battles, woodcutting tool	War Saw	Warsaw
15. 5th month has sight	May Sees	Macy's
16. Even score, wager	Tie Bet	Tibet
17. Murder a guy, glass can-cousin, 15th letter	Kill a man Jar "O"	Kilimanjaro
18. Me, place cookies on a________ to cool	I Rack	Iraq
19. "Old-play" opposite	New Work	Newark
20. Bag one Stanley	Pack a Stan	Pakistan
21. Weiner "IN" a German beer mug	Frank "IN" Stein	Frankenstein
22. Buddy, not high, low female voice	Pal Low Alto	Palo Alto
23. Duo, 5th letter	Pair "E"	Paris
24. One after bargain "L"	Sale "M"	Salem
25. Duel stumbles	Twin Falls	Twin Falls
26. 1 little piggie, opens a lock, 15th letter	Toe Key "O"	Tokyo
27. 6th month, yes opposite	June No	Juneau
28. Buddy, open up and say..., German mug	Pal Ah Stein	Palestine
29. Growth on roofs, Bovine	Moss Cow	Moscow
30. Sight organs, 14th letter, the "H' question word, 18th letter	Eyes, "N", How, "R"	Eisenhower
31. Kenneth, ____your shirt in, 5th letter	Ken Tuck "E"	Kentucky
32. Adult male, cap, 2000 lbs.	Man Hat Ton	Manhattan
33. Get on the horse, precipitation, close	Mount Rain Near	Mt. Rainier
34. Our star, English drink, open up and say___, green light	Sun Tea Ahh Go	Santiago
35. Indy 500, was observed	Race Seen	Racine
36. 1 little piggie, follow opposite, uncooked cookies	Toe Lead Dough	Toledo

	CLUE	Literal Answer	ANSWER
37.	Happy 14th letters	Cheery "O's"	Cheerios
38.	Queen's husband's, 2000 lbs.	King's Ton	Kingston
39.	Automobile grave/shrine	Car Tomb	Khartoum
40.	Maxi opposite, use needle & thread , te te cousin	Mini Sew Tah	Minnesota
41.	"3rd letter" visiting the 12th	"C" at "L"	Seattle
42.	Sun kicks like a horse	Star Bucks	Starbucks
43.	Test, smell appendage	Quiz Nose	Quiznos
44.	Sight organ "IN" a German beer mug	Eye "IN" Stein	Einstein
45.	24th letter, off opposite	"X" On	Exxon
46.	Sound of springs	Boing	Boeing
47.	21st letter becomes a sir, Queen stupid's husband	"U" Knighted King Dumb	United Kingdom
48.	Men's neck wear, Country	Tie Land	Thailand
49.	Finished the book after book "B"	Read "C"	Red Sea
50.	Wealthy, guys	Rich Men	Richmond
51.	____of the hand, coiled wire	Palm Springs	Palm Springs
52.	Beach dirt, 4th & 1st letters, green light	Sand "D" "A" Go	San Diego
53.	Sugary, 8,9, ___	Sweet Ten	Sweden
54.	Water drillings, "near-stop" opposite	Wells Far Go	Wells Fargo
55.	Me, bowel movement (abbrev.)	I BM	IBM
56.	Church bench, airplane, what we hear	Pew Jet Sound	Puget Sound
57.	Take to court, stumbles	Sue Falls	Sioux Falls
58.	Commercial bay, country	Port Land	Portland
59.	Pal, smarter	Bud Wiser	Budweiser
60.	Don't bring the sight organs	Leave Eyes	Levi's
61.	Apple middle, 5th letter, open up and say___	Core, "E" Ahhh	Korea
62.	19th letter, browned skin, male cow	"S" Tan Bull	Istanbul
63.	"Near-stop" opposite	Far Go	Fargo
64.	Horse homes "&" lacking a ringer	Barns "&" No Bell	Barnes & Noble

	CLUE	*Literal Answer*	*ANSWER*
65.	Ringer, quick	Bell Fast	Belfast
66.	Automobile, LLL, not good	Car, L's, Bad	Carlsbad
67.	60 minutes, tin jar, wood cutting tool	Hour Can Saw	Arkansas
68.	Trailer the 5th letter, lumber	Haul "E" Wood	Hollywood
69.	Sergeant, AC/DC	General Electric	General Electric
70.	"Macro-hard" opposite	Micro Soft	Microsoft
71.	Old opposite, bay	New Port	New Port
72.	Without clothes, Sandwich shop	Nude Deli	New Delhi
73.	Speak – past tense, tin jar	Spoke Can	Spokane
74.	Pet hair, lower part of face, Sight organ, countries	Fur Chin Eye Lands	Virgin Islands
75.	Grizzly, finger band, not crooked	Bear Ring Straight	Bering Strait
76.	Open up and say…., ignite	Ahh Burn	Auburn
77.	Take "S" to court, fire Albert	Sue "S" Can Al	Suez Canal
78.	Kitchen pot cousin, "A", ____ & Pa	Pan A Ma	Panama
79.	A golf ball holder "&" another Golf ball holder	A Tee "&" Tee	AT&T
80.	10th letter, ocean cousin, cent	"J" Sea Penny	JC Penny
81.	Gave food to the 24th letter	Fed "X"	FedEx
82.	Earth mound, 2000 lbs. 1/3 of Santa's laugh, explains	Hill Ton Ho Tells	Hilton Hotels
83.	Great 365 days, double knot the 18th letters	Good Year Tie "R's"	Goodyear Tires
84.	Guay guay	Pair of Guay	Paraguay
85.	Decay, 18th letter, beaver built	Rot "R" Dam	Rotterdam
86.	Given after a yawn, wine cousin, 5th letter, open up and say…	Sigh Beer "E" Ahh	Siberia
87.	Noah's boat, tock cousin	Ark Tick	Arctic
88.	$ charge after charge "F"	Fee "G"	Fiji
89.	Cold opposite coils	Hot Springs	Hot Springs
90.	Describes muscular person, Hi	Buff Hello	Buffalo
91.	Just purchased, football shirt	New Jersey	New Jersey
92.	Adams Family cousin ____, 12th then 15th letters	It, "L" "E"	Italy

	CLUE	Literal Answer	ANSWER
93.	Off mend opposite, 5th then 15th letter On Tear, "E" "O"	On Tear "E" "O"	Ontario
94.	Spleen & kidney cousin, Swim in a swimming _______	Liver Pool	Liverpool
95.	Beach dirt, dawn opposite, 5th letter	Sand Dusk "E"	Sandusky
96.	9th then 18th letters, country	"I" "R" Land	Ireland
97.	_____the whip, "UH", foot appendage, say______	Crack a Toe Ahh	Krakatoa
98.	Type of wind that blows off a hat, murmured when thinking	A Gust Uhhh	Augusta
99.	Light –skinned, financial institutions	Fair Banks	Fairbanks
100.	Ringer, not many	Bell Few	Bellevue
101.	Flowers in the spring, 2000 lbs.	Blooming Ton	Bloomington
102.	"Del" + "del", apply 1st ____ to the cut	Add "DEL" aid	Adelaide
103.	Rug's on the _____, "uh" + "uh"	Floor Add "uh"	Florida
104.	Me sprinted	I Ran	Iran
105.	Hello, "ENA"	Hi "Ena"	Hyena
106.	Vampire ____, 8,9,____ cheek cosmetic	Bat Ten Rouge	Baton Rouge
107.	Fish appendage, country	Fin Land	Finland
108.	Company shares, house	Stock Home	Stockholm
109.	#2 writing device, blood tube 5th letter, open up & say _____	Pencil Vein "E" Ahh	Pennsylvania
110.	Catholics partake of the ____ 15th letter	Sacrament "O"	Sacramento
111.	Harbor after "N", smell bad, 15th letter	Port "O" Reek "O"	Puerto Rico
112.	15th letters, Noah's boat	"O" arc	Ozark
113.	Me, ___self, and I, Sam I ___, I	My Am Me	Miami
114.	Harbor, plant part underground	Bay Root	Beirut
115.	Tin jar, pigeon sound, 14th letter	Can Coo "N"	Cancun
116.	Put father in a sack	Bag Dad	Baghdad
117.	Ma & Pa, what dog's tails do, Off opposite	Folks Wag On	Volkswagen
118.	Vim & vigor, ocean cousin	Pep Sea	Pepsi

	CLUE	*Literal Answer*	*ANSWER*
119.	5th month, sales sticker	May Tag	Maytag
120.	Take to court, skin turns brown	Sue Tan	Sudan
121.	Get hitched to "OTT"	Marry "OTT"	Marriott
122.	____& feather, other tense of got	Tar Get	Target
123.	Jonathon, M+M+M	Jon Add "M,s"	John Adams
124.	Row of shrubs, pig	Hedge Hog	Hedgehog
125.	Bash the pop	Club Soda	Club Soda
126.	Groovy, 15th letter	Hip "O"	Hippo
127.	Tear past tense, we	Tore Us	Taurus
128.	Horse sound, ___for Victory, ocean cousin, 12th letters	Neigh "V" Sea "L's"	Navy Seals
129.	Feline, ___M,N	Cat "L"	Cattle
130.	Have to, NASA orange drink	Must Tang	Mustang
131.	A deceit, off opposite	Lie On	Lion
132.	1,__,3, can't opposite	Two Can	Toucan
133.	Going, going, ____, B,C,___	Gone "D"	Gandhi
134.	Payment notice, "doors" to pastures	Bill Gates	Bill Gates
135.	"Wrong-sisters" opposite	Right Brothers	Wright Brothers
136.	___the bill, ___down the law	Pay Lay	Pele
137.	Pig meat, unlocks doors, ___cones (from trees)	Pork Key Pine	Porcupine
138.	Male nun, starts cars	Monk Key	Monkey
139.	Small wood piece (larger than sawdust), male nuns	Chip Monks	Chipmunks
140.	Payment notice, 5th letter, cracker used in smores	Bill "E" Graham	Billy Graham
141.	Hut, back of the foot, 15th letter, get down on your knees	Shack, Heel, "O" Kneel	Shaquille O'Neil

Two-Tips Trivia

Here's a fun little twist on knowledge recall. You will be given ***TWO*** clues. The first clue will apply to **ALL** the answers in a given section. The first section, for instance is **"A".** That means **that** ALL of the answers are going to start with that letter. The next **numbered** clue should be enough information to lead you to the answer.

More than just testing your knowledge…it's a game of "***How Fast Can You Get It***?!?!?!" Shouting is accepted.

Have fun!

Two-Tips Trivia

	Clue	Answer
1.	Everglade critter	Alligator
2.	Free from Dear Abby	Advice
3.	Military Unit	Army
4.	Love it or leave it	America
5.	Lost lady pilot	Amelia Earhart
6.	Squeezable music instrument	Accordion
7.	Most populated continent	Asia
8.	Taken for headaches	Aspirin
9.	Cleopatra's poison	Asp
10.	Colleges check this for entrance, Grade point_____	Average
11.	A person born in the USA	American
12.	Work it out before court	Arbitration
13.	Beings from space	Aliens
	Fights bacteria	Antibiotic

15. First song of the year	Auld Land Syne
16. Large soaring bird	Albatross
17. Painters, sculptors, singers, actors	Artists
18. Relates to wheels	Axle
19. Married to Uncle	Aunt
20. Questions elicit….	Answers
21. Taken for upset stomachs – it fizzes	Alka Seltzer
22. Annett's man…Frankie_________	Avalon
23. Road associate with the Beatles	Abbey Road
24. They try harder than Hertz	Avis
25. Dance studios	Arthur Murray
26. Scent	Aroma
27. Feline in the streets	Alley Cats
28. Seat with limbs	Armchair
29. Proper English race track neckwear	Ascot
30. Poison associated with old lace	Arsenic
31. Has magic lamp and flying carpet	Aladdin
32. Hans Christian _________	Anderson
33. Old age joint pain	Arthritis
34. Prayer ending word	Amen
35. Place to park planes	Airport
36. Government's head lawyer	Attorney General
37. TV news reporter	Anchorman
38. Famous ___________ Cookies	Amos
39. Study of Space	Astronomy
40. Study of Earth, Moon, & Sun alignments	Astrology
41. Snap-to military posture	Attention
42. Turns litmus paper blue	Acid
43. Colorado ski town	Aspen
44. Linkletter	Art
45. Live in Pennsylvania	Amish
46. Relieve pain through poking	Acupuncture
47. Space studier	Astronomer
48. Subtraction opposite	Addition
49. Round Table King	Arthur
50. Solicit business	Advertise
51. Self-Written self story	Autobiography
52. Fish container	Aquarium
53. Aquarium cud	Algae
54. First in animal names	Aardvark

	Clue	Answer
55.	Insect eater	Anteater
56.	Old	Antique
57.	Cools the car	Air conditioner
58.	IRS check	Audit
59.	War vets frat	American Legion
60.	Alaskan city	Anchorage
61.	Bridal path	Aisle
62.	Sport star	Athlete
63.	Country of knitted blankets	Afghanistan
64.	Famous orphan	Annie
65.	Morning hours	A.M.
66.	Belgium city	Antwerp
67.	Fables storyteller	Aesop
68.	Phosphoric precipitation	Acid rain
69.	Lawrence of ___________	Arabia
70.	The Spanish ___________	Armada
71.	Stomach	Abdomen
72.	Cousin IT is part of the ______________ Family	Adam's
73.	Pennsylvania City – Billy Joel	Allentown
74.	4-1 Day	April Fool's
75.	Rental	Apartment
76.	Snow monster	Abominable Snowman
77.	All in the Family man	Archie Bunker
78.	Supermarket row	Aisle
79.	He'll be back	Arnold Schwarzeneger
80.	Horns	Antlers
81.	Sold!	Auction
82.	Teenage	Adolescence
83.	Divorce payment	Alimony
84.	Einstein	Albert
85.	Big hair	Afro
86.	Fire power	Artillery
87.	She doesn't live here anymore	Alice
88.	Indian spear points	Arrowheads
89.	Dance fitness	Aerobics
90.	Little Rock	Arkansas
91.	Regional pronunciation	Accent
92.	Make it up	Ad-Lib
3.	Religious bench	Alter
	Fall	Autumn

95.	Earthquake encore	Aftershock
96.	Mud Homes	Adobe
97.	Good hay	Alfalfa
98.	Sunken city	Atlantis
99.	Sting like a bee boxer	Ali
100.	Map book	Atlas
101.	No name	Anonymous
102.	Cyborg	Android
103.	End of book info	Appendix
104.	I'm sorry	Apology
105.	Steel bird	Airplane
106.	"A" to "Z" consommé	Alphabet soup
107.	1st three numbers	Area code
108.	Steam the leaves, eat the heart	Artichoke
109.	Foreign Representative	Ambassador
110.	Fake grass	Astro-turf
111.	Vote from home	Absentee Ballot
112.	Oak nut	Acorn
113.	"You're in good hands"	Allstate
114.	Dick Clark	American Bandstand
115.	And battery	Assault
116.	Farmer's Book	Almanac
117.	Sweet Home _________	Alabama
118.	Plane letters	Air Mail
119.	And oranges	Apples
120.	Chinese counter	Abacus
121.	Oops	Accident
122.	And Costello	Abbott
123.	E-mail or home	Address
124.	North Pole	Arctic
125.	At the beep	Answering machine
126.	Not musketeers	Amigos
127.	Guacamole	Avocado
128.	Revolve around the	Axis
129.	Limb Struggle	Arm Wrestling
130.	Benedict	Arnold
131.	Canadian Province	Alberta
132.	He digs his works	Archaeologist
133.	Noah	Ark
134.	Heavenly	Angels

135.	Scottish socks	Argyles
136.	Second name	Alias
137.	Fire fiend	Arsonist
138.	Pain in the heart	Angina
139.	With nouns	Adjectives
140.	With verbs	Adverbs
141.	Thank you – thank you very much	Applause
142.	Nut	Almond
143.	Neck	Adam's Apple
144.	Fore and	Aft
145.	Hello Hawaii	Aloha
146.	And the lion	Androcles
147.	Small angle	Acute
148.	Math	Arithmetic
149.	Sky blue	Azure

	Clue	Answer
1.	Jewelry	Bracelet
2.	Kick it to die	Bucket
3.	Bleeding	Band-Aid
4.	Comforter	Blanket
5.	Machine marbles	Ball Bearings
6.	Clorox	Bleach
7.	Mel or Garth	Brooks
8.	Snoopy	Beagle
9.	Sniffer-pooch	Bloodhound
10.	And Decker	Black
11.	Hoss & Little Joe	Bonanza
12.	Groom's guy	Best man
13.	Groom's gal	Bride
14.	Eagle	Bald
15.	Surfin' Safari	Beach Boys
16.	Mczzanine	Balcony

17. George Foreman	Boxer
18. Arm & Hammer	Baking Soda
19. Chapter 11	Bankrupt
20. Dagwood's gal	Blondie
21. Toboggan	Bobsled
22. Constrictor	Boa
23. Alcohol	Booze
24. Tavern	Bar
25. Keg	Beer
26. Home Run King	Babe Ruth
27. Ocean	Beach
28. Moses	Burning Bush
29. Relationship issues	Baggage
30. Tom Hanks movie	Big
31. Willis	Bruce
32. Found on kitchen counter	Breadbox
33. Pants	Belt
34. Spoiled	Brat
35. Humphrey	Bogart
36. Bedtime for ______	Bonzo
37. Panther	Black
38. Become an Eagle	Boy Scout
39. Bread maker	Baker
40. Bazooka	Bubble Gum
41. Beg or	Borrow
42. Brady	Bunch
43. Sasquatch	Big Foot
44. Polka	Beer barrel
45. Bread and	Butter
46. Moose cartoon	Bullwinkle
47. Eyelids	Blink
48. Bread winner	Bacon
49. On the plains	Buffalo or Bison
50. 90210	Beverly Hills
51. NBC Tom	Brokaw
52. Self-service supper	Buffet
53. Chalk	Blackboard
54. On desk	Batter
55. 2 wings	Biplane
56. Kicks 'em out	Bouncer

57. Teeny-weeny tree	Bonsai
58. Big beak	Bill
59. 007	Bond
60. Fresh Prince	Bel Air
61. On the mark	Bull's eye
62. Shears	Barber
63. Investment	Bonds
64. Pedal	Bicycle
65. Aftermath of pop	Burp or belch
66. Flintstones	Barney Rubble
67. Derek or Diddley	Bo
68. Vulture	Buzzard
69. New York	Broadway
70. Cover eyes	Blindfold
71. Cerebral cloudburst	Brainstorm
72. Cincinnati Sports	Bengal
73. Ultimate drive	BMW
74. Easy break	Brittle
75. Music style	Blues or Bluegrass
76. Hocus-Pocus	Black Magic
77. Out of jail	Bail
78. Caterpillar	Butterfly
79. Disappearing planes and boats	Bermuda
80. Former Mrs. Jagger	Bianca
81. Legal papers	Briefs
82. Weightlifters use	Barbells
83. Glasses	Bifocals
84. Mixed metal	Bronze
85. Nuts and	Bolts
86. Little cabbages	Brussels Sprouts
87. Dollar	Buck
88. Vampire	Blood
89. And Robin	Batman
90. Hot embosser for cattle	Branding Iron
91. Underwear	Boxers/Boxer Shorts
92. Talcum	Baby Powder
93. Doe	Buck
94. Savings, Junk, or EE	Bonds
95. Prohibition	Bootleg
96. Financial Place	Bank

97. Ghost	Boo
98. Black and Blue	Bruise
99. Face and Fist	Black Eye
100. Do it to coffee	Brew
101. River Edge	Bank
102. Bill Gates	Billionaire
103. Yuppie Wheels	BMW
104. Space Void	Black Holes
105. Chocolate Dessert or points	Brownie
106. Wedding Gals	Bridesmaids
107. On Elvis' Feet	Blue Suede Shoes
108. 13	Baker's Dozen
109. Miss Shields	Brook
110. Pig	Boar
111. Contracts	Breach
112. Ice Cream Guys	Ben & Jerry
113. Half-price Cellar	Bargain Basement
114. Horseshoe maker	Blacksmith
115. Wide Street	Boulevard
116. Flutter Bug	Butterfly
117. Wooden Support	Beam
118. China Shops	Bull
119. Card Game	Bridge
120. Charts	Bar Graph
121. Portable Potty	Bed Pan
122. Sesame Seed Bun	Big Mac
123. "Stayin' Alive"	Bee Gees
124. And Robbins	Baskin
125. Star Ladle	Big Dipper
126. Head Only	Bust
127. Pocketless Pool	Billiards
128. Lucille	Ball
129. He Ain't Heavy	Brother
130. Frugal	Budget
131. Two in the	Bush
132. Shuttlecock	Badminton
133. Bird Watching	Binoculars
134. Yeltsin	Boris
135. And Cream Cheese	Bagels
136. Bunsen	Burner

137.	Tutu	Ballet / Ballerina
138.	And Eggs	Bacon
139.	Bogus Bullet	Blank
140.	Chess	Bishop
141.	Early Years	B.C.
142.	Lunar Sadness	Blue Moon
143.	Torture Tree	Bamboo
144.	Middle Man	Broker
145.	Can't be choosers	Beggars
146.	Cells are White or Red	Blood
147.	And Bailey	Barnum
148.	"It's None of Your ______"	Business or Beeswax
149.	Whooper	Burger King
150.	Brush's	Bristles
151.	Pitney's Partner	Bowes
152.	"Nonsense" meat	Bologna
153.	In Woodwind Family	Bassoon
154.	Corn, Oat, Wheat	Bran
155.	Jeeves	Butler
156.	Whales Have One	Blowhole
157.	Buster	Brown
158.	Flag Seamstress	Betsy Ross
159.	Simpson's Kid	Bart
160.	One Over	Bogie
161.	Mutiny	Bounty
162.	Pea	Black-Eyed Pea
163.	Bean	Black Bean
164.	One Under	Birdie
165.	Large English Clock	Big Ben
166.	Cheers	Boston
167.	Leave it to ________	Beaver
168.	Air Pressure	Barometer
169.	The Rock Irish Kiss	Blarney Stone
170.	Greg, Bobby, Peter, Marcia, Jan, Cindy	Brady Bunch

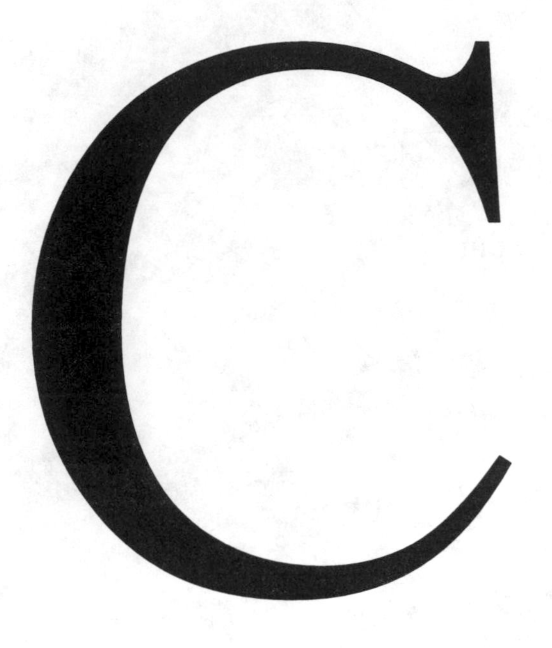

1. Boston Bar	Cheers
2. Saguaro	Cactus
3. Kids Hate These	Chores
4. Paraffin	Candles
5. Feline Boat	Catamaran
6. Bonnie &	Clyde
7. No-Talk game	Charades
8. Tennessee Train	Chattanooga Choo Choo
9. Stanley, Davis, or Tea	Cup
10. Dom Perignon	Champaign
11. 20's Dance	Cancan or The Charleton
12. Where in the World is She?	Carmen San Diego
13. Cowboys overpants	Chaps
14. Muscle	Calf
15. Ocean Flow	Currents

16. "Smile, You're on __________" Candid Camera
17. Military disguise Camouflage
18. Type of Skiing Cross-Country
19. Life unit Cell
20. Do the Twist Chubby Checker
21. Replaced antenna Cable
22. Nuns Convent
23. What Jack broke Crown
24. In a while ______________ Crocodile
25. Chocolate or potato Chips
26. Ice sport Curling
27. Fidel's mouthpiece Cigar
28. My Father's brother's son Cousin
29. Noodle Soup Chicken
30. Julius ________ Caesar
31. Peanut President Carter
32. Rhinestone Heroes Cowboys
33. Alamo's Davy Crocket
34. Grinned at Alice Cheshire Cat
35. City Slicker's Billy Crystal
36. "Give me an "A" Cheerleader
37. Pits Cherry
38. Banana brand Chiquita
39. Love sparks fly Chemistry
40. Newsman – Walter Cronkite
41. Champaign and ________________ Caviar
42. Golf gopher Caddy
43. Hannibal Lechter Cannibal
44. Cowboys drive them Cattle
45. Neanderthal apartment1 Cave
46. Kids do them in the yard Cartwheel
47. Seen between shows Commercials
48. 100 bug Centipede
49. And everything nice Cinnamon and Spice
50. ___________ of the board Chairman
51. Greatest show Circus
52. Curded cheese Cottage
53. 1 Hump or 2 Camel
54. Poo-Poo Pond Cesspool
55. Good Ghost Casper

56. Christmas candy	Candy Cane
57. Barbecue	Charcoal
58. Decipher the ___________	Code
59. Smoking	Cigarettes
60. Golf swing	Chip
61. Pushed while shopping	Cart
62. Found in a farm field	Cow Chips
63. Arnold smoke	Cigars
64. Valentine's Day Elf	Cupid
65. Rome's arena	Colosseum
66. Sonny &	Cher
67. And Abel	Cain
68. Around the neck	Collar
69. Used for future telling	Crystal Ball
70. Aladdin's flying _________	Carpet
71. Meat cutter	Cleaver
72. Dentist	Cavity
73. Tom, Joan, or Judy	Collins
74. ________Lace and a pretty face	Chantilly
75. Polite	Cordial
76. Kids	Children
77. Chilly deltoid	Cold Shoulder
78. Green growing pet	Chia
79. British bye-bye	Cheerio
80. Massachusetts place	Cape Cod
81. Catholic church leader	Cardinal
82. Life is this…old chum	Cabaret
83. End the shooting	Cease-Fire
84. Asian game	Chinese Checkers
85. Clock bird	Cuckoo
86. Missionary muncher	Cannibal
87. Congressional mound	Capitol Hill
88. Horse's gait	Cantor
89. Pulled muscle	Charley Horse
90. Record replacement	Compact Disc
91. In-ground vegetable	Carrot
92. Kernels of ___________	Corn
93. Vein fat	Cholesterol
94. Flue	Chimney
95. Plane seat	Cockpit

	Clue	Answer
96.	Back cracker	Chiropractor
97.	Chin dimple	Cleft
98.	Imitate feline	Copycat
99.	Smash	Crush
100.	Eating auditorium	Cafeteria
101.	Clothes storage	Closet
102.	Table protectors	Coasters
103.	Supersonic	Concord
104.	Rock around it	Clock
105.	Baby bed	Crib
106.	Salad bread	Croutons
107.	Type of pathway	Cobblestone
108.	Lady-like bow	Curtsy
109.	Kellogg's	Cereal
110.	Paris, Oslo, Rome, Tokyo	Capitals
111.	Clam soup	Chowder
112.	San Fran stadium	Candlestick Park
113.	Devil's Food or Angle Food	Cake
114.	Top Gun Tom	Cruise
115.	Paddle boat	Canoe
116.	Broccoli brother	Cauliflower
117.	Link fence	Chain
118.	TV ad	Commercial
119.	Fender bender	Crash
120.	Cathedral	Church
121.	Ice cream	Cone
122.	Simon, Theodore, Alvin	Chipmunks
123.	Cold-sounding hot beans	Chili
124.	Christmas song	Carol
125.	Balanced monthly	Checkbook
126.	Starbucks	Coffee
127.	Coffee	Caffeine
128.	Don Juan	Casanova
129.	Alaskan, Dungeness	Crabs
130.	England's Winston	Churchill
131.	Talented tramp	Charlie Chaplin
132.	Ralph Lauren fragrance	Chaps
133.	Glass slipper	Cinderella
134.	Graveyard	Cemetery
135.	Added to coffee	Cream

136.	California bird	Condor
137.	Flying corks	Champagne
138.	Boston ________Pie	Cream
139.	Bears, Bulls, & Cubs	Chicago
140.	La la land	California
141.	Expensive eggs	Caviar
142.	Light you might swing on	Chandelier
143.	Get a head of this vegetable	Cabbage
144.	Royal game	Chess
145.	Indian nation	Cherokee
146.	Ninja Turtles	Cowabunga!
147.	Limo	Chauffer
148.	Frugal	Cheap
149.	Italian goodbye	Ciao
150.	Witches stew	Cauldron

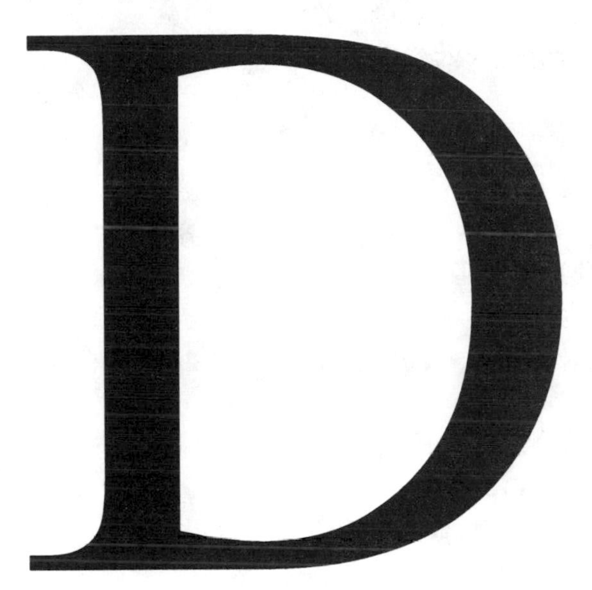

	Clue	Answer
1.	Hot and sandy	Desert
2.	Not zirconium	Diamond
3.	Pillsbury	Doughboy
4.	Donkey party	Democrats
5.	___________ Sergeant	Drill
6.	___________ Mites	Dust
7.	___________ Fir	Douglas
8.	101	Dalmatians
9.	What the farmer is in	Dell
10.	Look it up	Dictionary
11.	& Goliath	David
12.	Star Wars	Darth Vader
13.	Little boat	Dinghy
14.	Chicken & ________	Dumplings
15.	Cavities	Dentist
16.	Type of bad breath	Dragon

17.	Coin	Dime
18.	“Pirates” – Johnny	Depp
19.	No way out	Dead End
20.	Waterless wash	Dry Clean
21.	Postal Carriers and Pizza Hut	Deliver
22.	Loose weight	Diet
23.	Theodor Geisel	Dr. Seuss
24.	007 Enemy	Dr. No
25.	Talk to animals	Dr. Doolitle
26.	Flying elephant	Dumbo
27.	Pampers	Diapers
28.	Weed wine	Dandelion
29.	Big garbage container	Dumpster
30.	“Supremes’” leader	Diana Ross
31.	Texas “soap”	Dallas
32.	Of Hazard county	Dukes
33.	Plate cleaner	Dishwasher
34.	Rhea Perlman’s man	Danny DeVito
35.	Written by Thomas Jefferson	Declaration of Independence
36.	Basketball bouncing	Dribble
37.	Archeologist do this	Dig
38.	____________Longlegs	Daddy
39.	The seven___________	Dwarfs
40.	____________Perignon	Dom
41.	Forgetful dwarf	Dopey
42.	Caribbean hair	Dreadlocks
43.	Hawaiian hill	Diamond Head
44.	Chicken legs	Drumsticks
45.	Slam__________	Dunk
46.	Tie score in tennis	Deuce
47.	Blow ‘em before you roll ‘em	Dice
48.	Stock crash effect	Depression
49.	Original Biblical writings	Dead Sea Scrolls
50.	Weight lifters use	Dumbbells
51.	Shuffles the deck	Dealer
52.	The Menace	Dennis
53.	Visited Oz	Dorothy
54.	Pickle spice	Dill
55.	Mile-high City	Denver
56.	Sound measurement	Decibels

57. Cut Sampson's hair | Delilah
58. Number 1 club | Driver
59. Fake duck | Decoy
60. Sinatra refrain | Doo-Bee-Doo-Bee-Doo
61. Kids do this in class | Daydream
62. Krispie Kremes | Doughnuts
63. Dried fruit or going out with someone | Date
64. Gum for twins | Doublemint
65. Supper | Diner
66. Skin Doc | Dermatologist
67. Trump – King of the | Deal
68. Tom & Harry's friend | Dick
69. Hawaiian singer | Don Ho
70. Please don't eat the | Daisies
71. What you want to do first in a duel | Draw
72. Count ____________ | Dracula
73. Clint's Character | Dirty Harry
74. Laundry of dishwasher | Detergent
75. Back-to-back with guns | Duel
76. Mickey's home | Disneyland
77. Porpoise | Dolphin
78. Webster's | Dictionary
79. R.E.M. | Dreams
80. Photography | Dark room
81. Extinct bird | Dodo
82. Silly little song | Ditty
83. Doctor's guess | Diagnosis
84. Old testament book | Deuteronomy
85. Sad expression or look | Doleful
86. Last thing to eat | Desserts
87. Anne Frank | Diary
88. AC | DC
89. Knead this | Dough
90. Basketball blunder | Double Dribble

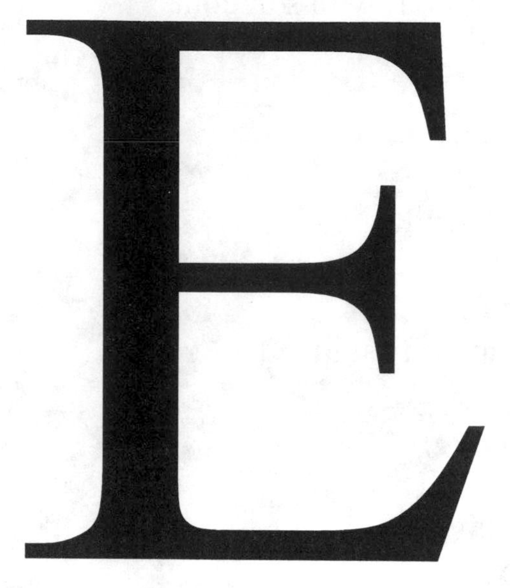

Clue	Answer
1. Roof extensions	Eaves
2. Adam &	Eve
3. Not deciduous	Evergreen
4. Fencing warning	En Garde
5. Scientists	Experiment
6. Albert___________	Einstein
7. Relativity equation	E=(mc)2
8. Great Lake	Erie
9. The Garden of	Eden
10. Pupils	Eyes
11. Yolks	Eggs
12. Contract	Expand
13. Fumes	Exhaust
14. Stuck sword	Excalibur
15. Corn	Ears
16. And so on…	Etc.

17. Phone home — E.T.
18. Not full — Empty
19. Archaeologists — Excavation
20. Cotton gin — Eli Whitney
21. Snail snack — Escargot
22. Ford's folly — Edsel
23. Light bulb — Edison
24. Christ arose — Easter
25. Foe — Enemy
26. Rocket man — Elton (John)
27. Paradise garden — Eden
28. Seal it – stamp it — Envelope
29. Water channel — English
30. AC/DC fixer — Electrician
31. Money movement — Economics
32. Small task — Errand
33. Make-shift marriage — Elope(ment)
34. "Going up?" — Elevator
35. Freud — Ego
36. Predict the future — E.S.P.
37. One or the other — Either
38. Scrambled — Eggs
39. Ocean's….(movie) — Eleven
40. Charcoal drawing — Etchings
41. Green Acres gal — Eva Gabor
42. West — East
43. Canyon, canyon, canyon — Echo
44. Moon block — Eclipse
45. 0 degrees — Equator
46. Hotel California — Eagles
47. Inuit — Eskimo
48. Pencil — Eraser
49. Feelings — Emotions
50. Funeral talk — Eulogy
51. Corn — Ears
52. Newspaper worker — Editor
53. Main course — Entrée
54. Death penalty — Electric chair
55. 911 — Emergency
56. Kicked out of school — Expelled

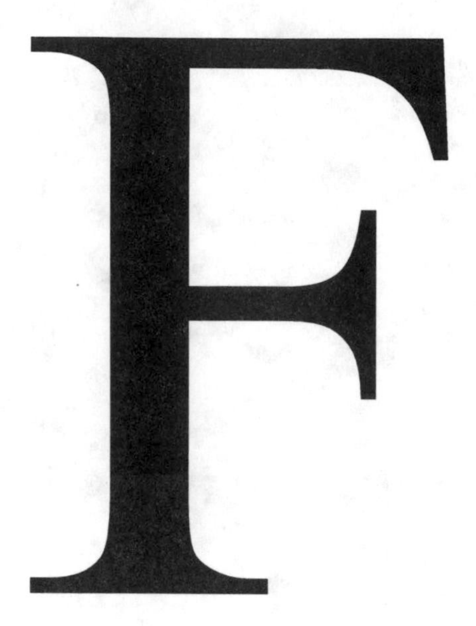

	Clue	Answer
1.	Gender	Female
2.	& Vegetables	Fruit
3.	San Andres	Fault
4.	Above 98.6	Fever
5.	Tooth	Fairy
6.	Corn	Flakes
7.	Adam's cover-up	Fig leaf
8.	Monday Night	Football
9.	Of the Loom	Fruit
10.	Tomorrow	Future
11.	& Square	Fair
12.	Barney Rubble's pal	Fred Flintstone
13.	"Boss…De plane!"	Fantasy Island
14.	TV Angel	Farrah Fawcett
15.	Crook identification	Fingerprints
16.	Toast	French
17.	Autumn	Fall

18. Pasta	Fettuccine
19. Heat degrees	Fahrenheit
20. Sheep	Flock
21. Autograph seeker	Fan
22. Barbed wire	Fence
23. Basic facts practice	Flash Cards
24. Mushrooms	Fungus
25. Empty	Full
26. 15 minutes of…	Fame
27. Mist	Fog
28. Parachuting	Free-Fall
29. Saturday Night	Fever
30. Model T	Ford
31. Bell-Bottoms, Pet-Rocks…	Fads
32. 31 Ice cream	Flavors
33. England's South American Islands	Falkland
34. Monster	Frankenstein
35. The Snowman	Frosty
36. Malcom ________ 500	Forbes
37. Build on it	Foundation
38. Telephone line copier	Fax
39. Niagara __________	Falls
40. Drinking	Fountain
41. Amusement ride	Ferris Wheel
42. Hot ________ Sundae	Fudge
43. Golf	Fairway
44. Inches	Feet
45. Ponce DeLeon	Fountain of youth
46. Holiday dessert	Fruit Cake
47. Auto bump	Fender Bender
48. Bascball	Foul Ball
49. Burial	Funeral
50. ….of Dreams	Field
51. Untrue	False
52. Ginger Rogers	Fred Astaire
53. Day	Friday
54. Sigmund	Freud
55. Feast or	Famine
56. Hot Dog	Frankfurt
57. On a horses foot	Frog

58.	Sun Spots	Freckles
59.	Dieting	Fasting
60.	Pallet lifter	Forklift
61.	No cost	Free
62.	Not domestic	Foreign
63.	Hands	Fingers
64.	Bank takes it all	Foreclose
65.	Lose color	Fade
66.	Ship team	Fleet
67.	Hot Cakes	Flapjacks
68.	__________Nightingale	Florence

1.	Johnny B. ………..	Goode
2.	Indian leader	Geronimo
3.	Proper Language	Grammar
4.	Lizard movie star	Godzilla
5.	Skimpy panties	G-String
6.	Exercise place	Gym
7.	Protector	Guard
8.	Pinch in the rear or bird	Goose
9.	Bird that's hunted	Grouse
10.	Cheese-head football players	Green Bay Packers
11.	__________ & Mercy	Grace
12.	Jerry Garcia	Grateful Dead
13.	Big homerun	Grand Slam
14.	Laughing, mustard, or tear	Gas
15.	"Frankly, my Dear,….	Gone with the Wind
16.	Milky Way	Galaxy

17. Presley home	Graceland
18. Harlem athletes	Globetrotters
19. Colosseum contestant	Gladiator
20. Bat town	Gotham City
21. "Who ya gonna call?"	Ghost Busters
22. Japanese entertainer	Geisha
23. Famous boy toy	G.I. Joe
24. Foods for home	Groceries
25. BBQ	Grill
26. Vandal art	Graffiti
27. Overeater	Glutton
28. Hand bomb	Grenade
29. Fore!	Golf
30. Mouthwash	Gargle
31. Dad's dad	Grandfather
32. Military leader	General
33. Mow	Grass
34. The big lakes	Great Lakes
35. Disney dwarf	Grumpy
36. Car mechanic	Grease Monkey
37. Olympics	Gold Medals
38. Farm animal	Goat
39. Race dog	Greyhound
40. Fortune tellers	Gypsies
41. Bullet filling	Gunpowder
42. Fruit	Guava
43. Promise	Guarantee
44. Plants starter	Greenhouse
45. Wrigley's	Gum
46. In the beginning…	Genesis
47. Simon & …	Garfunkel
48. Travolta & Olivia	Grease
49. Las Vegas	Gambling
50. Marlin Brando	Godfather
51. Chromosomes	Genes
52. Concord	Grapes
53. TV castaway show	Gilligan's Island
54. Castaway "movie star"	Ginger
55. World Records	Guinness
56. Casper	Ghost

57. Thirst quencher	Gatorade
58. Choke	Gag
59. Stole Christmas	Grinch
60. Front of car	Grill
61. Go!	Green
62. Baklava	Greek
63. Car storage	Garage
64. Dinner friends	Guests
65. Innards	Guts
66. Chocolate	Godiva
67. Parallel bars	Gymnastics
68. Puck stopper	Goalie
69. Talking gift	Gab
70. Wanna have fun	Girls
71. Frisco bridge	Golden Gate
72. Trash	Garbage
73. Mittens	Gloves
74. Bear	Grizzly
75. Shoot	Guns
76. Ulysses S. _________	Grant
77. Did the crime	Guilty
78. World Trade Center spot	Ground Zero
79. 144	Gross
80. Cracker	Graham
81. Angel	Gabriel
82. Mashed potatoes	Gravy
83. Turkey guts	Gizzards
84. Chortle	Giggle
85. Sea bird	Gull
86. Turkey sound	Gobble
87. Cow type	Guernsey
88. Atlanta	Georgia
89. Judge tool	Gavel
90. Elmer's	Glue

1. Church songs	Hymns
2. Bad idea	Half-Baked
3. Ice sport	Hockey
4. Shark type	Hammerhead
5. Grand slam	Home Run
6. Thumbs out	Hitchhike
7. Bee	Honey
8. Suggestion	Hint
9. Natural fence	Hedge
10. Laughing animal	Hyena
11. Kisses maker	Hershey

12. Beep beep	Honk
13. 24 in a day	Hours
14. Time of from work	Holiday
15. Commonly replaced bone	Hip
16. Ancient graffiti	Hieroglyphics
17. Angel instrument	Harp
18. Grades 9 – 12	High School
19. Wanting food	Hungry
20. Head protection	Helmet
21. Turn your head – cough	Hernia
22. Hover plane	Helicopter
23. Pork	Ham
24. Wife	Husband
25. Dirty clothes	Hamper
26. Allergic reaction	Hives
27. Mortgage	House/Home
28. Go seek	Hide
29. Low…	High
30. Sherlock	Holmes
31. Playground game	Hopscotch
32. Question	How
33. Texas city	Houston
34. Fire	Hose / Hydrant
35. Had a great fall	Humpty Dumpty
36. Tool	Hammer
37. Police tool	Handcuffs
38. Fir tree	Hemlock
39. Messiah composer	Handel
40. Frozen rain	Hail
41. Fur	Hair
42. Bugle	Horn
43. Crab type	Hermit
44. Idol	Hero
45. Elvis' dog	Hound
46. "Book 'em Danno"	Hawaii 5-0
47. S.O.S.	Help
48. McDonalds	Hamburgers
49. Oscar Meyer	Hot Dogs
50. I get Dad's stuff	Heir
51. Best policy	Honesty

52. Game show — Hollywood Squares
53. Space telescope — Hubbel
54. Afterlife — Heaven
55. House pet — Hamster
56. The horrible Viking — Hagar
57. Aloha — Hawaii
58. Purple haze — Hendrix
59. Alfred… — Hitchcock
60. Morning potatoes — Hash Browns
61. Monty, Carnegie, or Annie — Hall
62. Wind storm — Hurricane
63. Back hills folks — Hillbillies
64. Palominos — Horses
65. Quasimodo — Hunchback
66. Ghost infested — Haunted House
67. Drug effect — Hallucinations
68. Shootin' up — Heroine
69. Toy and game maker — Hasbro
70. New York river — Hudson
71. Rental car — Hertz
72. Jack-O-Lanterns — Halloween
73. Corn cover — Husk
74. Creamer — Half-and-Half
75. Induce trance — Hypnotize
76. Best part of the artichoke — Heart
77. Small ax — Hatchet
78. Boat belly — Hull
79. Cigar capital — Havana
80. Ford — Henry
81. Frat induction — Hazing
82. Arm bone — Humorous
83. …..and kisses — Hugs
84. Backyard game — Horseshoes
85. Pollen sneezing — Hay Fever
86. Whale type — Humpback
87. Backpackers — Hiking
88. Beer foam — Head
89. Iditarod — Huskies
90. Motorcycle — Harley-Davidson
91. Mt. Everest — Himalayas

Two-Tips Trivia

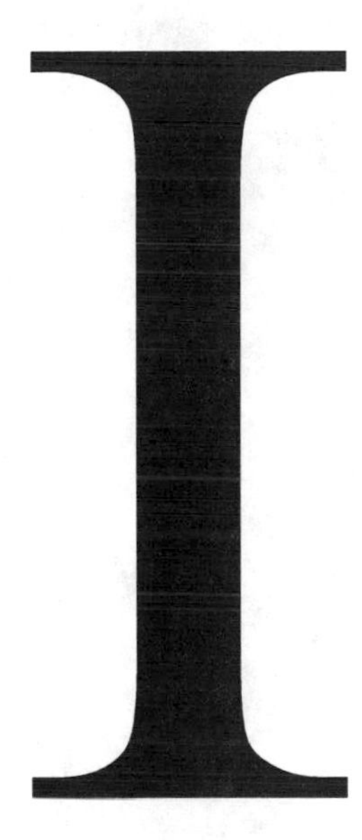

1. Measurement	Inch
2. Gilligan's	Island
3. Paragraph	Indent
4. Cherokee	Indian
5. Metal	Iron
6. Directions	Instructions
7. Mock	Imitate
8. Baby	Infant
9. Guts	Intestines
10. Worm type	Inch
11. Nine in baseball	Innings

12. Car starter	Ignition
13. Hanging on Santa's house	Icicles
14. Job talks	Interview
15. Joe meet Mary	Introduction
16. Some "Missions" are this	Impossible
17. Battalion	Infantry
18. Ice house	Igloo
19. Boot country	Italy
20. Debt letters	I.O.U.
21. Cigarettes	Inhale
22. It's bliss	Ignorance
23. Tusks	Ivory
24. A plays break	Intermission
25. Count up store items	Inventory
26. Columbus' Queen	Isabella
27. Added to injury	Insult
28. Fuji has over 300	Islands
29. Cars at stop lights	Idles
30. Eisenhower	Ike
31. Village dumby	Idiot
32. A feeling or premonition	Inkling
33. Bronze age cousin	Iron Age
34. The Terrible	Ivan
35. Jews home	Israel
36. Mensa = high…	I.Q.
37. Dog type	Irish Setter
38. Big Blue	IBM
39. Principal and	Interest
40. Used for blots	Ink
41. Eye part	Iris
42. College league	Ivy
43. Metallic monarch	Iron Butterfly
44. Cold country	Iceland
45. Sleepy Hollow	Ichabod Crane
46. 4th of July	Independence Day
47. Dessert	Ice Cream
48. Traveler's plan	Itinerary
49. No backbone	Invertebrate
50. Police questioning	Interrogate

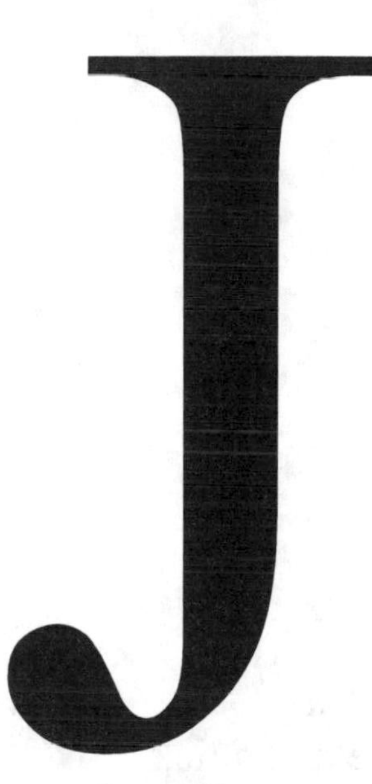

1. Rabbit type — Jack
2. Main vein — Jugular
3. Al little dance — Jig
4. Pop music Michael — Jackson
5. Basketball great Michael — Jordon
6. Airplane river — Jet stream
7. Wiggly jiggly food — Jell-O
8. Jump for this — Joy
9. Try to keep up with them — Joneses
10. Asian country — Japan
11. Before senior — Junior

12. Batman nemesis	Joker
13. Astor's owner	Jetsons
14. Black-robed lawyer	Judge
15. Criminal home	Jail
16. Trial by……	Jury
17. Boeing 747	Jumbo Jet
18. Carved pumpkin	Jack-O-Lantern
19. Clown skill	Juggle
20. Green stone	Jade
21. Hope to hit it at the casino	Jack Pot
22. In the whale's belly	Jonah
23. Pop and chips	Junk Food
24. Costly cat car	Jaguar
25. Medieval entertainer	Jester
26. Apostle	John
27. ________Cricket	Jiminy
28. JFK &	Jackie
29. Music style	Jazz
30. School cleaner	Janitor
31. Music machine	Jukebox
32. Climbed up the hill	Jack & Jill
33. Green Giant adjective	Jolly
34. Kind of mail	Junk
35. This can be hung in court	Jury
36. He needs to be nimble and quick	Jack
37. Nose nipper	Jack Frost
38. Race horse riders	Jockeys
39. Cow type	Jersey
40. To the center of the earth	Journey
41. Popes and toilets	Johns
42. Elbow, knee, hip	Joint
43. Illegal street crosser	Jaywalker
44. Orange, apple, grape…	Juice
45. Romeo	Juliet
46. Rock drill	Jackhammer
47. PB &	Jelly
48. Pants	Jeans
49. Coffee	Java
50. Diary	Journal

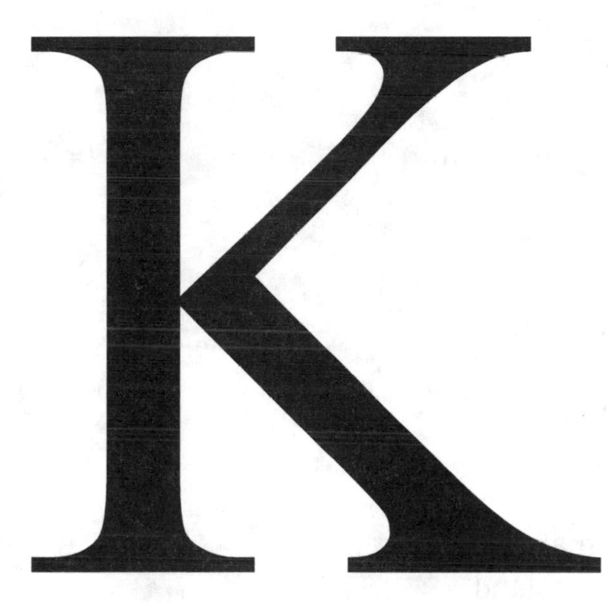

1. Seoul	Korea
2. Bed	King-size
3. Black belt	Karate
4. Mustard	Ketchup
5. Both bird and fruit	Kiwi
6. Lock	Key
7. Quilts	Knitting
8. Boxing finish	K.O. (Knock out)
9. Japanese garment	Kimono
10. Large pot	Kettle
11. Type of roll	Kaiser

12. Comes with caboodle — Kit
13. Tartan skirt — Kilt
14. Rope tying — Knots
15. Corn seed — Kernel
16. Start the football game — Kickoff
17. Pain in the neck — Kink
18. Cereal company — Kellogg's
19. Canoe cousin — Kayak
20. Wright brothers — Kitty Hawk
21. Done to bread dough — Kneading
22. Star Trek Captain — Kirk
23. Motorcycle type — Kawasaki
24. Chess piece — Knight
25. Bear type — Koala
26. Electrical measurement — Kilowatts
27. Smooch — Kiss
28. Pant color and type — Khakis
29. Biggest ape — King Kong
30. Superman weakness — Krypton
31. Pitch type — Knuckleball
32. Used to start fire — Kindling
33. Miss Piggy and — Kermit
34. Leg punch — Kick
35. Pouched animal — Kangaroo
36. Dorothy's homeland — Kansas
37. "Who's there?" — Knock Knock
38. Bumbler and stumbler — Klutz
39. Barbie and — Ken
40. Boat "backbone" — Keel

#	Clue	Answer
1.	Orange with black spot insect	Ladybug
2.	Military rank	Lieu ant
3.	First	Last
4.	Speech	Lecture
5.	Death	Life
6.	Same food	Leftovers
7.	Shaving cream	Lather
8.	Femur	Leg
9.	Last stand	Little Bighorn
10.	501's	Levis
11.	Late Night show	Letterman

12.	The Tonight Show	Leno
13.	Chortle	Laugh
14.	of Nations	League
15.	Solid….	Liquid
16.	You're pulling my…	Leg
17.	…I presume?	Livingston
18.	Irish ditty	Limerick
19.	Bread	Loaf
20.	How low?	Limbo
21.	Pay rent to…	Landlord
22.	Suntan oil	Lotion
23.	Speech impediment	Lisp
24.	Cattle capture	Lasso or Lariat
25.	Track meet leap	Long Jump
26.	Victoria's	Lingerie
27.	TV Collie	Lassie
28.	Fruit of the….	Loom
29.	Shirley's good ship	Lollipop
30.	Final vacation stop	Last Resort
31.	Cabaret singer	Liza Minnelli
32.	Dryer residue	Lint
33.	Brochure	Leaflet
34.	The Game of …	Life
35.	Driving permit	License
36.	Mallard with a limp	Lame Duck
37.	Skywalker	Luke
38.	Arkansas	Little Rock
39.	One-year contract	Lease
40.	Black candy	Licorice
41.	Mardi Gras state	Louisiana
42.	Frozen mandible	Lockjaw
43.	More or	Less
44.	Spotted jungle cat	Leopard
45.	Cracked Philly ringer	Liberty Bell
46.	Spirit of St……….	Louis
47.	Talk show host King	Larry
48.	Amorous jump	Lover's Leap
49.	Midday munch	Lunch
50.	Washer and Dryer	Laundry
51.	Genie's magic…	Lamp

	Clue	Answer
52.	Overboard saver	Life preserver
53.	Stairway to Heaven	Led Zeppelin
54.	3,2,1…ignition…	Lift-off
55.	Thunder	Lightning
56.	Jump-over game	Leap Frog
57.	& found	Lost
58.	Superman	Lois Lane
59.	Train	Locomotive
60.	Youth baseball	Little League
61.	The Blue ….	Lagoon
62.	Free book rental	Library
63.	Sung to a baby	Lullaby
64.	New England crustacean	Lobster
65.	Last, but not	Least
66.	Indian hockey	Lacrosse
67.	Abraham	Lincoln
68.	Watched sheep	Littlc Bo-Peep
69.	Top speed	Limit
70.	Hot rock	Lava
71.	Tree branch	Limb
72.	Keeps Rover from roving	Leash
73.	Stolen goods	Loot

Two-Tips Trivia

1.	________-Dixon Line	Mason
2.	Big Sky	Montana
3.	Mr. X	Malcolm
4.	Who's the greatest of them all?	Mirror Mirror
5.	The Rockies	Mountains
6.	Day	Monday
7.	End of river	Mouth
8.	Fast food	McDonald's
9.	Apple	Macintosh
10.	Soak the meat	Marinade
11.	Smore ingredient	Marshmallow

12. Muscle rub	Massage
13. Swimming game	Marco Polo
14. Holy fish	Mackerel
15. Samuel's Code	Morse
16. Run around this bush	Mulberry
17. Galaxy	Milky Way
18. Harley	Motorcycle
19. Out of Egypt	Moses
20. New York City	Manhattan
21. Baseball's Mickey	Mantle
22. High ……Low	Medium
23. Fridge door	Magnets
24. Old food fuzz	Mold
25. Islam starter	Mohammed
26. Indian shoe	Moccasin
27. First Ford	Model T
28. Syrup	Maple
29. 12 in a year	Months
30. Fur coat	Mink
31. Instruction book	Manual
32. Biceps – triceps	Muscles
33. Sherlock's tool	Magnifying Glass
34. Computer tool	Mouse
35. Doctors' insurance	Malpractice
36. Egyptian practice	Mummification
37. Finger soak	Manicure
38. Mixed dog	Mutt
39. American Patriots	Minutemen
40. Donkey	Mule
41. Exhaust	Muffler
42. Deaf	Mute
43. Angry	Mad
44. Police photo	Mug Shot
45. Mouse	Mickey
46. ½ woman – ½ fish	Mermaid
47. Smaller then big league	Minor
48. White condiment	Mayonnaise
49. Yellow condiment	Mustard
50. 3-Mile Island	Meltdown
51. A whale of tale	Moby Dick

52. Undercover agent	Mole
53. Tom Sawyer's river	Mississippi
54. Thermometer liquid	Mercury
55. Wooly animal	Mammoth
56. Shaken – not stirred	Martini
57. BIG house	Mansion
58. Snake hair	Medusa
59. Desert illusion	Mirage
60. Butterfly	Monarch
61. Robin Hood & …	Maid Marian
62. Evil's root	Money
63. Tom Cruise's Top Gun nickname	Maverick
64. Envelope type	Manila
65. Kermit the From	Muppet
66. Base, blush, eyeliner…	Make-Up
67. Funeral home	Morgue
68. Material girl	Madonna
69. Center hair only	Mohawk
70. Kitchen appliance	Microwave Oven
71. Created by humans	Man-Made
72. Boat parking lot	Marina
73. Jimmy Buffet's city	Margarita Ville
74. "Who Wants to Be a ……"	Millionaire
75. Syrup	Maple
76. Ten Commandments	Moses
77. They represent the lollipop kids	Munchkins
78. Just a spoonful of sugar….	Mary Poppins
79. School logo	Mascot
80. Playground toy	Monkey Bars
81. Motorized bike	Moped
82. Almost butter	Margarine
83. After minor leagues….	Major
84. Noodles with cheese	Macaroni
85. Fertilizer type	Manure
86. Joseph Smith's religion	Mormon
87. Telegraph language	Morse Code
88. Kiss under it	Mistletoe

Two-Tips Trivia

1. Not old	New
2. South	North
3. Primitive man	Neanderthal
4. Las Vega	Nevada
5. Bellybutton	Navel
6. Pins and ________	Needles
7. Bird home	Nest
8. No clothes	Naked
9. And bolts	Nuts

10.	Boy relative	Nephew
11.	Sciatic	Nerve
12.	Facial feature	Nose
13.	Coin	Nickel
14.	Light type	Neon
15.	Diet	Nutrition
16.	Middle C	Note
17.	Just married	Newlyweds
18.	Waterloo	Napoleon
19.	Hunchback	Notre Dame
20.	Profit type	Net
21.	Marry Poppins	Nanny
22.	October	November
23.	Old horse	Nag
24.	Macaroni	Noodles
25.	Positive	Negative
26.	Bad dream	Nightmare
27.	Hogwash – silliness	Nonsense
28.	Bonehead	Numbskull
29.	Spice	Nutmeg
30.	Next-door	Neighbors
31.	ABC – CBS -	NBC
32.	Giraffe	Neck
33.	Mother Theresa	Nun
34.	16-penny	Nails
35.	No gear	Neutral
36.	Cold outside	Nippy
37.	Nose on a hose	Nozzle
38.	Hangman	Noose
39.	Fig cookie	Newton
40.	Watergate	Nixon
41.	Military	Navy
42.	Zero zilch …	Nothing
43.	Explosive	Nitroglycerin
44.	Cashes, filbert, almond	Nut
45.	Big Apple	New York
46.	Shelled heroes	Ninja Turtles
47.	Atomic	Nuclear
48.	Children's network	Nickelodeon
49.	Cop baton	Nightstick

50.	Christmas Ballet	Nutcracker
51.	Yea or	Nay
52.	Horse talk	Neigh
53.	Santa Claus	Nicholas
54.	Longest river	Nile
55.	Wipe your mouth	Napkin
56.	Peach cousin	Nectarine
57.	Antsy	Nervous
58.	Chocolate	Nestlé's
59.	Salamander cousin	Newt
60.	Girl relative	Niece
61.	Stays up late	Night Owl
62.	Verb	Noun
63.	Storybook	Novel
64.	Not later	Now
65.	Digit	Number
66.	Denominator	Numerator
67.	Many	Numerous
68.	Push	Nudge
69.	Not wide	Narrow
70.	Country	Nation

Two-Tips Trivia

1. Apples and …	Oranges
2. Surgeon job	Operation
3. Genesis, Exodus….	Old Testament
4. 8 notes away	Octave
5. Antonyms	Opposites
6. Wise bird	Owl
7. Popeye's gal	Olive Oyl
8. Sanctioned minister	Ordained
9. Orange primate	Orangutan
10. Dead list	Obituary

11. Long Greek trip	Odyssey
12. Pearl factory	Oyster
13. OK state	Oklahoma
14. Realtor showing	Open House
15. Greek games	Olympics
16. Egg shape	Oval
17. Beast of burden	Ox
18. Fat	Obese
19. Stop sign	Octagon
20. Closed	Open
21. Kids card game	Old Maid
22. Squid cousin	Octopus
23. Sandwich cookie	Oreo
24. Fat-lady singing	Opera
25. Wilbur's brother	Orville
26. Annual movie awards	Oscars
27. Walla Walla sweets	Onions
28. Flightless bird	Ostrich
29. Police….	Officer
30. Breakfast food	Oatmeal
31. Under	Over
32. Story beginning	Once Upon a Time
33. Loneliest number	One
34. Hot dogs	Oscar Mayer
35. Not late	On time
36. Satellites	Orbit
37. Part of water	Oxygen
38. Parts of the body	Organs
39. Talk show host	Oprah
40. Check this in a car	Oil
41. Even	Odd
42. 3-egg	Omelet
43. Broken – not working	Out of Order
44. Perform in a pit	Orchestra
45. Telescopes	Observatory
46. Bathroom full	Occupied
47. Citizen Wells	Orson
48. Atlantic	Ocean
49. Mayberry	Opie
50. Popcorn man	Orville Reddenbocker

1. Arizona	Phoenix
2. Oysters	Pearls
3. Pumpkin Eater…	Peter
4. British legislators	Parliament
5. Oink	Pig
6. Teeth dirt	Plaque
7. Ebony and Ivory	Piano
8. Of the Opera	Phantom
9. France	Paris
10. City bird	Pigeon
11. Grated cheese	Parmesan

12. Disney puppet — Pinocchio
13. Fountain of youth — Ponce de Leon
14. Quills — Porcupine
15. Good guys finding bad guys — Posse
16. Billiards — Pool
17. Native-American meeting — Powwow
18. Twisted bread snack — Pretzel
19. Swimming — Pool
20. Spider Man — Peter Parker
21. Gift — Present
22. Birthday — Party
23. Almost an island — Peninsula
24. Planet — Pluto
25. Kangaroos & Possums have them — Pouches
26. Soda — Pop
27. Illegal hunting — Poaching
28. Best gas — Premium
29. Wall cover section — Panel
30. He's was with the wolf — Peter
31. Missile type — Patriot
32. Salt — Pepper
33. Charades — Pantomime
34. Boo hoo — Pout
35. Found in the Caribbean — Pirates
36. Overweight over — Potbellied Stove
37. Hog — Pig
38. Zit — Pimple
39. Elvis — Presley
40. Two-tone bear — Panda
41. Soccer great — Pele
42. Dolphin — Porpoise
43. Constipation fruit — Prunes
44. Dilled cucumber — Pickle
45. Antarctic bird — Penguin
46. Detective Clouseau – Peter Sellers — Pink Panther
47. Fat — Plump
48. These little toes — Piggies
49. Journalism award — Pulitzer
50. Already made – just put together — Prefabricated
51. Abstract artist — Picasso

52. Nylons	Pantyhose
53. Black of the eye	Pupil
54. Drool at the bell response	Pavlov
55. Plymouth rock	Pilgrims
56. Royalty home	Palace
57. Had pickled peppers	Peter Piper
58. English currency	Pound
59. Marionette	Puppet
60. Hawaiian fruit	Pineapple or Papaya
61. Drink served in a bowl at weddings	Punch
62. Marco….	Polo
63. Trousers	Pants
64. Peter Piper had these	Pickled Peppers
65. Type of dots	Polka
66. Fuzzy fruit	Peach
67. Jumping stick	Pogo
68. Tropical tree	Palm
69. Detective	Private Eye
70. Orchestra section	Percussion
71. Flintstone's daughter	Pebbles
72. Canal	Panama
73. "Little House" place	Prairie
74. Brotherly love city	Philadelphia
75. Nerd's Badge	Pocket Protector
76. Hit	Punch
77. Polish Dance	Polka
78. The Magic Dragon	Puff
79. Reddish spice	Paprika
80. Bedtime clothes	Pajamas
81. Baby' binkey	Pacifier
82. History	Past
83. Now	Present
84. Ocean	Pacific
85. European country	Poland
86. "Religious" insect	Praying Mantis
87. Backpackers tent	Pup Tent

	Clue	Answer
1.	King	Queen
2.	Patchwork	Quilt
3.	Hamburger type	Quarter-Pounder
4.	Ducks	Quack
5.	Theory type	Quantum
6.	Canada province	Quebec
7.	What they said	Quote
8.	Rock type	Quartz
9.	Barbershop group	Quartet
10.	Bird type	Quail
11.	Intelligence	Quotient

12. Fast	Quick
13. Five o'clock	Quitting time
14. Interrogate	Question
15. Isolate	Quarantine
16. Two bits	Quarter
17. Porcupine	Quills
18. Mini-test	Quiz
19. Tremble	Quake
20. Football position	Quarterback

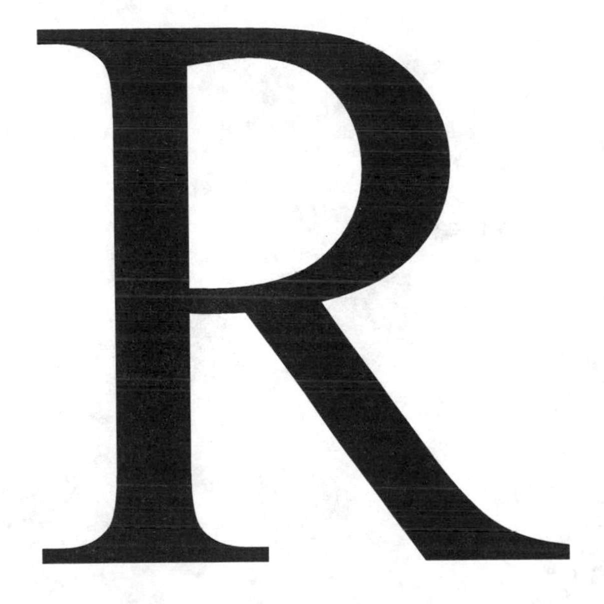

1. Chinese Taxi	Rickshaw
2. A shape	Rectangle
3. AM/FM	Radio
4. Precipitation	Rain
5. Thorny flower	Rose
6. Hare	Rabbit
7. Sherwood Forest thief	Robin Hood
8. Sly Stallone	Rocky
9. A Ninja Turtle	Raphael
10. Catholic string	Rosary

11. Rags to — Riches
12. Catskills 20-year sleeper — Rip Van Winkle
13. Igneous, Sedimentary, Metamorphic — Rocks
14. Albums — Records
15. Torn clothing — Rags
16. Cook with a spit — Rotisserie
17. Part of a ladder — Rung
18. Mice, rats, etc. — Rodents
19. Kings, Queens, etc. — Royalty
20. Mountain of Presidents — Rushmore
21. Wherefore art thou… — Romeo
22. Type of cube puzzle — Rubik's
23. Tires — Rubber or Radial
24. Casino wheel — Roulette
25. Wheeled shoes — Roller Skates (Blades)
26. Chess castle — Rook
27. Crow — Raven
28. Presidential Mountain — Rushmore
29. Hilltop sheep — Ram
30. Long pistol — Rifle
31. Quake scale — Richter
32. American mountain range — Rockies
33. Response request — RSVP
34. Second place — Runner-Up
35. Sounds similar — Rhymes
36. Parsley, sage,….. — Rosemary
37. Precipitation prism — Rainbow
38. Let down your hair…. — Rapunzel
39. Cowboy circus — Rodeo
40. Virginia capital — Richmond
41. Red gem — Ruby
42. Cracker type — Ritz
43. Not common — Rare
44. Plant part — Roots
45. Stereo — Receiver
46. String of mountains — Range
47. Saturn has them — Rings
48. Late-night flight — Red-Eye
49. Tape measure cousin — Ruler
50. Used in tennis — Racket

51.	Sir Lancelot's furniture	Round Table
52.	Bathtub toy	Rubber Duck
53.	Caribbean music style	Reggae
54.	Wasn't built in a day	Rome
55.	Have ridges	Ruffles
56.	Space vehicle	Rocket
57.	Not smooth	Rough
58.	Deadly gamble game	Russian Roulette
59.	Say again	Repeat
60.	Chicken	Rooster
61.	Tire material	Rubber
62.	Bound carpet	Rug
63.	Old phone type	Rotary
64.	Pot of Gold	Rainbow
65.	Farm	Ranch
66.	Mid-day school break	Recess
67.	Formally approve	Ratify
68.	Great Barrier	Reef
69.	Sleigh pullers	Reindeer
70.	Summary of work experience	Resume'

Two-Tips Trivia

1. Church panes	Stained Glass
2. Mint type	Spearmint
3. Find it with fire	Smoke
4. Collect	Save
5. Buy	Spend
6. Wise Biblical king	Solomon
7. Poetry or Nissan car	Stanza
8. Ghostly meeting	Séance
9. Kilt origin	Scotland
10. Japan "bye-bye"	Sayonara

11. Good on shortcake — Strawberries
12. Marriage partner — Spouse
13. Achoo — Sneeze
14. Groggy — Sleepy
15. Farmers belt — Suspenders
16. Celestial lights — Stars
17. Robin Hood's home — Sherwood Forest
18. Baby deliverer — Stork
19. Drool — Salivate
20. Hair removal — Shave
21. Facial hair — Sideburns
22. Pocket knife type — Swiss Army
23. Of the foot — Sole
24. Beer mug — Stein
25. Great Lake — Superior
26. Frosty… — Snowman
27. And Cher — Sony
28. Boat — Ship
29. Drum type — Snare
30. Chit chat — Small talk
31. Wonders of the World — Seven
32. Right angle dance — Square
33. Chip dip type — Salsa
34. Card mixing — Shuffle
35. Christmas Carol — Scrooge
36. Big Bird's road — Sesame Street
37. Roof covering — Shingles
38. Clam cover — Shell
39. Canal — Suez
40. Fork — Spoon
41. Mayday — S.O.S.
42. Coho — Salmon
43. Pig house — Sty
44. And the Seven Dwarfs — Snow White
45. Peter Parker — Spider-Man
46. Pepper — Salt
47. Bees do this — Sting
48. Lollipop — Sucker
49. Head over heals — Somersault
50. Engine type — Steam

51.	Canonized	Saint
52.	Turkey filling	Stuffing
53.	…Square Pants	Sponge-Bob
54.	Horse house	Stable
55.	Chicken noodle	Soup
56.	Black card type	Spades
57.	Word chunks	Syllables
58.	Ice cream treat	Sundae
59.	Sticky cellophane	Scotch Tape
60.	Ringed planet	Saturn
61.	Horse type	Shetland
62.	Boat type	Submarine
63.	On a beach	Sand
64.	Feet	Socks or Shoes
65.	Cattle overdrive	Stampede
66.	Oriental cat	Siamese
67.	Weapon type	Sword
68.	Japanese Warrior	Samurai
69.	Japanese athlete	Suma Wrestler
70.	Steam room	Sauna
71.	Charlie Brown's dog	Snoopy
72.	Lonely Hearts Club bandleader	Sgt. Pepper
73.	Rocky actor	Sylvester Stallone
74.	Clark Kent	Superman
75.	…the Bear	Smokey
76.	Met a pieman	Simple Simon
77.	Terminator Arnold	Schwarzenegger
78.	Pasta type	Spaghetti
79.	Tossed lettuce	Salad
80.	Green soup	Split Pea
81.	Golden Gate	San Francisco
82.	Zucchini	Squash
83.	Mail attachment	Stamp
84.	Phillips or regular	Screwdriver
85.	Used to fix a bad cut	Stitches
86.	Captain Kirk	Star Trek
87.	Frame by frame	Slow Motion
88.	Couch	Sofa
89.	Split sofa	Sectional
90.	Popeye	Spinach

91.	Underwater RADAR	Sonar
92.	Little plate	Saucer
93.	Hockey trophy	Stanley Cup
94.	Spring toy	Slinky
95.	India instrument	Sitar
96.	George Lucas	Star Wars
97.	Canned fish	Sardines
98.	Growls when hungry	Stomach
99.	Jewish cathedral	Synagogue
100.	Bath	Shower
101.	Lesson on the mount	Sermon
102.	Lots of bees	Swarm
103.	Card game	Solitaire
104.	PB&J	Sandwich
105.	Between meals	Snacks
106.	Boing	Spring
107.	Hot months	Summer
108.	Oops…	Sorry
109.	Change gears	Shift
110.	Hair cleaner	Shampoo
111.	Safety strap	Seat Belt
112.	Flight attendant	Steward or Stewardess
113.	Hawaiian sport	Surfing
114.	Pancakes	Syrup
115.	& Roebuck	Sears
116.	Ugly duckling	Swan
117.	Small prawn	Shrimp
118.	Autograph	Signature
119.	Twist and….	Shout
120.	& gold	Silver
121.	Z's	Sleep
122.	Wizard of Oz character	Scarecrow
123.	Clover	Shamrock
124.	Baa Baa	Sheep
125.	Timid	Shy
126.	Trousers	Slacks
127.	Bones	Skeleton
128.	Rough drawing	Sketch
129.	Lemons	Sour
130.	Run	Sprint

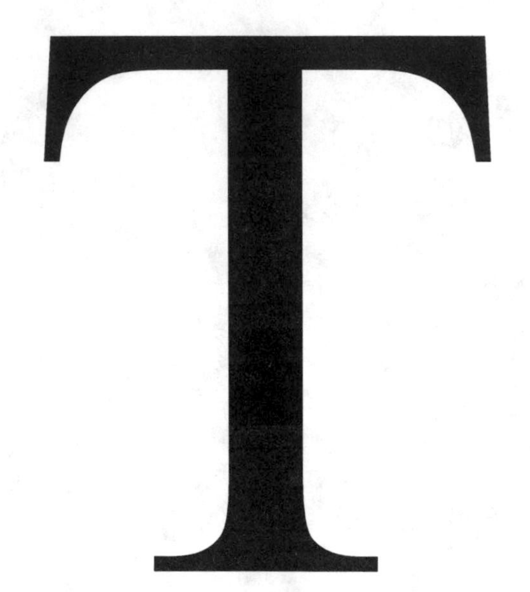

1. Commuting	Traffic Jam
2. Teenage Ninja	Turtles
3. Dental gel	Toothpaste
4. Egyptian King	Tut
5. Sliver tool	Tweezers
6. And the Hare	Tortoise
7. Animal stuffer	Taxidermist
8. All-for-one…	Three Musketeers
9. Sled cousin	Toboggan

10. "Unsinkable" — Titanic
11. Unlucky number — Thirteen
12. Football move — Tackle
13. It "flies" — Time
14. Ten Commandments — Tablets
15. Ocean changes — Tide
16. Aim at the… — Target
17. Gratuity — Tip
18. The Donald — Trump
19. And Jane — Tarzan
20. "Stuffed" bird — Turkey
21. Horse races — Triple Crown
22. Bacon, Lettuce and — Tomato
23. "Shake it up baby now…" — Twist and Shout
24. Canned fish — Tuna
25. "Give 'em hell, Harry" — Truman
26. Wonderland's twins — Tweedledee & Tweedledum
27. Clock sounds — Tic Toc
28. Cake type — Torte
29. Perfect vision — Twenty/Twenty
30. Skin art — Tattoo
31. Heat reader — Thermometer
32. Forbidden — Taboo
33. Boat type — Tug
34. Fruit Loops bird — Toucan
35. When the lion sleeps — Tonight
36. Lyme Disease carrier — Tick
37. Movie Studio — Twentieth-Century Fox
38. Breakfast jewel — Tiffany's
39. Benedict Arnold — Traitor
40. Bike cousin — Tricycle
41. Audio – Visual — Television
42. Dentist — Teeth
43. In cheek — Tongue
44. Native American weapon — Tomahawk
45. Dracula home — Transylvania
46. Type of crown for a horse — Triple
47. Florida — Tallahassee
48. Little star — Twinkle Twinkle
49. Drinking glass type — Tumbler

50. Car part	Tire
51. On edge	Testy
52. Of little importance	Trifle
53. Try to overthrow the government	Treason
54. Tom cruising in the sky	Top Gun
55. Instant orange drink	Tang
56. Blackjack	Twenty-One
57. Beats per minute	Tempo
58. Hurricane cousin	Tornado
59. Lone Star	Texas
60. Graduate hats	Tassels
61. Piano tool	Tuning Fork
62. Cigarettes	Tobacco
63. Elf-like dolls	Trolls
64. Found in a bathroom	Toilet
65. Big ping-pong	Tennis
66. Clock	Tick-Tock
67. Flip chips game	Tiddlywinks
68. Dorothy's dog	Toto
69. Neck knot	Tie
70. Engine control	Throttle
71. Thor	Thunder
72. Done to ribs	Tickles
73. Pulled behind cars	Trailer
74. Mexican sandwich	Taco
75. Gypsy instrument	Tambourine
76. Lance Armstrong	Tour de France
77. Dynamite	TNT
78. Christmas tree fringe	Tinsel
79. Orange cousin	Tangerine
80. Carved tree	Totem pole
81. Wood eaters	Termites
82. Airport	Terminal
83. Takes two…	Tango
84. Teenie	Weenie
85. Hubble	Telescope
86. Singing range	Tenor
87. …and shout	Twist
88. Military vehicle	Tank
89. Grave marker	Tombstone

90. 76 led the big parade	Trombones
91. Santa's gifts to kids	Toys
92. Man wig	Toupee
93. House of worship	Temple
94. Stretched story	Tall Tale
95. Hitchhiker tool	Thumb
96. Elephant tooth	Tusk
97. Throw it in when giving up	Towel

1.	Black light	Ultraviolet
2.	Bono	U2
3.	Aunt	Uncle
4.	Piano type	Upright
5.	"You're out!"	Umpire
6.	Bumbershoot	Umbrella
7.	Milk dispensers	Udders
8.	Church attendant	Usher
9.	A-bomb material	Uranium
10.	Cake type	Upside-down

11. German ship — U-Boat
12. VHF cousin — UHF
13. Salmon mating direction — Upstream
14. Big bang — Universe
15. Hawaiian instrument — Ukulele
16. British flag — Union Jack
17. What the swan was — Ugly duckling
18. What stress can give you — Ulcers
19. Joins baby to mom — Umbilical cord
20. Where fish live — Underwater
21. Wild child — Unruly
22. Institution — University
23. One of a kind — Unique
24. Workers organization — Union
25. Needed now — Urgent
26. City life — Urban
27. Not new — Used
28. Fork, spoon…. — Utensils
29. Ideal place — Utopia
30. Police outfit — Uniform

1. Reindeer	Vixen
2. Animal Doc	Veterinarian
3. Rug cleaner	Vacuum
4. Shot in the arm	Vaccination
5. Fake leather	Vinyl
6. Vapor rub	Vicks
7. Rrrrrrip fastener	Velcro
8. T.J. home state	Virginia
9. Mt St. Helens	Volcano
10. Zodiac sign	Virgo

11. U. S. President — Van Buren
12. City with canals — Venice
13. Bug car maker — Volkswagen
14. Sweater type — V-Neck
15. Carnivorous plant — Venus Flytrap
16. Work for no pay — Volunteers
17. Color or flower type — Violet
18. Animal poison — Venom
19. Grapes cut from these — Vines
20. February — Valentines (Day)
21. Break from work — Vacation
22. Motel opening — Vacancy
23. Car Parker — Valet
24. Letter turner — Vanna White
25. Popeville — Vatican City
26. Gardens — Vegetables
27. Chrysler mini….. — Van
28. Elections — Votes
29. Ravine — Valley
30. Set, spike, side-out — Volleyball
31. Loudness — Volume
32. Hides bride — Veil
33. Albert's queen — Victoria
34. Multi pill — Vitamin
35. Savage — Vicious
36. Mr. Borge — Victor
37. Dracula — Vampire
38. Had an ear for art — Vincent Van Gogh
39. Maple syrup & cheddar state — Vermont
40. Computer bug — Virus
41. Literary rabbit — Velveteen
42. Sausage type — Vienna
43. Spock's bloodline — Vulcan
44. Dignitary initials — VIP
45. Nothingness — Void
46. Offensive or rude — Vulgar
47. Promise — Vow
48. Deer meat — Venison
49. Speed — Velocity
50. Not clear — Vague

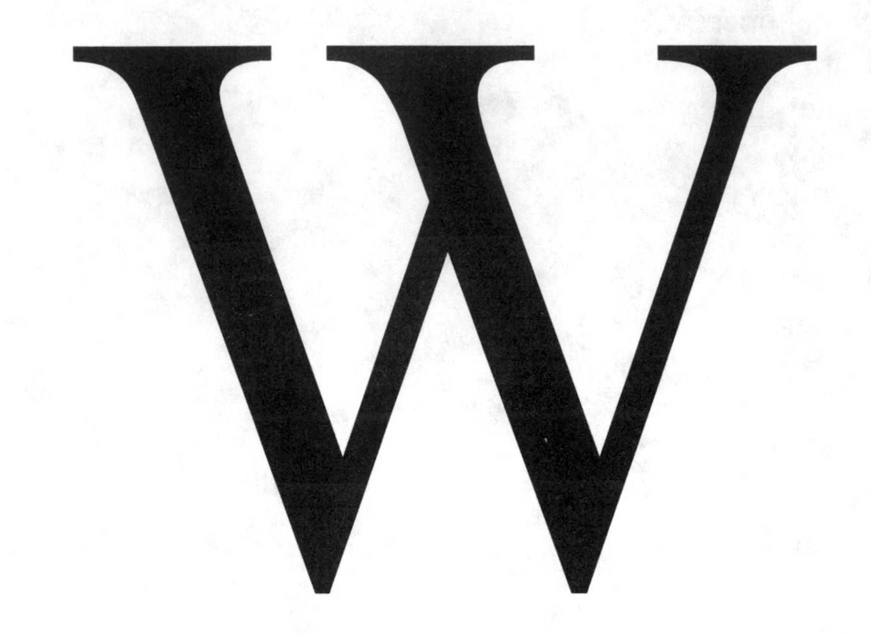

1. Shirts professionals wear	White Collar
2. English tennis championship	Wimbledon
3. Done to cream	Whipped
4. Thank you	Welcome
5. Dictionary dude	Webster
6. Four balls	Walk
7. Sheep hair	Wool
8. Appliance maker	Whirlpool
9. Timepiece	Watch
10. Bet	Wager

11. Belt line — Waist
12. Garbage — Waste
13. Right opposite — Wrong
14. Weaved furniture — Wicker
15. On top of barns — Weather Vane
16. Red-headed bird type — Woodpecker
17. Breakfast cereal of champions — Wheaties
18. Woodrow president — Wilson
19. Stock market street — Wall Street
20. Dive gear — Wet suit
21. Sea Lion cousin — Walrus
22. Red Flyer — Wagon
23. Female — Woman
24. Wicked — Witch
25. BBQ Buffalo — Wings
26. Duck walk — Waddle
27. Office garbage bin — Wastebasket
28. Croquet piece — Wicket
29. Buggy accelerator — Whip
30. Al Yankovic — Weird
31. Knock on it — Wood
32. Square burgers — Wendy's
33. Dance style — Waltz
34. Blink — Wink
35. Architect — Frank Lloyd Wright
36. Mid week — Wednesday
37. Middle measurement — Waist
38. Dances with... — Wolves
39. Puns = play on ____________ — Words
40. Tsunami — Wave
41. Teepee — Wigwam
42. Shoe type — Wing Tip
43. Restaurant — Waiter
44. Pancakes — Waffle
45. Car protection — Wax
46. Fat fighters — Weight Watchers
47. First plane — Wright Brothers
48. A Fish Called ______________ — Wanda
49. Bruce "Die-Hard" — Willis
50. First Pres. — Washington

1.	Instrument	Xylophone
2.	Superman	X-Ray Vision
3.	Men – 1, Women – 2	X Chromosomes
4.	Millionaire's boat	Yacht
5.	Egg	Yolk
6.	Oxen	Yoke
7.	Dot com biggie	Yahoo!
8.	Bread lifter	Yeast
9.	Village People	YMCA
10.	National Park	Yellowstone
11.	Knit	Yarn
12.	Grape squeezer	Wine Press
13.	Beatle's ship	Yellow Submarine
14.	365	Year
15.	Toy	Yo-Yo
16.	Switzerland singing	Yodel
17.	3 feet	Yard
18.	Day before the day before tomorrow	Yesterday
19.	Sign of tiredness	Yawn
20.	Bad taste reply	Yuck
21.	Good taste reply	Yum

Clue	Answer
22. Ox cousin	Yak
23. Cowboy Sam	Yosemite
24. Potato cousin	Yam
25. Doodle song	Yankee
26. School memory book	Yearbook
27. Cartoon bear	Yogi
28. Wizard of Oz	Yellow Brick Road
29. Flintstone saying	"Yabba Dabba Do!"
30. Yami ___________	Yogurt
31. Phone book	Yellow Pages
32. Traffic sign	Yield
33. Nothing	Zero, Zilch, Zip
34. "AA-bottom" opposite	ZZ Top
35. This way, that way	Zig Zag
36. Living dead	Zombie
37. Hindenburg	Zeppelin
38. Mail	Zip Code
39. African horse cousin	Zebra
40. Twilight ___________	Zone

Say What?

These intriguing little puzzles require the readers to LISTEN carefully and go beyond what they are saying and on to what they are HEARING! There are many ways to share these riddles. First…let us show you an example:

Say each of the following words – ***slowly*** – and ***blend*** them together as you do.
Do you hear it?

ABLE OWE KNEES HAND WHICH = A Bologna Sandwich

Cool, huh?!?!

So, here is what you can do.

- *Cover up the answers and see if you can figure them out.*
- *Write them on a bigger piece of paper and see if your friends, family, or students can figure them out.*
- *Give a friend clues to each word. Once they have guessed each word…see if they can figure out the completed phrase.*

Have FUN!

1. A DOLL FIDDLER	Adolph Hitler
2. ABE AN AN APPEAL	A Banana Peel
3. ABE AN AN AS PULL HIT	A Banana Split
4. ABE AUTUMN LISP HIT	A Bottomless Pit
5. ABE AX HEAT ARRIVE HER	A Back Seat Driver
6. ABE AX TAB HER	A Back Stabber
7. ABE AX TREE TALLY	A Back Street Alley
8. ABE BARF SSS! HOPE	A Bar Of Soap
9. ABE EACH DWELL	A Beached Whale
10. ABE EARTH TAPE RACE HINT	A Birthday Present
11. ABE EASY SUPPORTS	ABC Sports
12. ABE EARTH DAZE HOOT	A Birthday Suit
13. ABE HAG AWFUL OUR	A Bag Of Flour
14. ABE HAIR HEAT RASH YOU'RE	A Buried Treasure
15. ABE HAT CHILL HARP ADD	A Bachelor Pad
16. ABE HAT CHILL HARP HEARTY	A Bachelor Party
17. ABE HE KEEN HE	A Bikini
18. ABE HER DOUSE	A Birdhouse
19. ABE HIS NEIGH SCARRED	A Business Card
20. ABE HUM PEN THIN HEIGHT	A Bump In The Night
21. ABE HUT TON KNOLL	A Button Hole
22. ABE LINCOLN LIED	A Blinkin' Light
23. ABE LINED EIGHT	A Blind Date
24. ABE ODD HULL UP HOP	A Bottle Of Pop
25. ABE OX SUCK HANDY	A Box Of Candy
26. ABE PAWN HUFF HIGH DOLL FUR	A Bonafide Offer
27. ABE RAN OOZE HOOT	A Brand New Suit
28. ABE REIGN FORTH HUSK HAIR GROW	A Brain For A Scarecrow
29. ABE RYE TIDY YEAH	A Bright Idea
30. ABE WHO BEAT WRAP	A Booby Trap
31. ABLE ANKLE HOOK	A Blank Look
32. ABLE EATING ART	A Bleeding Heart
33. ABLE HIGH GUY	A Black Eye
34. ABLE HISS HEARD	A Blizzard
35. ABLE OWE KNEES HAND WHICH	A Bologna Sandwich
36. ABLE SAYS SHUN	A Bull Session
37. ACE AIN'T BARNYARD	A Saint Bernard
38. ACE CARED EKE HAT	A Scaredy Cat
39. ACE DATE TOUGH GAY HOSS	A State Of Chaos
40. ACE ETHER WHO BULL HOUSE	A See Through Blouse
41. ACE HACK SOFA OWN	A Saxophone
42. ACE HAY CRUD GAL	A Sacred Cow
43. ACE HEAL INK VAN	A Ceiling Fan
44. ACE HECK HUNCH ANTS	A Second Chance

45. ACE HEIGHT FORCE OR RISE	A Sight For Sore Eyes
46. ACE HIGH ENOUGH THUD I'M SSS!	A Sign Of The Times
47. ACE HUM ARF! ACHE ASIAN	A Summer Vacation
48. ACE KITS OFFER IN HICK	A Schizophrenic
49. ACE LEAP LESSON HEIGHT	A Sleepless Night
50. ACE LIE SOAP EYE	A Slice Of Pie
51. ACE LIE TOUGH AND	A Slight Of Hand
52. ACE LIP PUFF THAT HUNG	A Slip Of The Tongue
53. ACE LOBE OIL	A Slow Boil
54. ACE LOPE OAK	A Slow-Poke
55. ACE NEIGH KIN THICKER AS	A Snake In The Grass
56. ACE NOSE DORM	A Snowstorm
57. ACE OFF BOWL DIG	A Soft Boiled Egg
58. ACE PAY SHALLOW CASE SHUN	A Special Occasion
59. ACE PEA DING TEA KIT	A Speeding Ticket
60. ACE TANNED HENS TART	A Standing Start
61. ACE TORE MISS BURR WHO WING	A Storm Is Brewing
62. ACE TRAY TASTE WHO DENT	A Straight "A" Student
63. ACE WOMEN PULL	A Swimming Pool
64. ACHE ALLOWED HEED HAY	A Cloudy Day
65. ACHE AN TOLL HOPE	A Cantaloupe
66. ACHE ARF! OWN	A Car Phone
67. ACHE COMET HE AFFAIR HEARSE	A Comedy Of Errors
68. ACHE HAND HE EYE PULL	A Candy Apple
69. ACHE HAS SIR HOLE	A Casserole
70. ACHE HAT BURR GLARE	A Cat Burglar
71. ACHE HAT DILL HACK	A Cadillac
72. ACHE HEAP UN- CHOPPER HATER	A Key Punch Operator
73. ACHE HEARTY HACKER WRIST	A Cardiac Arrest
74. ACHE HEY SOLVE DIARY AH	A Case Of Diarrhea
75. ACHE HICK KIN TUB HUT	A Kick In The Butt
76. ACHE HILLY SEAL	Achilles Heel
77. ACHE HIT AWAKE ARE	A Get-Away Car
78. ACHE HOOD SIN SEW FUME HER	A Good Sense Of Humor
79. ACHE HOP HE MUSH SHEEN	A Copy Machine
80. ACHE HOP PICK HAT	A Copy Cat
81. ACHE HOW CUE LATER	A Calculator
82. ACHE HULL LEG SHH! ENOUGH STAMPS	A Collection Of Stamps
83. ACHE HUNT TREES TORE	A Country Store
84. ACHE HUNT TRICKLE HUB	A Country Club
85. ACHE HUNT TRIM AISLE	A Country Mile
86. ACHE INKS HIGH SPED	A King Size Bed
87. ACHE LASS EH? KEG SAMPLE	A Classic Example
88. ACHE LEANS LATE	A Clean Slate
89. ACHE LOCK RAID HE OWE	A Clock Radio
90. ACHE OAR VETS TEEN GRAY	A Corvette Stingray

91. ACHE OFF CORES	A Golf Course
92. ACHE OFF FANNED HE GAP	A Golf Handicap
93. ACHE ORDER	A Quarter
94. ACHE UN- HAIRY	A Canary
95. ACHE UP PUCK OFF HE	A Cup Of Coffee
96. ACHE WAND TUMBLE HEAP	A Quantum Leap
97. ACRE AGE US SPUR SUN	A Courageous Person
98. ACRE EACH HER ROVE HIGH BIT	A Creature Of Habit
99. ACRE HALLS TUB HOARD	Across The Board
100. ACRE HEY OWE LUCK RAY YAWN	A Crayola Crayon
101. ACRE HIGH MUFF PIE SHUN	A Crime Passion
102. ACRE HILL UH	A Gorilla
103. ACRE HISS MUSK HARD	A Christmas Card
104. ACRE HISSED MUSTER HE	A Christmas Tree
105. ACRE HIT TICKLE DOES ASIAN	A Critical Decision
106. ACRE LEAK YOU	A Curly Q
107. ACRE REAL CHIEFS HAND WITCH	A Grilled Cheese Sandwich
108. ACRES WHIRRED	A Curse Word
109. AID US SINNER OWE HOSES	A Dozen Roses
110. ADJUST DAWN KIT HIT	I Just Don't Get It
111. ADORE PURR EYES	A Door Prize
112. AGE ANT HUB BLOWS HEAVEN	Agent Double-0-Seven
113. AGE ANT SOLVE SHH! OURS	A Chance Of Showers
114. AGE ARE COKE REAL	A Charcoal Grill
115. AGE HAIRY GEE SKATE	A Cherry Cheese Cake
116. AGE HAPPEN HE SCAR	A Japanese Car
117. AGE HE STAIN HUSH	A Cheese Danish
118. AGE HIGH HUNTS GUYS GRAPE HER	A Giant Skyscraper
119. AGE HIGH KNEES WEST WANT	A Chinese Restaurant
120. AGE HIP OFF TOLD BULL LOCK	A Chip Off The Old Block
121. AGE HOOF ANNULLED HEAL INK WENT	A Juvenile Delinquent
122. AGE JOB RAKE ARE	A Jaw Breaker
123. AGE OAR CHIP EACH	A Georgia Peach
124. AGE US DISSOLVED HIP EASE	A Justice Of The Peace
125. AGED WHO WOE	H2O
126. AGHAST HANK	A Gas Tank
127. AGREE NAP HULL	A Green Apple
128. AGREE SUMMON KEY	A Grease Monkey
129. AH! GNARL BALM ENGINE	Honorable Mention
130. AID AID REAM HER	A Daydreamer
131. AID ARE COARSE	A Dark Horse
132. AID ARE CRANK LOUD	A Dark Rain Cloud
133. AID ARRIVE HEN THEY UTTER	A Drive-In Theater
134. AID ARRIVE HER SLICE SINS	A Driver's License
135. AID ARRIVING ARRANGE	A Driving Range
136. AID HAY HUFF ACHE ASIAN	A Day Of Vacation

137. AID HEAD HOG KIN THERE OWED	A Dead Dog In The Road
138. AID HID DULLED HID DULL	Hey Diddle Diddle
139. AID HIGHNESS TEA	A Dynasty
140. AID HOG WITHER HAY BEES	A Dog With Rabies
141. AID HUB BLADE GENT	A Double Agent
142. AID HUB BULB LAY	A Double Play
143. AID HYMN OAK RAT	A Democrat
144. AID I'M UN- DEN THERE HUFF	A Diamond In The Rough
145. AID INN HEARSE OWL ADD	A Dinner Salad
146. AID ITCH IT TALK LOCK	A Digital Clock
147. AID RAFT PIER	A Draft Beer
148. AID RIDE HYPER	A Dry Diaper
149. AID ROBIN TUB UH KIT	A Drop In The Bucket
150. AIM ACRE BRAKES HITCH AWAY SHIN	A Make Or Break Situation
151. AIM ADDER ROUGH OPEN YEN	A Matter Of Opinion
152. AIM AGE HER ROBBER ASIAN	A Major Operation
153. AIM AHH! MOSS BEAU WE	A Mama's Boy
154. AIM AIR EGG GORE ROUND	A Merry-Go-Round
155. AIM ASH YOU'RE RINK UP	A Measuring Cup
156. AIM HAY JERK RICE HISS	A Major Crisis
157. AIM HIKER OWES COPE	A Microscope
158. AIM HOME HINT HINT I'M	A Moment In Time
159. AIM HONEY BAG CARE RUNT HE	A Money Back Guarantee
160. AIM HUNKER HEAR INCH	A Monkey Wrench
161. AIM ODD AILS HIT HIS HEN	A Model Citizen
162. AIM ODD HULK ARE	A Model Car
163. AIM OTHER RANCH HOWLED	A Mother And Child
164. AIM UH SAND DANDY	Amos And Andy
165. AIM UN- THUS UNDIES	A Month Of Sundays
166. AIM US KEY TUB HEIGHT	A Mosquito Bite
167. AIM WHO FAKE RID TICK	A Movie Critic
168. AIM WHO VERY VIEW	A Movie Review
169. AIR EGG YULE ARE WHY SKY	A Regular Wise Guy
170. AIR EIGHTY HATER	A Radiator
171. AIR EVER FULL OWE STEW THESE HE	A River Flows To The Sea
172. AIR HAY SUCK HINTS THICK LOCK	A Race Against The Clock
173. AIR HEAD LET HEARD HAY	A Red-Letter Day
174. AIR HEN TALK ARE	A Rental Car
175. AIR HOUND DOVE COUGH	A Round Of Golf
176. AIR HUB HERB HAND	A Rubber Band
177. AIR HUFF FRIDAY HEAD	A Rough Ride Ahead
178. AIR HUSH HENS PIE	A Russian Spy
179. AIR WHOM WIDTH HALF YOU	A Room With A View
180. AIRY LEDGES PURSE SUN	A Religious Person
181. AIRY MIND HER	A Reminder
182. AISLE BEER HEIGHT THEY HAIR	I'll Be Right There

183. AISLE HIKE CUE	I Like You
184. AISLE ME CHEW HAVE WEIGH	I'll Meet You Half Way
185. AISLE ME JEWEL HATER	I'll Meet You Later
186. AISLE OF LOOSELY	I Love Lucy
187. AISLE OH VIEW	I Love You
188. AISLE UH FIT	I Love It
189. ALE EDGE INDIAN HISS OWNED I'M	A Legend In His Own Time
190. ALE HAWK CAB HEN	A Log Cabin
191. ALE HAZE HEED HEY	A Lazy Day
192. ALE HEIGHTS WITCH	A Light Switch
193. ALE HEY BURR OVAL OF	A Labor Of Love
194. ALE HISS DOVE THAT HOPPED INN	A List Of The Top Ten
195. ALE HOT TREAT HICK HIT	A Lottery Ticket
196. ALE HUM PEN MOTH WROTE	A Lump In My Throat
197. ALE IF ANGLE HEDGE END	A Living Legend
198. ALE LIT HOLD APPLE DUE HUE	A Little Dab'll Do Ya
199. ALE OF HUFF AIR	A Love Affair
200. ALE OF HUFF AIR HOLLOW DAZE ALE	Holiday Sale
201. ALE OF TRY ANKLE	A Love Triangle
202. ALLEY MAKE LAMP HIT	Elly May Clampett
203. ALLIED ATTACKED HER	A Lie Detector
204. ALLOT HURRY	A Lottery
205. ALOE COW HURRIED HIGH YET	A Low Calorie Diet
206. ALONG BUY CRIED	A Long Bike Ride
207. AMEN ASK HURT	A Mini-Skirt
208. AMEN EASE EERIE SEWN TEA FEE	A Mini-Series On TV
209. AMEN HISSED HER	A Minister
210. AMMO BULLS HEY YULE ARF! OWN	A Mobile Cellular Phone
211. AN AN YOU WOOLY VENT	An Annual Event
212. ANGER SAY WAY	Anchors Away!
213. ANNEX GLUM NATION POINT	An Exclamation Point
214. ANNEX TIN CHUNK HOARD	Am Extension Cord
215. ANNOY STIR BAR	An Oyster Bar
216. ANTIDOTE MAIN MAY BEE	And I Don't Mean Maybe
217. ANY LACK TRICKED BULL HANK HIT	An Electric Blanket
218. ANY LICK TRICKLES DORM	An Electrical Storm
219. APART RID CHIN-UP HAIR TRAY	"... A Partridge In A Pear Tree"
220. APE AGE HECK	A Paycheck
221. APE ANY FUR YOUTH HALTS	A Penny For Your Thoughts
222. APE ARE KENNEL HOT	A Parking Lot
223. APE ARROW FACES	A Pair Of Aces
224. APE ARROWS HANDLES	A Pair Of Sandals
225. APE ARROWS OX	A Pair Of Socks
226. APE ARROWS UNCLE AS HIS	A Pair Of Sunglasses
227. APE HACK AWFUL EYES	A Pack Of Lies
228. APE HAND HUB HAIR	A Panda Bear

229. APE HATE HAIL HUFF OWN	A Pay Telephone
230. APE HAY CHOW TOUGH FIST TREE	A Page Out Of History
231. APE HEN SEALS HARP INNER	A Pencil Sharpener
232. APE HICK CHEER RAIL BUM	A Picture Album
233. APE HICK HIT FINS	A Picket Fence
234. APE HICK KETTLE LINE	A Picket Line
235. APE HOURS TRUCK HULL	A Power Struggle
236. APE I LOVED RASH	A Pile Of Trash
237. APE IN HEAP INCH HER	A Penny Pincher
238. APE LAY ONWARDS	A Play On Words
239. APE LAY TOUGH SCRAM BULL DIGS	A Plate Of Scrambled Eggs
240. APE RASHES MOW MEANT	A Precious Moment
241. APE ROB HUB HULK HALLS	A Probable Cause
242. APE RYE FAT TIE	A Private Eye
243. AROUND DOVE APPLE LAWS	A Round Of Applause
244. ARRANGE HECK	A Rain Check
245. ARREST HAIRY AHH!	Rest Area
246. ARREST MIKE ACE	I Rest My Case
247. ARROW LOVED OIL IT TISSUE	A Roll Of Toilet Tissue
248. ARROW LURK HOLSTER	A Roller Coaster
249. ARROW ME OWE	A Romeo
250. ART BRAY COAT HAIL	Heart Break Hotel
251. AS CARE SAYS INNS TEETH	As Scarce As Hen's Teeth
252. AS CURE BALLS FRAY FAKE ASIAN	Ask Your Boss For A Vacation
253. AS PRINT APPLE HITS	Aspirin Tablets
254. AS PUNK HOLLOW ROD OWE	Aspen, Colorado
255. AS THICKER OAF LIES	As The Crow Flies
256. ASBESTOS HIKE AN	As Best As I Can
257. ASH HA! CUBS OR BURR	A Shock Absorber
258. ASH HER TANNED HIGH	A Shirt And Tie
259. ASH HOLD HURT HOOK RYE YAWN	A Shoulder To Cry On
260 ASH HOOD OVEN BED HER	I Should Of (Have) Known Better
261. ASH HOOD OVEN ON KNIT	I Should Of Known It
262. ASK LEER ESSAY BALE	As Clear As A Bell
263. ASK RUDE ARRIVE HER	A Screwdriver
264. ASK WIG CUSS AWFUL ASH	As Quick As A Flash
265. AT TEN CHINS HA! PURSE	"Attention, Shoppers..."
266. ATE APE REEK QUARTER	A Tape Recorder
267. ATE ALL GRADE HE OWE SHH! OWE	A Talk Radio Show
268. ATE HIGH BURR ACRE	A Tie- Breaker
269. ATE OOZE TORE HE OWLS	A Two Story House
270. ATE RASH YOU'RE RUNT	A Treasure Hunt
271. ATE RIP TOOT HIS KNEEL HAND	A Trip To Disneyland
272. ATE WHOLE FREAK HAUL	A Toll Free Call
273. ATTACK CEDAR MISSED	A Taxidermist
274. AUTHOR WHO THICKEN THEN	All Through Thick And Thin

275. AWARD DEN HEDGE WIVES	A Word In Edgewise
276. AWE HAY SPY MICE HIDE	Always By My Side
277. AWE LAD WON SIT TAP END	All At Once It Happened
278. AWE LINT THIEF HAM HILLY	All In The Family
279. AWE MOW STAIR	Almost There
280. AWE MUM HOT HER	Alma Mater
281. AWE THICK LITTER SIS KNOCK OLD	All That Glitters Is Not Gold
282. AWE TOOTH HUG HOOD	All To The Good
283. AWED SAND DENS	Odds And Ends
284. AWFULLY MITTS	Off Limits
285. BACKED OOZE QUEER WON	Back To Square One
286. BAGGED WHO THIEF HUGE HER	Back To The Future
287. BAGPIPE HOP YOU LARD HE MANNED	Back By Popular Demand
288. BAH! FOLLOW	Buffalo
289. BAIL HEED ANT SIR	Belly Dancer
290. BALDY GULL	Bald Eagle
291. BALL STINT HEAP HEARTY	Boston Tea Party
292. BALL STUNS ALE TICKS	Boston Celtics
293. BAR BEAK USE HALLS	Barbecue Sauce
294. BAR BRUSHED RISE HAND	Barbara Streisand
295. BAR CUPPED THEIR RUNG TREE	Barked Up The Wrong Tree
296. BARE LOVE MONK EASE	Barrel Of Monkeys
297. BAT END HOUND THAT CHESS	Batten Down The Hatches
298. BAT ERUPT WHO DEEP LATE	Batter Up To The Plate
299. BAT HULL LACKS	Battle Ax
300. BAT TREE SNOT INK LOOTED	Batteries Not Included
301. BAT WRECKS WEIGHS SEA	Patrick Swayze
302. BAWL LOVE HIRE	Ball Of Fire
303. BAY HARASS BRAN	Bayer Aspirin
304. BAY SCISSORS LOOTED	Bases Are Loaded
305. BAYS DAWN EIGHT ROOST OR HE	Based On A True Story
306. BE TAR HOUND TUB HUSH	Beat Around The Bush
307. BEAK HALL SIZE HEADS HOE	Because I Said So
308. BEAM HIVE HOWL LINT I'M	Be My Valentine
309. BEAR OMIT TRICK PRAY SHORE	Barometric Pressure
310. BEAST ILL MA ART	Be Still My Heart
311. BEAU RISK ARE ALOFT	Boris Karloff
312. BED HERB HILLY FIT	Better Believe It
313. BEE COMMON EGG SPURT	Become An Expert
314. BEE LEAGUE RAM	Billy Graham
315. BEE TOOTH HEAP HUNCH	Beat To The Punch
316. BEE WAY ROUGH THUD HOG	Beware Of The Dog
317. BEE YAWN THICK HOLLOW DO TEA	Beyond The Call Of Duty
318. BEEN GARTER HEIGHT	Ben Cartwright
319. BEEP HAY TREE EROTIC	Be Patriotic
320. BEEP REAP AIRED	Be Prepared

321. BEES ITEMS SAY ELF	Beside Himself
322. BEES LOAD WHO ANCHOR	Be Slow To Anger
323. BELLY THICK HID	Billy The Kid
324. BELOW THEY WHIZ ILL	Blow The Whistle
325. BELOW YAWNED RUMP PET	Blow Your Trumpet
326. BERRY THATCH HIT	Bury The Hatchet
327. BET RELATE THIN HEIFER	Better Late Than Never
328. BET TERM AISLE STRAP	Better Mousetrap
329. BETTER HOSES	Bed Of Roses
330. BEYOND NEST WIT CHORES ELF	Be Honest With Yourself
331. BEYOND THEY'LL HOOK OUT	Be On The Look Out
332. BIBLE EYE CUB ROOK	Babble Like A Brook
333. BIGGER SCANT BEACH WHO SEA	Beggars Can't Be Choosy
334. BILL LEAK WRIST HULL	Billy Crystal
335. BILL LEDGE OILS	Billy Joel
336. BILL OFFER HEIGHTS	Bill Of Rights
337. BILLS PAIR READ OH-BOY!	"Pillsbury Doughboy"
338. BILLY FITTER NAUGHT	Believe It Or Not
339. BITE THESE WET TOUGHEST PROWL	By The Sweat Of His Brow
340. BLEW WHEN THIEF ACE	Blue In The Face
341. BOB BOBBLE AXE HEAP	Baa Baa Black Sheep
342. BOG HULL THUMB HIND	Boggle The Mind
343. BOOK HE MAN	Boogie Man
344. BORE NAG HEN	Born Again
345. BOW LAWNS SALVE MORPHIN	Blondes Have More Fun
346. BOWEL LAID ANSWER	Ballet Dancer
347. BREW SWILL HISS	Bruce Willis
348. BROTH ERRANDS HISSED HER	Brother And Sister
349. BRR! STUFFS BEAD	Burst Of Speed
350. BUCK SPUN HE	Bugs Bunny
351. BUFF EARLY HEAL BELLIES	Beverly Hillbillies
352. BUFF ELOPE HEEL	Buffalo Bill
353. BULL LINE DAYS SUB HAT	Blind As A Bat
354. BUN CHEEK HOARD	Bungee Cord
355. BURN DEATH THUS TAKE	Burned At The Stake
356. BURN THE CANDLE AT BOTH ENDS	Burn The Candle At Both Ends
357. BURNED THUMB HIDDEN HEIGHT OIL	Burn The Midnight Oil
358. BURR NUB THEIR OWED	Burn Up The Road
359. BURR SIGN FEW	Bird's Eye View
360. BURR SOFA FAITH HER	Birds Of A Feather
361. BURR STAT THESE AIMS	Burst At The Seams
362. BURR TRAIN HOLDS	Burt Reynolds
363. BURROW KIN ART HID	Broken Hearted
364. BUS TOUGH BEAU TWIRLS	Best Of Both Worlds
365. BUS WHO CUB HUB HULK HUM	Bazooka Bubble Gum
366. BUT HURT HOSE TINGE ALLEY	Buttered Toast And Jelly

367. BUTCH CHIRP AUTUMN DOLL HER	Bet Your Bottom Dollar
368. BUTTON HEN KNEE OF HINT	But In Any Event
369. BUY FOLK HULLS	Bifocals
370. BY CHORE DUNG	Bite Your Tongue
371. BYE YAM ERA GUN	Buy American
372. CAGE HUNK HOOK KING	Cajun Cooking
373. CALL FEET HE WORM ELK	Coffee, Tea, Or Milk
374. CALL FIBBER RAKE	Coffee Break
375. CALL TIN EIGHT RAP	Caught In A Trap
376. CALL TREAD AND HID	Caught Red Handed
377. CALM HAND DRENCH HEAVE	Commander In Chief
378. CALM HUNGER HOUND	Common Ground
379. CALM MASS HUE WIRE	Come As You Are
380. CALM TOOTH HEN COVE FIT	Come To Think Of It
381. CALMS HE YES HUMMED I'M	Come See Us Sometime
382. CAN CHEW WHACK CHORE RAGE	Can't You Act Your Age
383. CAN TWIN FOIL WHO SING	Can't Win For Losing
384. CANNED ACHE MY HIGH SAW FEW	Can't Take My Eyes Off (Of) You
385. CANOE BILLY FIT SAP INNING	Can You Believe It's Happening
386. CANOE FILTHY EAT	Can You Feel The Heat?
387. CANOE KEY PACE HE GRIT	Can You Keep A Secret?
388. CANOE KEY PIT WHO YEARS ELF	Can You Keep It Yourself?
389. CAPPED TIN CAN GREW	Captain Kangaroo
390. CAR DENIALS HEN	Cardinal Sin
391. CARE HUNT EDEN RIGHT HEN	Guaranteed In Writing
392. CARESS TOUGHER CLUMP US	Christopher Columbus
393. CAT CHUM SEAS	CATCH SOME "Z's"
394. CAT HER ENOUGH HIT	Katarina Witt
395. CAUSE COT LAND CHARRED	Call Scotland Yard
396. CAUSE MID TICKS URGE JURY	Cosmetic Surgery
397. CAUSE TAP RID TIP ANY	Cost A Pretty Penny
398. CAW LITTLE HIGH CUES HE HIT	Call It Like You See It
399. CELL WHO THIEF LAG	Salute The Flag
400. CHAIN CHORE SEASON MIST REAM	Change Horses In Midstream
401. CHAIN SHOVE SEEN HURRY	Change Of Scenery
402. CHAIN SHOVES EASE SONS	A Change Of Seasons
403. CHAIR HOLD DEAN FUR ARROW	Geraldine Ferraro
404. CHECK CAN TUB ENDS TALK	Jack And The Beanstalk
405. CHECK COVE FAULT RAIDS	Jack Of All Trades
406. CHECK ENOUGH THESE HE	Chic Ken Of The Sea
407. CHECK HINGE ILL	Jack And Jill
408. CHECK HOLE ANT TURN	Jack-O-Lantern
409. CHECK KENNEL IF HEARSE	Chicken Livers
410. CHECK NICKEL US	Jack Nicklaus
411. CHESS SANE HOE	Just Say No
412. CHESS SIEGE ACTION	Jesse Jackson

413. CHESS TAME HOME HINT	Just A Moment
414. CHESS TANG GLUES	Just Hang Loose
415. CHESS TOP PANS MAIL THROW SAYS	Just Stop And Smell The Roses
416. CHEST ACHE HIT TONE TEACH HEN	Just Take It On The Chin
417. CHEST BEAT WEAN HUSK HURLS	Just Between Us Girls
418. CHEST HAY KIT TEASE HE	Just Take It Easy
419. CHEST HOLE DEBTOR HEIGHT THEIR	Just Hold It Right There
420. CHEST HUFF EH? CUE ROVES PEACH	Just A Figure Of Speech
421. CHEST IT THIGHS POTS	Just Hit The High Spots
422. CHEST LEAF MEOW TOUGH FIT	Just Leave Me Out Of It
423. CHEST MICE EYES	Just My Size
424. CHEST RIGHT HOOT HEY KITTY SEE	Just Try To Take It Easy
425. CHEST SKI FILM HIGH FUDGE ANTS	Just Give Him Half A Chance
426. CHEST TAN JERK ROUND	Just Stand Your Ground
427. CHEST WRITE TOUR HIM EMBER	Just Try To Remember
428. CHEW RULE SOLEMN	Jerusalem
429. CHEWS EASED ACHES	Juicy Steaks
430. CHIEF EACH ACE	Chevy Chase
431. CHILL HEAP EH? PURSE	Chili Peppers
432. CHIN ROLE MOAT OARS	General Motors
433. CHORE JUT HECK	Georgia Tech
434. CHUCK HE TUB AN AN US	Chiquita Bananas
435. CHUNK MALE	Junk Mail
436. CLAN TEASED WOOD	Clint Eastwood
437. CLOSE MMM! ACHE THUMB AN	Clothes Make The Man
438. CLOTHES HORIZON SAY UP RARE	Clothes Your Eyes And Say A Prayer
439. CLOTHES TUB HOOK SONNET	Close The Books On It
440. COKE OAK WHIP EASE	Cocoa Crispies
441. COMB BEE FORTH EASE DORM	Calm Before The Storm
442. COMB MELLOW RYE WATT HER	Come Hell Or High Water
443. COMBED HOUND WHO WORTH	Come Down To Earth
444. COMBED HOUND WIDTH ACHE HOLD	Come Down With A Cold
445. COMMON FIRM THERE RAIN	Come In From The Rain
446. CON FACE SHORES HENS	Confess Your Sins
447. CONE WIDTH THAW END	Gone With The Wind
448. CONNIVE YEAR RAW TUG RAFT	Can I Have Your Autograph?
449. CORE TEASE INNS EH? SHIN	Court Is In Session
450. COTTON KNEE I.D. UH	Got Any Idea?
451. COUCH ORAL UH KISS TARS	Count Your Lucky Stars
452. COUGH HE ANCHOR REAM	Coffee And Cream
453. COULD DREAD HINTS	Good Riddance
454. COULD GUYS MY LEDGE	Good Gas Mileage
455. COULD TOOTH HULL ASKED DROP	Good To The Last Drop
456. COW CHANNEL HUFFS EAT	Couch And Love Seat
457. CRATE BOSS HUFF HIRE	Great Balls Of Fire

458. CRAWL OUT HEARS	Crocodile Tears
459. CRAWL SHORE FIEND CURSE	Cross Your Fingers
460. CRAWLS CON TREE	Cross Country
461. CREASED MY SIEVE	Christmas Eve
462. CRIES LURK OPERATION	Chrysler Corporation
463. CROWN DOGGED HAY	Ground Hog Day
464. CRY CUSS MILE	Crack A Smile
465. CRY SHAPE HEARTY	Crash A Party
466. CUDDLE EVER ROYAL	Cod Liver Oil
467. CURLS COUNT GOO KEYS	Girl Scout Cookies
468. CUSSED HUM AID	Custom Made
469. CUTE HIPS GOTTEN SWAPS	Q-Tips Cotton Swabs
470. DAD AS ADORN ALE	Dead As A Doornail
471. DAD DONOR EYEFUL	Dead On Arrival
472. DAD TOOTH WHIRLED	Dead To The World
473. DEAD CHUM HISS MAY	Did You Miss Me?
474. DANG SAW CURL	Dance Hall Girl
475. DARE CHESS LUG HE HIGH GAS	They're Just Lucky, I Guess
476. DARE SNOW WINDOW WIT	There's No End To It
477. DARE SPAT CENT HE BALE FREE	There's Bats In The Belfry
478. DARE SUNNY SEIZE HULL WHO SHUN	There's An Easy Solution
479. DARE SWAN FOURTH HUB HOOKS	There's One For The Books
480. DATE OWN HUFF HIVE HUNT DREAD	Daytona 500
481. DAWN AHH! SCUM HE	Don't Ask Me
482. DAWN BEACH AISLE DISH	Don't Be Childish
483. DAWN BED TONE KNIT	Don't Bet On It
484. DAWN BEES HOSE HILLY	Don't Be So Silly
485. DAWN BEES HUTCH APE EGG	Don't Be Such A Pig
486. DAWN BEES OWE ARE DEAD HID	Don't Be So Hard Headed
487. DAWN BILL EIGHT	Don't Be Late
488. DAWN BIZARRE CAST TICK	Don't Be Sarcastic
489. DAWN BURIED HICK YULE US	Don't Be Ridiculous
490. DAWN CHEW BILL EVEN MAY	Don't You Believe Me?
491. DAWN CHOOSE TART WIDTH MAY	Don't Start With Me
492. DAWN GIFT UP THESE HIP	Don't Give Up The Ship
493. DAWN HECK CONNED GAS ME	Don't Second Guess Me
494. DAWN HUT SANK HALL FEE	Doughnuts And Coffee
495. DAWN JULY TOMB HE	Don't You Lie To Me
496. DAWN JURY MEMBER	Don't You Remember
497. DAWN KITS MARRED WIDTH MAY	Don't Get Smart With Me
498. DAWN LAY JERK HARD TOWN	Don't Let Your Guard Down
499. DAWN MAY COME MEAL HALF	Don't Make Me Laugh
500. DAWN MAY KICKS CUES SIS	Don't Make Excuses
501. DAWN PLAGUE AIM SWIFT ME	Don't Play Games With Me
502. DAWN TALL QUIT CHORE MILE FULL	Don't Talk With Your Mouth Full
503. DAWN TALL QUITS TRAY INJURES	Don't Talk With Strangers

504. DAWN TASK FORM OR	Don't Ask For More
505. DAWN TENDER UP MAY	Don't Interrupt Me
506. DAWN WAY ROUT CHORE WILL COMB	Don't Wear Out Your Welcome
507. DAWN WAYS CHORE TIE MOAN KNIT	Don't Waste Your Time
508. DAWN WERE RIB OUT HIT	Don't Worry About It
509. DAWNED ACHED HAT LINE TOWN	Don't Take That Lying Down
510. DAWNED B.M. OCEAN HULL	Don't Be Emotional
511. DAWNED HAWK BAG TOMB HE	Don't Talk Back To Me
512. DAWNED HAY GUINEA CHANTS HIS	Don't Take Any Chances
513. DAWNED HAY KIT FORK RANTED	Don't Take It For Granted
514. DAWNED LIEU SHARK WHO'LL	Don't Lose Your Cool
515. DAWNED RINK HAND ARRIVE	Don't Drink And Drive
516. DAWNED WHO DEBT HUG HEN	Don't Do That Again
517. DAWNS BOIL YEARS UPPER	Don't Spoil Your Supper
518. DAWNS PEA TENTH OWE END	Don't Spit In The Wind
519. DAWNS TALL PAWN MY COUNT	Don't Stop On My Account
520. DAWNS TEA COUCH OR DUNG	Don't Stick Out Your Tongue!
521. DAWNS WAYS MIGHT I'M	Don't Waste My Time
522. DAY FIDDLE ADDER MAN	David Letterman
523. DAY FIG RAW KIT	Davy Crocket
524. DEAD ANT HALF AGE ANTS	Didn't Have A Chance
525. DEAD DEBT CRAWL SHORE MINE	Did It Cross Your Mind
526. DEAD HEAP HOP THICK WEST CHIN	Did He Pop The Question?
527. DEADEN CONE	Dead And Gone
528. DEAF VILLAIN DISK HIGHS	Devil In Disguise
529. DEAL EVER THUG HOODS	Deliver The Goods
530. DEATH WORM DOUGH FUR	Death Warmed Over
531. DEBT ONCE DUMPED ME	That One Stumped Me
532. DEBT SICK SACK LAYER HEIGHT	That's Exactly Right
533. DEBT SNOT MUST AISLE	That's Not My Style
534. DEBT SOAK HAY WIDTH MAY	That's Ok With Me
535. DEBT SUPPER AH! MISS	That's A Promise
536. DEBTS ALIKE LEAST OAR HE	That's A Likely Story
537. DEBTS THIN HAY MUFF THUG AIM	That's The Name Of The Game
538. DECK HEY DOVE D.A. TEASE	Decade of The 80's
539. DEEP HITS PERKS TILL HEARS	Thc Pittsburgh Steelers
540. DEEPER LEAGUE HATES	The Pearly Gates
541. DELIGHTS HAVENS DIME	Daylight Savings Time
542. DEN NEST AMEN US	Dennis The Menace
543. DEPEND HE ARE TOUGHED HICK SEA	Deep In The Heart Of Dixie
544. DEPOT KNEE EGG SUPPRESS	The Pony Express
545. DEPOT STALL FIZZ	The Post Office
546. DIAMOND DIME HUG HEN	Time And Time Again
547. DIARRHEA FAN FRANK	Diary Of Anne Frank
548. DIME TOMB OATH HUG HARASS	Time To Mow The Grass
549. DISC POSSIBLE DYE PURSE	Disposable Diapers

550. DISGUISE GRAY SEA	This Guy's Crazy
551. DISGUISE THEY'LL HIM HIT	The Sky's The Limit
552. DITCH CHEWS HAZE HUM THIN	Did You Say Something?
553. DOCKED HEARSE WHOSE	Dr. Seuss
554. DOCKED URBAN CASE HE	Dr. Ben Casey
555. DOES TENTH HE WHEN	Dust In The Wind
556. DOLL ARSON SINCE	Dollars And Cents
557. DOUBLE USE HE FEE YIELDS	W.C. Fields
558. DOUSE HOPE	Dial Soap
559. DOWEL LIST EXCESS	Dallas, Texas
560. DOZEN MADDER TOMB HE	Doesn't Matter To Me
561. DRAGON FILL DOVE HINTS	Track And Field Events
562. DRIED HOG FEUD	Don't Leave Home Without It
563. DRY FEW THAW ALL	Drive You Up The Wall
564. DRY FIN MIST HAZY	Driving Miss Daisy
565. DUCK HEAVEN HATED CALL FEE	Decaffeinated Coffee
566. DUE HUE HEAVEN HIGHER RAY	Do You Have And I.R.A.
567. DUE SCISSORS WOW!	Deuces Are Wild
568. DUNE HOT FEED THAN HYMN HULLS	Do Not Feed The Animals
569. DUNK RYE OWE FURS BUILT MILK	Don't Cry Over Spilt Milk
570. DUTY LOW COME OCEAN	Do The Locomotion
571. EACH OAR HARD TOUT	Eat Your Heart Out
572. EAR STEW HUE	Here's To You
573. EAR SWAN FORTH ERODE	Here's One For The Road
574. EAR WIG HOE HUG HEN	Here We Go Again
575. EASE ACE LIFE OX	He's A Sly Fox
576. EASE BAG KIN THESE HAD DULL	He's Back In The Saddle
577. EASE CHEST TUCK HID DEBT TART	He's Just A Kid At Heart
578. EASE COT THICK HEFT HUFF CAB	He's Got The Gift Of Gab
579. EASE COTTAGE HIP PONIES HOLDER	He's Got A Chip On His Shoulder
580. EASE EARS HEAD THINNED UN-	Easier Said Than Done
581. EASE EIGHTH INK HER	He's A Thinker
582. EASE HOMES HICK KIN BED	He's Home Sick In Bed
583. EASE OATH OUGHT FULL	He's So Thoughtful
584. EASE OWE KNEE SNEEZE	He's On His Knees
585. EASE SADDLE HOSS FORWARDS	He's At A Loss For Words
586. EASE SEEK HOMEY SAG HOE	Easy Come, Easy Go
587. EASE SOAP AIR ANNOYED	He's So Paranoid
588. EASE SOFT WHO ABE ADDS TART	He's Off To A Bad Start
589. EASEL AID EASE MAN	He's A Lady's Man
590. EASEL HIGH TONE EASE FEAT	He's Light On His Feet
591. EAST HAG HEARD HOME	He Staggered Home
592. EASY HUSTLE HEAP	Is He Asleep?
593. EAT HER NULL OF	Eternal Love
594. ECHOED UH FIFTH HICKS	A Code Of Ethics
595. EGG AIM MUCH EGG CURSE	A Game Of Checkers

596. EGG HIT TARP HICK — A Guitar Pick
597. EGG HOOD I'M WAS SAD BUY Y'ALL — A Good Time Was Had By All
598. EGG HOOD TRY CRACK CORD — A Good Track Record
599. EGG HULL ART EVE HE — A Color TV
600. EGG HUNT RIG HURL — Egg Country Girl
601. EGG HUT TREE HACK SHIN — A Gut Reaction
602. EGG KNOW RINSES BLESS — Ignorance Is Bliss
603. EGG LASSO FOREIGN JEWS — A Glass Of Orange Juice
604. EGG RAN DOPE INNING — A Grand Opening
605. EGG RAY SPEAR HE HID — A Grace Period
606. EGG SLACKS IT IF — Ex-Lax Laxative
607. EGGS CRAMS LAMB — A Grand Slam
608. EGGS PIER HEN SOLVE ALIVE DIME — Experience Of A Lifetime
609. EGGS PIN SIFT HASTE — Expensive Taste
610. EGGS TRUCK ITCH UP — Extra Ketchup
611. HIT TONE LEG HIT SPAT HER — It Only Gets Better
612. EIGHT ACED UH FUNNY — A Taste Of Honey
613. EIGHT ALE HUFF HONK AWE — A Telephone Call
614. EIGHT EVE EERIE PORT HER — A TV Reporter
615. EIGHT EYES CORE — A Tie Score
616. EIGHT HAY BULL EGG — A Table Leg
617. EIGHT HE MUFF FORCES — A Team Of Horses
618. EIGHT HER MOM UTTER — A Thermometer
619. EIGHT HEY BLUFF CON TENSE — A Table Of Contents
620. EIGHT HIP PICKLE ANT SIR — A Typical Answer
621. EIGHT HOPPER FORMER — A Top Performer
622. EIGHT I'M EGG SWATCH — A Timex Watch
623. EIGHT OAT HULL LEAK LIPS — A Total Eclipse
624. EIGHT OWE WHEAT REIGN — A Toy Train
625. EIGHT REIGNED RACK — A Train Track
626. EIGHT REINDEER — A Trained Ear
627. EIGHT ROOF AN ATTIC — A True Fanatic
628. EIGHT UH FACT HOOF HOLLOW — A Tough Act To Follow
629. EIGHT UPPER WHERE PAR TEA — A Tupperware Party
630. EIGHT WHO BUFF FLIPS TICK — A Tube Of Lipstick
631. EIGHTH HAIR — Hey There!
632. EIGHTY FIN SAT EARN HE — As Defense Attorney
633. EIGHTY PARTS MINTS TORE — A Department Store
634. ELF HABITS HOOP — Alphabet Soup
635. ELF REAP IDEAS PROP PLUMS — Everybody Has Problems
636. ELF WREATH INK FUR MATE OOZE HE — Everything From A To Z
637. END DUKE HORSE — In Due Course
638. END HE YEN REIGNED ANTS — Indian Rain Dance
639. END HEAP WHAT HER — In Deep Water
640. END HOE ROUT TORQUE HARP HIT — Indoor-Outdoor Carpet
641. END HOOT I'M — In Due Time

642. END TUB EGG INNING	In The Beginning
643. ERECT ANGLE	A Rectangle
644. ERODE MY YAP	A Road Map
645. ESSAY GLASS SACKED	It's A Class Act
646. ESSAY MADDER ROUGH ACT	As A Matter Of Fact
647. ESTATE YOU KNEE VARSITY	A State University
648. EUROPE ART TOUGH FIT	You're Part Of It
649. EUROPE AS CHIRP RHYME	You're Past Your Prime
650. EUROPE LAY SORE MINE	Your Place Or Mine
651. EVE LIE	Evil Eye
652. EVEN CHEW WOOLY	Eventually
653. EVERY TIME DEACON AIRY	Every Tom, Dick And Harry
654. EVICT UH MUFF SIR GUM STANCE	A Victim Of Circumstance
655. EYE WE SHINE WHO	I Wish I Knew
656. EYE AGE HUE FOURTH HAT	I Hat You For That
657. EYE BELLY FEWER HEIGHT	I Believe You Were Right
658. EYE BEND REAM ENOUGH FEW	I Been Dreaming Of You
659. EYE FAD DEBT UPPED WHO EAR	I've Had It Up To Here
660. EYE FELT HOUR	Eiffel Tower
661. EYE HARASS	I.R.S.
662. EYE HEY JERK HUTS	I Hate Your Guts
663. EYE KNEE THUMB UH KNEE	I Need The Money
664. EYE MAP HILLY MAYOR HEED	I'm Happily Married
665. EYE MENTION GNAW LOAFER	I'm Itchin' All Over
666. EYE MILE TOUGH GUESS	I'm Out Of Gas
667. EYE MINNOW FIRM AHEAD	I'm In Over My Head
668. EYE MINNOW HER HE	I'm In No Hurry
669. EYE MOAN PENSION KNEE DULLS	I'm On Pins And Needles
670. EYE MUG HURL WHAT CHORE	I'm A Girl Watcher
671. EYE MULL HEIGHTS LEAP HER	I'm A Lights Sleeper
672. EYE MULL HER CHECKED WHO WIT	I'm Allergic To It
673. EYE NEEDLE AX EIGHT IF	I Need A Laxative
674. EYE NEEDLE OVEN	I Need Lovin'
675. EYE PEW PRO FIN	Ibuprofen
676. EYE PILLOW FIZZ SIGH	Apple Of His Eye
677. EYE WASTE HUNG TIDE	I Was Tongue-Tied
678. EYE WON SMACK SHIN	I Want Some Action
679. FACTOR FIG SHIN	Fact Or Fiction
680. FAD ACE APE EGG	Fat As A Pig
681. FADE DULL HUT TRACTION	Fatal Attraction
682. FAIRWAY THEIR FUR END	Fair Weather Friend
683. FALL LAWYER KNOWS	Follow Your Nose
684. FALL OATH HELLO PRICK CROWED	"Follow The Yellow Brick Road"
685. FALL SACK USE ASIANS	False Accusations
686. FANS SEEP ANTS	Fancy Pants
687. FARTHER STAY	Father's Day

688. FASTEN FURRY YES HACK SHIN — Fast And Furious Action
689. FEAT SLY KEG LOVE — Fits Like A Glove
690. FEE ADORE ROSE FELT — Theodore Roosevelt
691. FEE IT TUBE EAT HIDE — Fit To Be Tied
692. FEE NECK SOUR REZONE AHH! — Phoenix Arizona
693. FEE SUCK HARD — Visa Card
694. FEW OWN LEAN HEW — If You Only Knew
695. FIEND GIRLY KING HOOD — Finger Licking Good
696. FILTHY BE ILL — Fill The Bill
697. FILTHY PEA INCH — Feel The Pinch
698. FINE OWN OAT HISS — Final Notice
699. FINK HOW LICKS HAMS — Final Exams
700. FIRM RACK STEW REACH HISS — From Rags To Riches
701. FIRM TUB AUTUMN MUFF MY ART — From The Bottom Of My Heart
702. FIT TEASE HEAVEN SHOVE HE — 57 Chevy
703. FLAMING YAWN — Filet Mignon
704. FLIP EARTH HEED ALL FIN — Flipper The Dolphin
705. FLOOR HINT SNIDE TEEN GALE — Florence Nightingale
706. FOE REELED ARRIVE — Four Wheel Drive
707. FOE ROOM TUB BELT HOLES — For Whom The Bell Tolls
708. FOE WASTE HOP — Four Way Stop
709. FOOL HAD ESTEEM — Full Head Of Steam
710. FOOLED FOURTH HOT — Food For Thought
711. FORCE HAY LOWER HINT — For Sale Or Rent
712. FORK HIT MEAN HOT — Forget Me Not
713. FORK HOOD NESTS ACHES — For Goodness Sakes
714. FORK OAR NOR SOFTY HEARTH — Four Corners Of The Earth
715. FORK RYE IN HALT ALLOWED — For Crying Out Loud
716. FORK WAITS HUMPED I'M — For Quite Some Time
717. FORM HUE LAUGH OR OWN NINE — Formula 409
718. FORTH HUB HERDS — For The Birds
719. FOUR KIT TOE FUR — Fork It Over
720. FOURTH HULL LAWN GUEST TIME — For The Longest Time
721. FOURTH ARREST TOUGH MILE HIVE — For The Rest Of My Life
722. FOURTH WRECK GOURD — For The Record
723. FOYER OWNS ACHE — For Your Own Sake
724. FRAY DOVE URINE SHY DOUGH — Afraid Of Your Own Shadow
725. FULL HIP MILE HID — Flip My Lid
726. FULL OATH LITER — Follow The Leader
727. FUN STING KIN THUMB WARNING — First Thing In The Morning
728. FUR HEAD FULL HINTS TONE — Fred Flinstone
729. FUR HEAD US STARE — Fred Astaire
730. FUR SCUM FUR SURFED — First Come, First Served
731. FUR STAND FIRM HOST — First And Foremost
732. FURS TANNED HEN — First And Ten
733. FURS TAR RISE HEAT WHO NIGHT — First Star I See Tonight

734. GALE LOG SCORN FULL ACHES	Kellogg's Corn Flakes
735. GAY SWAT	Guess What?
736. GEL HOW SIR HOCK	Jailhouse Rock
737. GEM HE OFF UH!	Jimmy Hoffa
738. GENE YEN HUB AWED HULL	Genie In A Bottle
739. GHOST TICKET	Go Stick It
740. GIFT FIT ATE RYE	Give It A Try
741. GLOW ROCKS BULL EACH	Clorox Bleach
742. GNAT SHUN ALIGN THUMB	National Anthem
743. GNAW LAMB ERA GUN BEAU WE	An All-American Boy
744. GNAW TAIL EGG TOAST HAND OWN	Not A Leg To Stand On
745. GOAT HOOP EASE HIS	Go To Pieces
746. GOAT THREW THEM OCEANS	Go Through The Motions
747. GOAT TOOTH THUD HOGS	Go To The Dogs
748. GOES LOW WINDY BUG INNING	Go Slow In The Beginning
749. GOLF LIE ACHE HEIGHT	Go Fly A Kite
750. GOOD CHEW POLICE FORK IF FUSS	Could You Please Forgive Us?
751. GOPHER THUG HOLD	Go For The Gold
752. GOWN CHIRP LESS SINGS	Count Your Blessings
753. GOWN TRACK YOU'LL AHH!	Count Dracula
754. GRADE EGGS PECKED ASIANS	Great Expectations
755. GRASS PASTA RAW	Grasp A Straw
756. GRIST HULL BLOOPERS WAY SHUN	Crystal Blue Persuasion
757. GULL ICICLE MOO SICK	Classical Music
758. GUN TREND WASTE TURN MOO SICK	Country And Western Music
759. GUT MEAT WHO THICK WICK	Cut Me To The Quick
760. GUT THUMB US STIRRED	Cut The Mustard
761. GUT TOOTH HECK WICK	Cut To The Quick
762. HA! PIG HOLE YUCKY	Happy Go Lucky
763. HA! TANK HOLD RUN INN WATT HER	Hot And Cold Running Water
764. HA! TON DIRTY CALLER	Hot Under The Collar
765. HABIT TANNED COST HELLO	Abbott And Costello
766. HAD DEMAND HEAVE	Adam And Eve
767. HAIL PURSE ELF TOMB OAR	Help Yourself To More
768. HAIRIEST ROOM UN-	Harry S. Truman
769. HAIRY MOO FUR	Hair Remover
770. HALF HUE COT US CRUEL OOZE	Have You Got A Screw Loose?
771. HALF FUSE HE KNITTER HOUND	Have You Seen It Around?
772. HALLWAY SENT RUBBLE	Always In Trouble
773. HAMPER GRAND FUR INCH FUR EYES	Hamburger And French Fries
774. HANDLING LOVE	Hand In Glove
775. HANG CARE RUN	Hank Aaron
776. HANKY KNOWN BATH RED	Hanging On By A Thread
777. HAPPEN DECIDE US	Appendicitis
778. HARASS FEE PEA	R.S.V.P.
779. HASTE HAT ASSEMBLE	A Status Symbol

780. HASTE HER EIGHTS HOOTER	A Straight Shooter
781. HASTE HUNT MAN	A Stunt Man
782. HASTE RAKE HAT	A Stray Cat
783. HASTE ROBBER HEAP HATCH	A Strawberry Patch
784. HASTE WRONG WILT WHO SURF HIVE	A Strong Will To Survive
785. HAT CHORE BACON CAW	At Your Beck And Call
786. HAUL HE WOULD	Hollywood
787. HAUL MAY DIE SCREAM	Homemade Ice Cream
788. HAUL WEIGH SEWN MIME HIND	Always On Your Mind
789. HAVE PRY SAIL	Half-Price Sale
790. HAVE THIEF HONEY SKIDDING THEIR	Half The Fun Is Getting There
791. HAWK HIDDEN US HIDE	All Kidding Aside
792. HAY CHAIN JAW PAYS	A Change Of Pace
793. HAY DENS HOLDER SUB OF ARREST	Head And Shoulder Above The Rest
794. HAY FEE WAIT BALK SIR	Heavyweight Boxer
795. HAY HIM ELF HYMNS TEARY HOE	Am-Fm Stereo
796. HAZE SEND HE WHOLE	Ace In The Hole
797. HE KNEE MEAN AIM HIGH NAME OWE	Eeny, Meeny, Miney, Mo
798. HE CHORES PEN HITCH	Eat Your Spinach
799. HE LEGS SHUNNED HAY	Election Day
800. HE MAY DAY PIE SADDER	He Made A Pass At Her
801. HE MERGE HEN SEIZE HER JURY	Emergency Surgery
802. HE SNOT HUB REIGNS URGE INN	He's Not A Brain Surgeon
803. HE SOWN WORSEN NUMB HE	His Own Worst Enemy
804. HE SPIN FULL INNER HOUND	He's Been Fooling Around
805. HE SUNNY CURB HE FUR	He's An Eager Beaver
806. HE YES PEN	ESPN
807. HE'S YES SPY	Easy As A Pie
808. HEADS FULL IF UN-	Ed Sullivan
809. HEAP HE POUR HAY	Hip, Hip, Hooray
810. HEAP LAID THIEF HEALED	He Played The Field
811. HEART TOUGH FISH HULK HOLLER	Artificial Color
812. HEAT HOOK ABE HUM PONIES HEAD	He Took A Bump On His Head
813. HEAT WHO CALL PHYSICAL LOWS	He Took Off His Clothes
814. HEAVEN ACTS TOOK RIND	Have An Ax To Grind
815. HEAVEN ICED HAY	Have A Nice Day
816. HEED ANT SIS TUNA THERE TUNE	He Dances To Another Tune
817. HEFT BEE EYE	F.B.I.
818. HEFT HUSH HOOF HIT SWEAR RAT	If The Shoe Fits Wear It
819. HELLO MINT TREE WHAT SUN	"Elementary, Watson"
820. HEN DITTO FUR	Hand It Over
821. HEN EIGHT HANG GALE STEER	Anything Else, Dear?
822. HEN EIGHT HANG OWES	Anything Goes
823. HEN FIN HIT WHIZ DUMB	Infinite Wisdom
824. HEN OF SIN OF	Enough's Enough
825. HEN TUB LEAN COVE FUN NIGH	In The Blink Of An Eye

826. HER CHEW WHIR REAL — Heard You Were Ill
827. HER DEATH ROOF THICK RAPE FINE — Her It Through The Grapevine
828. HEY SOP HISS LEAVE — Ace Up His Sleeve
829. HI ANKLE LESS DRAWL — High In Cholesterol
830. HI HAND MY TEA — High And Mighty
831. HI HOSE ILL FRAY WEIGH — "Hi Ho, Silver! Away!"
832. HI MOAN AID HI YET — I'm On A Diet
833. HI PEA YES SCAN BEE — Happy As Can Be
834. HI WIRE HUE — How Are You?
835. HI! HAND RYE — High And Dry
836. HI! RED JEW CASE SHUN — Higher Education
837. HI! WIPER TROLL — Highway Patrol
838. HI-FI GOOD DIE WOOD — If I Could, I Would
839. HICK HITS WORSEN WHIRS — It Gets Worse And Worse
840. HICKS CUES MAY — Excuse Me
841. HIDE EIGHT TUBE HE INN ISSUES — I'd Hate To Be In His Shoes
842. HIDE HAUNT DESSERT FIT — I Don't Deserve It
843. HIDE HAUNT PLACE HECK UNFIT DULL — I Don't Play Second Fiddle
844. HIDE HAUNT WHO WHEN DOES — I Don't Do Windows
845. HIDE HEN TICKLED WINS — Identical Twins
846. HIDE HID DEBT OFFER HUE — I Did It All For You
847. HIDE HID ITCH US FOIL HALVES — I Did It Just For Laughs
848. HIDE HOOT WHO — I Do, Too
849. HIDE OWN HUNTERS TAN DEBT TALL — I Don't Understand At All
850. HIDE OWN TRICK RED HIT — I Don't Regret It
851. HIDE REAM MUFF GEE KNEE — I Dream Of Jeannie
852. HIDE WRATH HERD HIGH — I'd Rather Die
853. HIGH CANCEL HEAP — I Can't Sleep
854. HIGH DAWN OWE OUT OOZE HAY YET — I Don't Know How To Say It
855. HIGH KNEE DUD RINK — I Need A Drink
856. HIGH MENTION TOOT RIOT — I'm Itching To Try It
857. HIGH MILE TOE FEAR — I'm Out Of Here
858. HIGH MINT RUBBLE — I'm In Trouble
859. HIGH MOAN LEAK HIDDEN — I'm Only Kidding
860. HIGH MOSS YET TUG HOE — I'm All Set To Go
861. HIGH MY TOUGH GUEST — I Might Of Guessed
862. HIGH PIANO FURS HAIRY — Happy Anniversary
863. HIGH THIN CUE BET HURL EVE — I Think You Better Leave
864. HIGH VIEW HEW THIN WHOSE — Have You Heard The News?
865. HIGH WE SHY GOOD — I Wish I Could
866. HIGH WEIGHT WHO HAVE IN — Highway To Heaven
867. HIGH WOW! BOUT AND EIGHT — How About A Date?
868. HIGHER HACKED MOB REIGNS — I Racked My Brains
869. HIKE AIR HUB OUCH WHO — I Care About You
870. HIKE AN TELL PIT — I Can't Help It
871. HIKE ANT THAN CUE WHEN HUFF — I Can't Thank You Enough

872. HIKE ANTS TOPPLE OVEN KNEW	I Can't Stop Loving You
873. HIKE CANNED WHO WIT	I Can Do It
874. HIKE HEN SIT HEN YEAR RISE	I Can See It In Your Eyes
875. HIKE HIDDEN WAND HOOT WHO WIT	I Didn't Want To Do It
876. HIKE HOOP UH FAD HUFFY EIGHT	I Could Have Had A V-8
877. HINEY DAIRY SEAT	I Need A Receipt
878. HINEY DEBT BUFF RIDE HAY	I Need It By Friday
879. HINEY DUCK HOLE SHH! OUR	I Need A Cold Shower
880. OW! HUTCH CASHEW COT	How Much Cash (Have) You Got?
881. HIRE HINT DISK TRICKED	High Rent District
882. HIS UPPER HEAD HE	Is Supper Ready?
883. HISTORIAN KNITS ELF	A Story In Itself
884. HIT ACHE STEW TOOT HANG OWE	It Takes Two To Tango
885. HIT ACHE SWINE TUNA WON	It Takes One To Know One
886. HIT CELL SLY COT CAKES	It Sells Like Hotcakes
887. HIT CHAIR HIDE	Hitch A Ride
888. HIT CHIN HAIR HIDE	Hitching A Ride
889. HIT CHORE WAG UNTO US TAR	Hitch Your Wagon To A Star
890. HIT GUTS MYTH RUIN THREW	It Cuts Me Through And Through
891. HIT HOOK FUR RIVER	It Took Forever
892. HIT KNEAD STEW BEES HEAD	It Needs To Be Said
893. HIT ONE TAP HEN NAG HEN	It' Won't Happen Again
894. HIT SAG AS	It's A Gas
895. HIT SAID HEAD DISH SHOE	It's A Dead Issue
896. HIT SAP ARE TOUGH MAY	It's Part Of Me
897. HIT SASS HEN	It's A Sin
898. HIT SAW CREST TALK LAYER	It's All Crystal Clear
899. HIT SAW LOAFER BUD THICK RYE YEN	It's All Over But The Crying
900. HIT SAW MY FOUGHT	It's All My Fault
901. HIT SAWN HATCH HER HULL	It's All Natural
902. HIT SAY HOW SOLD WHIRRED	It's A Household Word
903. HIT SAYS MALL WHIRLED	It's A Small World
904. HIT SEEP HIT SEIZE PATTER	Itsy Bitsy Spider
905. HIT SEVEN CENT	It's Heaven Sent
906. HIT SEWN LEAN ACHOO! RAW AL	It's Only Natural
907. HIT SEWN LEAP LAME HONEY	It's Only Play Money
908. HIT SEWN LID REAM	It's Only A Dream
909. HIT SEWN LIMO ROUGH THUS AIM	It's Only More Of The Same
910. HIT SHORE JOYS	It's Your Choice
911. HIT SHORES FOURTH YES KING	It's Yours For The Asking
912. HIT SIN MICE HEIGHTS	It's In My Sights
913. HIT SKIDDING SOUL EIGHT	It's Getting So Late
914. HIT SMILE HUG KISS TAR	It's My Lucky Star
915. HIT SNOT MIKE ABOVE TEE	It's Not My Cup Of Tea
916. HIT SNOTTY FIN CLOTHES	It's Not Even Close
917. HIT SNOW LIE FILM ADDER	It's No Laughing Matter

918. HIT SNOWED ICE	It's No Dice
919. HIT SOME HAT ROUGHED I'M	It's A Matter Of Time
920. HIT SOWN LADY BEAK INNING	It's Only The Beginning
921. HIT SPIN COULD FORM HE	It's Been Good For Me
922. HIT STEW WHAT TANNED DULL	It's Too Hot To Handle
923. HIT STEW WORD EYE	It's Do Or Die
924. HIT STOOP ADD	It's Too Bad
925. HIT STUFF PUTT WEAKEN MAY KIT	It's Tough, But We Can Make It
926. HIT SUCK RHYME	It's A Crime
927. HIT SUN HEIGHT TREE MEMBER	It's A Night To Remember
928. HIT SUN OWE BULK HALLS	It' A Noble Cause
929. HIT SUN YOU BOG AIM	It's A New Ball Game
930. HIT SUPPER HIVE HAT MADDER	It's A Private Matter
931. HIT SWAN HINT THUS AIM	It's One In The Same
932. HIT TALL DEEP ENDS	It All Depends
933. HIT TONE LATE ACHE SOME HEN HIT	It Only Takes A Minute
934. HIT WHEELIE KNEAD STUPID UN-	It Really Needs To Be Done
935. HITS AGE ANT SOLVE ALE I'VE DIME	It's A Chance Of A Lifetime
936. HITS AIM SLY CUD REAM	It Seems Like A Dream
937. HITS AMISS SIR HOUND EAR	It's A Mess Around Here
938. HITS APE AIR HEAD ICE	It's A Paradise
939. HITS CHESS TOUCH OAK	It' S Just S Joke
940. HITS DIME FOREST TUG HOE	It's Time For Us To Go
941. HITS DIME TOUPEE HUP	It's Time To Pay Up
942. HITS ELEVEN	It's A Living
943. HITS ERASE STEW THE FIN HUSH	It's A Race To The Finish
944. HITS FORK HEAPS	It's Up For Keeps
945. HITS HAY FORTH HEN YOUTH INK	It's Safer Than You Think
946. HITS HURT IN LEAD US	It Certainly Does
947. HITS HUSTLE OWE GO	It's A Slow Go
948. HITS LEAPED MIME HIND	It Slipped My Mind
949. HITS LIP HURRY WIN WIT	It's Slippery When Wet
950. HITS NEEDLE EH? STEWS HEY	It's Needless To Say
951. HITS OAK WHOLE DOUBTS HIDE	It's So Cold Outside
952. HITS OFF HOWLED HUP	It's All Fouled Up
953. HITS OWE WAD	It' So Odd
954. HITS PEN ABE ADD HEY	It's Been A Bad Day
955. HITS REIGN INK HATS SAND HOGS	It's Raining Cats And Dogs
956. HITS RELEASE ADD	It's Really Sad
957. HITS SEW WHIRLY INN THUMB WARNING	It' So Early In The Morning
958. HITS SNOT LIE CUE	It's Not Like You
959. HITS STOOL ATE FOURTH HAT	It's To Late For That
960. HITS TAN TREASON	It Stands To Reason
961. HITS TEETH INK TOO WHO	It's The Thing To Do
962. HITS THIGH SING GONE THICK ACHE	It's The Icing On The Cake
963. HITS US HOOP HEARD ILL	It's A Super Deal

964. HITTER UN- SIN THIEF HAM HILLY	It Runs In The Family
965. HIVE COT HIT INN MICE HEIGHTS	I've Got It In My Sights
966. HIVE COT WHOM HOP THIEF LOWER	I've Got To Mop The Floor
967. HIVE COTTON HUP SITS THUMB ACHE	I've Got An Upset Stomach
968. HIVE ELLS HICK	I Feel Sick
969. HIVE ERASE HOPE	Ivory Soap
970. HIVE HIGH DEPT WIDTH HUE	I've Had It With You
971. HOBBY CALL SAW FEW	All Because Of You
972. HOE FIRM ODD HEAD BALDY	Over My Dead Body
973. HOE KEYED OAK HE	Okey-Dokey
974. HOE LEAN WON	Hole In One
975. HOE LIMB HACK HURL	Holy Mackerel
976. HOE MULL OWNED WHO	Home Alone 2
977. HOE PEW HEAVEN ICE HUM HER	Hope You Have A Nice Summer
978. HOE PUKE HIT WHALE SOON	Hope You Get Well Soon
979. HOG REEK TOMB HE	A Greek To Me
980. HOLDS AIN'T NICKEL LESS	Old St. Nicholas
981. HOLDS MOPE ILL	Oldsmobile
982. HOLE CHORE HOE OR SAYS	Hold Your Horses
983. HOLE DEBT GLOW STEW YO! ART	Hold It Close To Your Heart
984. HOLE GRAY NOTES EERIE HULL	Whole Grain Oats Cereal
985. HOLE KITTEN CUP POODLE	Whole Kit And Caboodle
986. HOLLOW FOIL	Olive Oil
987. HOLLOW PAIN YEP EH? PURSE	Jalapeno Peppers
988. HOLLY SWIRL LEAGUE HOODS	All His Worldly Goods
989. HOME ACT ANNULLED ADD HUFF ARM	Old McDonald Had a Farm
990. HOME FILL DAD FANNED HEDGE	Home Field Advantage
991. HONK ALLOWED NINE	On Cloud Nine
992. HOP US HIT SAT RACKED	Opposites Attract
993. HOPE HEN THICK HURT TEN	Open The Curtain
994. HOPPER TUNE HIT TEEN OX	Opportunity Knocks
995. HOSE ACHE HEN USE HE	"Oh, Say Can You See..."
996. HOUR DAY LIBRA HEAD	Our Daily Bread
997. HOUSE MIND ARRIVING	How's My Driving?
998. HOUSE SANE HOME OR	I'll Say No More
999. HOW CUSS ELSE HER	Alka Seltzer
1000. HOW DEPART NOR	Howdy Partner
1001. HOW SOLVED HORIZONS UN-	House Of The Rising Sun
1002. HOWL HAY TAR WIG HOEING TUB HE	How Late Are We Going To Be
1003. HOWL KIN HIKE GUN FENCE SHOE	How Can I Convince You?
1004. HUB ADD DECK SPEAR HE HINTS	A Bad Experience
1005. HUBBY YELL TEA	A B.L.T.
1006. HUE AS EIGHT HOOD HAY	U.S.A. Today
1007. HUE BED CHIRP HOOTS	You Bet Your Boots
1008. HUE CAN TWIN THE MALL	You Can't Win Them All
1009. HUE EH? SMELL	U.S. Mail

1010. HUE ESSAY	U.S.A.
1011. HUE FORGOT TUBE BEAK HIDDEN	You've Got To Be Kidding
1012. HUE INN SUMMON YULE OOZE HUM	You Win Some And You Lose Some
1013. HUE STUNNED EGG SIS	Houston, Texas
1014. HUE WIT THIN A LOAN THEY HID	You Hit The Nail On The Head
1015. HUE WRECKS ACT LAYER HEIGHT	You're Exactly Right
1016. HUFF AHH! STIR ROAM	A Foster Home
1017. HUFF HAIRY YACHT CLIMB IT	A Very Hot Climate
1018. HUFF OAT HUG RAFT	A Photograph
1019. HUFF OFF RUM GRAYS	A Fall From Grace
1020. HUFF ORAL HEAVE GLOW FUR	A Four Leaf Clover
1021. HUFF REEF ORAL	A Free For All
1022. HUFF WHO DUDE HAUL	A Voodoo Doll
1023. HUFFF HAM LIMB AN	A Family Man
1024. HUG ANTSY ROWS	Hogan's Heroes
1025. HUM AN OFFICE WHIRRED	A Man Of His Word
1026. HUM MINE DOUGH FEE ZONE	A Mind Of His Own
1027. HUMS HOE WICKS HEIGHT HID	I'm So Excited
1028. HUNT ILL THIN DOVE DIME	Until The End Of Time
1029. HURT HIGH MASK HUM	Her Time Has Come
1030. HUSH HOT HINT THUD ARK	A Shot In The Dark
1031. HUSTLE HAPPEN THIEF ACE	A Slap In The Face
1032. HUSTLE HE PIMP HEAL	A Sleeping Pill
1033. HYPE EGG CURE PAR DONE	I Beg Your Pardon
1034. I PULL JEWS	Apple Juice
1035. I SIN TOBACCO FEWER	Eyes In The Back Of Your Head
1036. I'LL LISTEN WON DARE LEND	Alice In Wonderland
1037. I'M ISSUES HOME HUTCH	I Miss You So Much
1038. I.D. MAN DONE ANT SIR	I Demand An Answer
1039. ICE HIM PLAGUE IF UP	I Simply Give Up
1040. ICE HIM PLEAD HAUNT CARE	I Simply Don't Care
1041. ICE HOOD OVEN ON	I Should Have Known
1042. ICE HULL WHO CHEW	I Salute You
1043. ICE MAIL ASK HUNK	I Smell A Skunk
1044. ICE TILL OWE VIEW HEN AWAY	I Still Love You Anyway
1045. ICON SALTED APE ROW	I Consulted A Pro
1046. IDLE OF TWO	I'd Love To
1047. INDEED HALL COWS	In The Dog House
1048. INDIAN AHH! NUDGE OWNS	Indiana Jones
1049. INK HEY SOLVE HIM URGENT SEA	In Case Of Emergency
1050. INK ODD WHEAT RUST	In God We Trust
1051. INK WIRING MINE SWAN TUNE HOE	"Inquiring Minds Want To Know"
1052. INN NAP EGG SIGH	In A Pig's Eye
1053. INN THREAD	In The Red
1054. INNER G.G FISH HUNT	Energy Efficient

1055. IOWA US SUFFER HAY DOVE THAT	I Was Afraid Of That
1056. IOWA US UH PAWN HEIGHT	I Was Up All Night
1057. IRAN FORK HOVER	I Ran For Cover
1058. IVORY TIRED	I've Retired
1059. JACKED HER HIP HER	Jack The Ripper
1060. JAIL HEN OWE	Jay Leno
1061. JAR LEECH APPLE IN	Charlie Chaplain
1062. JAR LIBRA HOUND HANDS NEW PEA	Charlie Brown And Snoopy
1063. JAW HECK HUM LAID LAY	Johnny Come Lately
1064. JAW KNEE MAY THUS	Johnny Matthis
1065. JAW NEON THIS POT	Johnny On The Spot
1066. JAW NICK ARSON	Johnny Carson
1067. JEW HEAVEN KNEEL HUCK	Did You Have Any Luck?
1068. JEW LIGHT HUFF WORTH	July The Fourth
1069. JEW YES SCISSOR	Julius Caesar
1070. JOG CLAY DIE SCREAM	Chocolate Ice Cream
1071. JOSTLE IF HANDLE EARN	Just Live And Learn
1072. JUSTICE HYMN PULL REEK WEST	Just A Simple Request
1073. KEP PURE RISE SOAP PIN	Keep You Eyes Open
1074. KEY HICK TUB HUG KIT	Kick The Bucket
1075. KEY PACE TRADE PHASE	Keep A Straight Face
1076. KEY PALM ERA CUB YOU TEA FULL	Keep America Beautiful
1077. KEY PASTE IF UH PEARL HIP	Keep A Stiff Upper Lip
1078. KEY PAY WATCH FLY YAWN KNIT	Keep A Watchful Eye On It
1079. KEY PERCH HEN UP	Keep Your Chin Up
1080. KEY PIT WHO YEARS ELF	Keep It To Yourself
1081. KEY POP WIDTH EACH OWN SIS	Keep Up With The Jones's
1082. KEY POUT	Keep Out
1083. KEY PUP THUG HOOD QUIRK	Keep Up The Good Work
1084. KEY PURE BRIT CHESS SEWN	Keep Your Britches On
1085. KEY PURE CARD HUP	Keep Your Guard Up
1086. KEY PURE HEY DAWNS TRAIT	Keep Your Head On Straight
1087. KEY PURE PAINT SEWN	Keep Your Pants On
1088. KEY PURE RED HUB HUFF WHAT HER	Keep Your Head Above Water
1089. KILL AGAIN SIGH LEND	Gilligan's Island
1090. KIN NEAR ODD JARS	Kenny Rogers
1091. KIN USE HE IT	Can You See It?
1092. KIT BAG TUMMY HEY ESSAY PEA	Get Back To Me A.S.A.P.
1093. KIT CHIRP HE SOLVED HEAP EYE	Get A Piece Of The Pie
1094. KIT CHORE HACKED WHO GATHER	Get Your Act Together
1095. KIT CHORE REARS LORD	Get Your Ears Lowered
1096. KIT HOW TOUGH FEAR	Get Out Of Here
1097. KIT HUFF FOOT TENTH HEED ORE	Get A Foot In The Door
1098. KIT THEY'LL HEAD DOUBT	Get The Lead Out
1099. KIT TILE TOUGH MILE HIVE	Get Out Of My Life
1100. KIT WIDTH HEAP ROW CRAM	Get With The Program

1101. KITTEN SCENE GULF AISLE	Get In Single File
1102. KNACK TOUGH BEAT RAIL	An Act Of Betrayal
1103. KNEAD LINEN HASTE HACK	A Needle In A Haystack
1104. KNEE PANT HUCK	Nip An Tuck
1105. KNOLL HEFT EARN	No Left Turn
1106. KNOT FORCE HURT TIN	Not For Certain
1107. KNOT UP ANY LEST	Not A Penny Less
1108. KNOT UP PEN HYMN OAR	Not A Penny More
1109. KNOW AN HUE WOLF HE	No Annual Fee
1110. KNOW THINK TOOT WHO	Nothing To Do
1111. KNOW WHEN DENS HEIGHT	No End In Sight
1112. KNOW WHIFF FANS HERB HUTS	No If, Ands, Or Buts
1113. KNOW WON CANDY HIGH YET	No One Can Deny It
1114. KNOWN YOU SIS COULD NOOSE	No News Is Good News
1115. KNOWS HER FIVE HEARSE	No Survivors
1116. KNOWS MOW KEEN	No Smoking
1117. KNOWS WET	No Sweat
1118. LAID HOUND DULL AWE	Lay Down The Law
1119. LASS BUTTON HOTLY EAST	Last But Not Least
1120. LASS TOUGH DEMO EKE INNS	Last Of The Mohicans
1121. LASS TWILL ANT SYSTEM HINT	Last Will And Testament
1122. LATE ROUGH HE KNOW	Lee Trevino
1123. LAUGH TAN DID	Left Handed
1124. LAUGHED WHOLE DENT HUB HAG	Left Holding The Bag
1125. LAUNCH HARES	Lawn Chairs
1126. LAW RENT SWAY ELK	Lawerence Welk
1127. LAW SAND JEALOUS	Los Angeles
1128. LAWS TEASE MAR BULLS	Lost His Marbles
1129. LAWS TINS PAYS	Lost In Space
1130. LAY BIRD HEY WE KIN	Labor Day Weekend
1131. LAY DESCEND CHANT OMEN	Ladies And Gentlemen
1132. LAY DISCLOSE	Ladies' Clothes
1133. LAY HITS LEAP END HOG SLY	Let Sleeping Dogs Lie
1134. LAY HITS MOO FAWN	Let's Move On
1135. LAY SEIZE HUM HEARD HAZE	Lazy Summer Days
1136. LAY THICK HAT OW! TOUGH TUB HAG	Let The Cat Out Of The Bag
1137. LAYER GUARD SEWN DEBT ABLE	Lay Your Cards On The Table
1138. LEAF FIT TUBE HE FEAR	Leave It To Beaver
1139. LEAF KNOWS TONE UNDER EARNED	Leave No Stone Unturned
1140. LEAF MEAL OWN	Leaf Me Alone
1141. LEAVE HEIST AROUSE	Levi Strauss
1142. LECTURE CON CHUNKS BEER GUIDE	Let Your Conscience Be Your Guide
1143. LED SAID FOURTH HEALS	Let's Head For The Hills
1144. LESS HUNT WHOM HE	Listen To Me
1145. LET IRK HAIRIER	Letter Carrier

1146. LET OFFICE HUMS TEAM — Let Off Steam
1147. LETTUCE HIT BUY THIEF HIGHER — Let Us Sit By The Fire
1148. LETTUCE MAKEUP ACT — Let Us Make A Pact
1149. LICK KIN MUCH HOPS — Licking My Chops
1150. LID ALLOW SEWN HIP RARE HE — Little House On The Prairie
1151. LIE C ARE HABIT TIN NUB RARE PITCH — Like A Rabbit In A Briar Patch
1152. LIE COMBAT OW! TOE FELL — Like A Bat Out Of Hell
1153. LIE FIN PRISM — Life In Prison
1154. LIE FIN THIEF AS LAME — Life In The Fast Lane
1155. LIE GAIN HA! TUNNEL HOG — Like A Knot On A Log
1156. LIE GUYS HEAD — Like I Said
1157. LIE QUARTER RAW FAD DUCTS BACK — Like Water Off A Duck's Back
1158. LIE SUMMON ALLEY — Liza Minnelli
1159. LIEU KIN TOMB EYE HIGHS — Look Into My Eyes
1160. LIEU WE FOLK INN TUG HE — Louisville, Kentucky
1161. LIEU WEIGH HARM STIR WRONG — Louis Armstrong
1162. LILAC AID HOG — Lie Like A Dog
1163. LIST HAIL HER — Liz Taylor
1164. LIT HOLLER HEAD DRY DEN GOOD — Little Red Riding Hood
1165. LIT HULL CHOKE HEART WRITE — Little Joe Cartwright
1166. LIT LOWER FUN NANNY — Little Orphan Annie
1167. LIT ME BANJO REAR — Let Me Bend Your Ear
1168. LIT SKIT AUTO FEAR — Let's Get Out Of Here
1169. LIT SKIT TONE WIDTH HIT — Let’s Get On With It
1170. LIT STALKED HER KEY — Let's Talk Turkey
1171. LIT STAY CAGE ANT SEWN KNIT — Let's Take A Chance
1172. LIT SUPPRESS SEWN — Let's Press On
1173. LIT TOLD HID HIGH NO — Little Did I Know
1174. LOAD HOUNDS GOWN DRILL — Low Down Scoundrel
1175. LOAF MEAT HINDER — Love Me Tender
1176. LOANED I'M NOSE HE — Long Time, No See
1177. LOPE RYE SCARE HUNT HE — Low Price Guarantee
1178. LOSS FAKE UH SNUFF ODD AHH! — Las Vegas, Nevada
1179. LOW EH? SLAIN — Lois Lane
1180. LOW WEST PRY SIS SENT TOWN — Lowest Prices In Town
1181. LOWERED HALF IMMERSE HE — Lord Have Mercy
1182. LOWERED SPRAYER — Lord’s Prayer
1183. LUG COVE THUD RAW — Luck Of The Draw
1184. LUG OUT RUB HULL SCUM HEN — Look Out, Trouble’s Coming
1185. MA MAN NAP PULP EYE — Mom And Apple Pie
1186. MA NEED TOWN THUD REIGN — Money Down The Drain
1187. MA THORN HOSE PEST — Mother Knows Best
1188. MAD CHICK HARP HIT — Magic Carpet
1189. MAKES SEEK COAST SEEDY — Mexico City
1190. MAN HUFF RUM HALF FIN — Manna From Heaven
1191. MANES TREE CHEW ESSAY — Main Street, U.S.A.

1192. MARRY RANT WON NET	Marie Antoinette
1193. MASH HURT KNEADS EYE RUNNING	My Shirt Needs Ironing
1194. MASH WHO SUN TIDE	My Shoe's Untied
1195. MASK CON FEW SHUN	Mass Confusion
1196. MASS TUCK HARD	MasterCard
1197. MAY BEAN HEX CHEER	Maybe Next Year
1198. MAY CANE AIM FOYERS ELF	Make A Name For Yourself
1199. MAY COUSIN ALL FUR	Make Us An Offer
1200. MAY CUP PURE MINE	Make Up Your Mind
1201. MAY CURES ELVES CARES	Make Yourself Scarce
1202. MAY CUSS SUCK CHEST CHIN	Make A Suggestion
1203. MAY DENIM AIR HICK AHH!	Made In America
1204. MAY GUN HIGH TOUGH FIT	Make A Night Of It
1205. MAY KITS NAP PEA	Make It Snappy
1206. MAY LOWER DARK HAT HULL HOG	Mail Order Catalog
1207. MAY RIP HOP PINS	Mary Poppins
1208. MAY WEED ANTS	May We Dance?
1209. MAYOR ACRE HISS MISS	Merry Christmas
1210. MAYOR HINGE HOSE IF	Mary And Joseph
1211. MAYOR ITCH MAIDEN HAVE FUN	Marriage Made In Heaven
1212. MAYOR LEMON ROW	Marilyn Monroe
1213. MAYOR STERN INK RAY	My Hair's Turning Gray
1214. ME AFFAIR OWE	Mia Farrow
1215. ME SINGING KNACK SHIN	Missing In Action
1216. MEAT ARE SIN HUE CHAIN	"Me Tarzan, You Jane"
1217. MEATY FULL DAZE	Medieval Days
1218. MEEK CAME HOW'S	Mickey Mouse
1219. MENACE OAT TOUGH HATS	Minnesota Fats
1220. MERCY DAY SPINS	Mercedes Benz
1221. MERGER HEIGHT AHH! HEAD	Merge Right Ahead
1222. MICE HAY FINGER ACE	My Saving Grace
1223. MID LOVE THEIR OWED	Middle Of The Road
1224. MIGHT HUNG WASTE HIDE	My Tongue Was Tied
1225. MIKE UN- TREAT HIS SOLVED HE	My Country 'Tis Of Thee
1226. MIKE UPPER UN- EIGHTH OWE FUR	My Cup Runneth Over
1227. MILE HIPS IRIS HEALED	My Lips Are Sealed
1228. MILE HIVE LASHED BEE FORM HE	My Life Flashed Before Me
1229. MILE TANNED WHO	Mountain Dew
1230. MILK HIPS UN-	Mel Gibson
1231. MINE CHORE HONE BUS NEST	Mind Your Own Business
1232. MINE HEY MISS POND CHAINS POND	My Name Is Bond, James Bond
1233. MINE YUPPIES ACCUSE	Mind Your P's And Q's
1234. MISS HER HEEL OF SCUM PENNY	Misery Loves Company
1235. MISS TURN HIGH SKY	Me. Nice Guy
1236. MMM! ABE EEL LATER	Maybe Later
1237. MMM! HAY HIKE HISS SHOE	May I Kiss You?

1238. MOB ODD ESSAY KIN — My Body's Achin'
1239. MONK KISS HOOT — Monkey Suit
1240. MOO SICK COUCH HAIRS — Musical Chairs
1241. MOPE OW! WART WHO HUE — More Power To You
1242. MOUND DEAF ARREST — Mount Everest
1243. MOW BEAD HICK — Moby Dick
1244. MOW EARTH HEN AIM MOUTH FULL — More Than A Mouthful
1245. MOW REAR THIN MEATS THIGH — More Here Than Meets The Eye
1246. MOWER FOYER MY KNEE — More For Your Money
1247. MOWER THIN HIKE HANDSTAND — More Than I Can Stand
1248. MOWER THIN NUKE INCH WHO — More Than You Can Chew
1249. MOWS TOUGH FUME HAY RIM EMBER — Most Of You May Remember
1250. MOWS VOW HUE BULB LAYER — Most Valuable Player
1251. MRS. HAS COULD HAS SAME I'LL — Miss Is As Good As A Mile
1252. MUD OARS HALLWAY SOAP HEN — My Door's Always Open
1253. MUSH ELF HIGH FUR — Michele Pfeiffer
1254. MY CALL KEY TON — Micheal Keaton
1255. MY CULLED HUG LESS — Michael Douglas
1256. MY GLAND DONE — Michael Landon
1257. MY GULCH HOARD UN- — Michael Jordan
1258. MY KOJACK SUN — Michael Jackson
1259. MYRRH FIB AROUND — Murphy Brown
1260. NAG ROUGH HALLS — Niagara Falls
1261. NAIL SUNDAY ROCKY FILLER — Nelson D. Rockefeller
1262. NAIL WIVES HE KNIT TALL — Now I've Seen It All
1263. NECK HUT IF FREE ACTION — Negative Reaction
1264. NEIGH AILED TOOTH THICK ROSS — Nailed To The Cross
1265. NEIGH FIRM AISLE OF — Never My Love
1266. NEIGH FORT HOOKED I'M TOOT RYE — Never Took Time To Try
1267. NEIGH JERK HALLS — Nature Calls
1268. NEIGH VERB HEN BED HER — Never Been Better
1269. NEIGH VERSE SANE HEIFER — Never Say Never
1270. NINE TD GREASE — Ninety Degrees
1271. NOAH'S CAPE FERMENT — No Escape From It
1272. NOD AID HOLLERED WHO MINE AIM — Not A Dollar To My Name
1273. NOD ITCH ANTS — Not A Chance
1274. NOD SLANTING — Knot's Landing
1275. NOGGIN HOCK OOZE DARE — Knock Knock. Who's There?
1276. NOOSE HE LEND — New Zealand
1277. NOPE ARK KINGS OWN — No Parking Zone
1278. NOPE EVER CHISEL LOUD — No Beverages Allowed
1279. NOPE LAYS TOO WIDE — No Place To Hide
1280. NOPE ODD HEED UH SIT BET HER — Nobody Does It Better
1281. NOPE ROB LIMB — No Problem
1282. NOPE YET SALE LOUD — Not Pets Allowed
1283. NOR MANNER HOG WHALE — Norman Rockwell

1284. NOR WHOM FORD OUT	No Room For Doubt
1285. NOSE AILS MINNOW LOUD	No Salesman Allowed
1286. NOSE HOLE IS SITTING	No Soliciting
1287. NOSED RING SAT HATCHED	No Strings Attached
1288. NOTE I'M FOE RANK HEAP HANK KEY	No Time Of Hanky Panky
1289. NUDGE EATING GAY LOUD	No Cheating Allowed
1290. NUT HANG LIE KIT	Nothing Like It
1291. NUT THIN GALES REAM MANES	Nothing Else Remains
1292. OAK ACRE OWL	O.K. Corral
1293. OAR SOFA DEAF ORIENT COLLAR	Horse Of A Different Color
1294. OCCUR INN TOUGH HARE	A Current Affair
1295. OF BOY DEBT LIKED HEAP LEG	Avoid It Like The Plague
1296. HOG HEAP HUCK	Hockey Puck
1297. OLD MEAT HEIGHT	Hold Me Tight
1298. ONCE TAP OPEN TOAST HIPS BAG	One Step Up Two Steps Back
1299. ONCE TIP CLOTHES HER	One Step Closer
1300. OOZE TAR TAD DEBT	Who Started It?
1301. ORE CAN HEIST GRIME	Organized Crime
1302. OUT ACHE ARROW VIEW	I'll Take Care Of You
1303. OW! DEAF OAKS	Howdy, Folks
1304. OW! FRAY DITCH CAULK	Alfred Hitchcock
1305. OW! TEN THICK OLD	Out In The Cold
1306. OW! TIN LIFT FEE YIELD	Out In Left Field
1307. OW! TOOL HUNCH	Out To Lunch
1308. OW! TOUGH CARE ACTOR	Out Of Character
1309. OW! TOUGH FOR DOOR	Out Of Order
1310. OW! TOUGH SIGH TILE TOUGH MINE	Out Of Sight Out Of Mind
1311. OW! TOUGH WHY HACK	Out Of Whack
1312. OW! TUNNEL HYMN	Out On A Limb
1313. OW! WHIRRED USE	Howard Hughs
1314. OWE CHASE HIM SUN	O.J. Simpson
1315. OWE FOURTH ACCOUNT HERD RUGS	Over The Counter Drugs
1316. OWE HIGH HOST ATE BUG GUYS	Ohio State Buckeyes
1317. OWE LIMB PICKY FENCE	Olympic Events
1318. OWE LOVE FILLET	Oil Of Olay
1319. OWE PENCIL OWE LEAP LEASE	Open Slowly, Please
1320. OWE PIN ARTS HER JURY	Open Heart Surgery
1321. OWL BEEP HACK KIN AMEN HIT	I'll Be Back In A Minute
1322. OWL LICKS HAND IRK RAM BAIL	Alexander Graham Bell
1323. OWL TENTH US NO	Out In The Snow
1324. OWN LEAF FOURTH EGG CUFF HIT	Only For The Heck Of It
1325. OWN LETHAL ONLY	Only The Lonely
1326. OWN THICK RAY FEET RAIN	On The Gravy Train
1327. OWN THIN HOSE	On The Nose
1328. OWN TUB HUT TON	On The Button
1329. OWNED HA! PUFF FOLDS MOW KEY	On Top Of Old Smokey

1330. PAIR HINT DULL HINT STINK — Parental Instinct
1331. PAIR RIM ACE UN- — Perry Mason
1332. PALM HICK HEART KNEE — PAUL McCartney
1333. PAN NUMB HOG KIN NOW — Panama Canal
1334. PAR CALF EH? NEW — Park Avenue
1335. PARCEL ONUS PAIN — Barcelona, Spain
1336. PART LEASE UN- EASE GUYS — Partly Sunny Skies
1337. PASTURE BET I'M — Past Your Bedtime
1338. PATCH RECKON RAY — Patrick Henry
1339. PAW BUN YEN — Paul Bunyan
1340. PAY PURPLE EIGHT — Paper Plate
1341. PEA CUB WHO ICY HUE — Peek-A-Boo! I See You
1342. PEA CUP TEEPEE SIS — Pick Up The Pieces
1343. PEA HEARSE DEARS — Pierced Ears
1344. PEA KISS BURR RAIN — Pick His Brain
1345. PEA SANK WHITE — Peace And Quiet
1346. PEA STALKS — Peace Talks
1347. PEA TARP AN — Peter Pan
1348. PEA YELLED EASE HAND WITCH — B.L.T. Sandwich
1349. PEANUT HAIL OWN THUD OWN KEY — Pin The Tail On The Donkey
1350. PECAN CHEW OOZE — Pick And Choose
1351. PEN NIP IN SURE — Penny Pincher
1352. PEP SICK HOLE AHH! — Pepsi-Cola
1353. PEP TUBBY SMALL — Pepto-Bismol
1354. PEW EARLY COINS HID DENTAL — Purely Coincidental
1355. PEW REST THUD RIBBONS KNOW — Pure As The Driven Snow
1356. PHASE THIEF AX — Face The Facts
1357. PIE CURE BEGS — Pack Your Bags
1358. PIE CURES HOOT CASE — Pack Your Suitcase
1359. PIE PINE HOLLOW FOIL — Popeye And Olive Oyl
1360. PIE SOWN THEY'LL HEFT — Pass On The Left
1361. PIECE SUN UP ODD — Peas In A Pod
1362. PINE THIS GUY — Pie In The Sky
1363. PINS LAND PAY PURR — Pencil And Paper
1364. PITCHER AND SOP — Put Your Hands Up
1365. PITCHER HID STEW GATHER — Put Your Heads Together
1366. PITCHER MINE DEBT TEASE — Put Your Mind At Ease
1367. PITCHER THIN KIN GAP SOWN — Put Your Thinking Caps On
1368. PITCHERS ELF HEN MOP LACE — Put Yourself In My Place
1369. PITCHERS HOLDER TOOTH WE ILL — Put Your Shoulder To The Wheel
1370. PLATE HUG INNS HAM — "Play It Again, Sam"
1371. PLAY JAW FULL AGENTS — Pledge Of Allegiance
1372. PLAY SOLVE ARREST — Place Of The Rest
1373. PLEA SAIL PUS — Please Help Us
1374. PLEA SOLD THIS FORM HE — Please Hold This For Me
1375. PLEA SUPPRESS MASH HURT — Please Press My Shirt

1376. PLEA SWAY TUBE EASE HEATED	Please Wait To Be Seated
1377. PLEA SWIPE PURE FEAT	Please Wipe Your Feet
1378. PLUM PRAY SINS	Plump Raisins
1379. POLICE BESS EERIE US	Please Be Serious
1380. POLICE BURR EASE NUB HULL	Please Be Reasonable
1381. POLICE COMMA KIN	Please Come Again
1382. POLICE COUGH FOREIGN FORMATION	Please Call For Information
1383. POLICE HYMN THEY'LL HEIGHTS	Please Dim The Lights
1384. POLICE MEAT MIME ALMOND ADD	Please Meet My Mom And Dad
1385. POLICE PEA CURE PEAS	Please Speak Your Piece
1386. POOH ALLOW TALL THESE TOPS	Pull Out All The Stops
1387. POROUS SUCH ARCH MILES	Poor As Church Mouse
1388. POSE TRAYS EMBER RAN	Post Raisin Bran
1389. PRAY CHEWED HISSED	Prejudiced
1390. PRAY PARADE SHUN AGE	Preparation H
1391. PROWL DOVE VIEW	Proud Of You
1392. PRY SCISSORS HEIGHT	Price Is Right
1393. PUB LICKED DRESSES STEM	Public Address System
1394. PUB LICKED HAIL HE VISION	Public Television
1395. PUFFED HUM HATCHET DRAG GUN	Puff The Magic Dragon
1396. PULL LAY THUMB ARC KIT	Play The Market
1397. PULL LEASED TOMB HE CHEW	Pleased To Meet You
1398. PULLEY SKIM HE HUB RAKE	Please Give Me A Break
1399. PUTT EIGHT HOSE ANGER HAY FEE	Potatoes And Gravy
1400. PUTT MEOW TOUGH MISS HURRY	Put Me Out Of Misery
1401. PUTT THICK LOVE SEWN	Put The Gloves On
1402. PUTT UPPER SHH! HUT HUP	Put Up, Or Shut Up
1403. PUTTY STALE BEET WEENIES LAGS	Put His Tail Between His Legs
1404. RAGE HURLS	Ray Charles
1405. RAID HARDY TACK TORE	Radar Detector
1406. RAID HE WE NEW WIRE	Ready When You Are
1407. RAIDED PEACH HE	Rated P.G.
1408. RAISE PECK CHORES ELF	Respect Yourself
1409. RARE WHEN DOUGH DEAF AUGER	Rear Window Defogger
1410. RATS HULLED AS HULL	Razzle Dazzle
1411. RAW CAN HER HOLE	Rock And Roll
1412. RAW PEN SUNK GREW SEW	Robinson Crusoe
1413. RAW SPUR OWE	Ross Perot
1414. RAY COVER THICK HOLES	Rake Over The Coals
1415. RAYS DIE BROWSE	Raised Eyebrows
1416. REACH ARE DIM NECK SUN	Richard M. Nixon
1417. RECKON DREW IN	Wreck And Ruin
1418. RED EAR KNOTTIER HIKE HUM	Ready Or Not, Here I Come
1419. RICH CHEEK HONEY CAM	Richie Cunningham
1420. RIM ELM BIRTH OW! LIMO	Remember The Alamo
1421. RINGER HOUND THEIR HOSES	Ring Around The Roses

1422. RISER OWN KNEE	Rice-A-Roni
1423. ROB THICKER HAY DULL	Rob The Cradle
1424. ROBBER TREAD FORWARD	Robert Redford
1425. ROE RIVER ENDEAVOR	Forever And Ever
1426. ROT INTO THICK OAR	Rotten To The Score
1427. ROW LINEN THUMB HONEY	Rolling In The Money
1428. ROW LOAF RAMP LAID HEAD	Roll Over And Play Dead
1429. ROW MITT HULL HE	Rome, Italy
1430. RUMOR TOY DART WRITE US	Rheumatoid Arthritis
1431. RYE DOUBT THESE DORM	Ride Out The Storm
1432. RYE PURE HARM SIR HOUND MAY	Wrap Your Arms Around Me
1433. RYE TEEN SOWN THOUGH HALL	Writing's On The Wall
1434. RYE TONE BRR! OTHER	Right On, Brother!
1435. RYE TOUR FOREIGN OOZE PAY PURPLE	Writer For A Newspaper
1436. SAFARI SIGH CAN'T HAIL	So Far As I Can Tell
1437. SAIL FRY SINFUL HOUR	Self-Rising Flour
1438. SAND TACKLE LAWS	Santa Claus
1439. SAND US OWE KNEE SWAY	Santa's On His Way
1440. SASS MISTER EAT	Sesame Street
1441. SAT HOLD HOUND	Settle Down
1442. SAT HULL THIS CORE	Settle The Score
1443. SAT JERK LOCK	Set Your Clock
1444. SAVE FANNED HEY SAW EEK	Seven Days A Week
1445. SAVE HEN YEAR RICH	Seven Year Itch
1446. SAVE TEASE OWN	Safety Zone
1447. SAW REHAB OUT HAT	Sorry About That
1448. SAWED AMEN GUM AURA	Sodom And Gomorrah
1449. SAY CHORES HEIGHT SIGH	Set Your Sights High
1450. SAY FANS HOUND	Safe And Sound
1451. SAY FINGER ACE	Saving Grace
1452. SAY FIT FRAY RAY NEED HEY	Save It For A Rainy Day
1453. SCAR LOTTO ERA	Scarlett O'Harra
1454. SCENE CURSE WHIM	Sink Or Swim
1455. SEA BEE EH? SNOOZE	CBS News
1456. SEA CAN'T HIGHER DOVE FIT	Sick And Tired Of It
1457. SEA CAN'T HIRED	Sick And Tired
1458. SEA ROW WHEN KNOWN	Zero In On
1459. SEA YEAR HOUND	See You Around
1460. SEAT BACON HINGE AHOY! HIT	Sit Back And Enjoy It
1461. SEE CASE AID HOG	Sick As A Dog
1462. SEE HIGH YEA!	C.I.A.
1463. SEEK TOMB MICE THUMB ACHE	Sick To My Stomach
1464. SEEN GAY DEAF FRIEND TUNE	Sing A Different Tune
1465. SEEN YOURS IT IS IN	Senior Citizen
1466. SEW MAYOR HOVER THEIR AIM BEAU	Somewhere Over The Rainbow
1467. SEWN LEAP UPHILL OF	(It's) Only Puppy Love

1468. SHAM PAY NIL ANNOY	Champaign, Illinois
1469. SHAWL PINS INNER	Shopping Center
1470. SHE EVER LAY	Chevrolet
1471. SHE FIRM HEAT EMBERS	"Shiver Me Timbers"
1472. SHE STEW WINNER FAIRY BEST	She's Doing Her Very Best
1473. SHEIK RIDE BIT HURT HEARS	She Cried Bitter Tears
1474. SHELL OF SHOE	She Loves You
1475. SHH! APE UPPER SHH? POUT	Shape Up Or Ship Out
1476. SHH! ACHE CUSSED HICK HAT	Shake A Stick At
1477. SHH! EASE HEATING FORT WHO	She's Eating For Two
1478. SHH! EASEL EIGHTY	She's A Lady
1479. SHH! HAT HEARD REAMS	Shattered Dreams
1480. SHH! HOE MEOW	Show Me How
1481. SHEIK HOG OAK HUBS	Chicago Cubs
1482. SHOCK CUSSED TOE	Jacques Cousteau
1483. SHOE GRAND SPIES	Sugar And Spice
1484. SHOE TOOK ILL	Shoot To Kill
1485. SHOOK A RAIL IN HEARD	Sugar Ray Leonard
1486. SHORE TANS WHEAT	Short And Sweet
1487. SHUCK HOG OBEY AIRS	Chicago Bears
1488. SICK STEAM HOUSE SIN OUR	Sixty Miles An Hour
1489. SICK STEAMY KNITS	60 Minutes
1490. SICK SUCK LAW CONE THUD HOT	Six O'clock On The Dot
1491. SICKEN TUNE UN-	Second To None
1492. SIGH MISSED WINS	Siamese Twins
1493. SIGH SOLVE THESE OWED YAK	Signs Of The Zodiac
1494. SIN MINNOWS FLYERS	Send Me No Flowers
1495. SIN TRIALS TAN DIRT I'M	Central Standard Time
1496. SIN TURF ELDER	Center Fielder
1497. SIN TURF HOLD	Centerfold
1498. SINGS BILL LEAVING	Seeing Is Believing
1499. SINK FOYERS UP HER	Sing For Your Supper
1500. SINKING HEN THERE REIGN	Singing In The Rain
1501. SIR CHIN FOREIGN WHY HIDE	Searching Far And Wide
1502. SIR CHORES HOLE	Search Your Soul
1503. SIR GUMS TAN CHILL AVID ANTS	Circumstantial Evidence
1504. SIT THREW TOOTHY HEN	See It Through To The End
1505. SKI KNEW WOOL HIVE	Skin You Alive
1506. SKIN NEED HIP INK	Skinny Dipping
1507. SLUM BURP HEARTY	Slumber Party
1508. SKI NECK HAT	Skin A Cat
1509. SNOW BEGGED EEL	It's No Big Deal
1510. SNOW UNDER	(It's) No Wonder
1511. SOAK LATCH HUE THAW DOVE FIT	So Glad You Thought Of It
1512. SOCKET TUMMY	Sock It To Me
1513. SOFA HARSH OAK HOOD	So Far So Good

1514. SON DAME WARNING	Sunday Morning
1515. SON KNEES HIDE HUP	Sunny Side Up
1516. SOUP HERB HOLE	Super Bowl
1517. SPAY SAVE HALO BULL	Space Available
1518. SPIN HIGH STALK HINT WHO HUE	(It's) Been Nice Talking To You
1519. SSS! HEAVEN THIN INK STIR ETCH	Seventh Inning Stretch
1520. SSS! MY LANDS AGE EASE	Smile And Say Cheese
1521. STAINED OPEN BEAK HOUND TAD	Stand Up And Be Counted
1522. STALL PROWL SHH! HOOT	Stop Or I'll Shoot
1523. STAR CHARRED HAY ALL FRIGHT	Start Your Day Off Right
1524. STAR GRAY FIN MY ADD	Stark Raving Mad
1525. STAR TIN FIRMS CRY HATCH	Starting From Scratch
1526. STAR TIN TOOL WHO SUN UP	Starting To Loosen Up
1527. STARTLE LOAFER	Start All Over
1528. STATE WHO THEIR HEIGHT	Stay To The Right
1529. STAY CAKE LAME	Stake A Claim
1530. STAY PAWN THUG AS	Step On The Gas
1531. STAY TOUGH THEY HEART	State Of The Art
1532. STIRRING BEAK HE KNEE	String Bikini
1533. STRAW GAS UH KNOCKS	Strong As An Ox
1534. STUB HER NEIGH SAME YULE	Stubborn As A Mule
1535. SUE PANS OW! LAD	Soup And Salad
1536. SUMMER BET EARTH HEN UH THEIRS	Some Are Better Than Others
1537. SUNNED APE APE HER	Sunday Paper
1538. SURE LAW COMBS	Sherlock Holmes
1539. SURF HIVE ALOFT DEFEAT HISSED	Survival Of The Fittest
1540. SWEEP HUT EIGHT HOPE HIGH	Sweet Potato Pie
1541. TAKE NOPE RISEN HEARSE	Take No Prisoners
1542. TAKEN DOWEL NAP EGG	Taken Down A Peg
1543. TALL CANS HER GULLS	Talk In Circles
1544. TALL CURE REAR OFF	Tear Your Ear Off
1545. TALL KIN MILE HANG WEDGE	Talking My Language
1546. TALL MISCHIEF HER SUN	Thomas Jefferson
1547. TEA CHURCH SPAT	Teacher's Pet
1548. TEA INCOME HAND MINTS	Ten Commandments
1549. TEA PUFF MIGHT HUNG	Tip Of My Tongue
1550. TEACH HECK SIN THEM ALE	The Check's In The Mail
1551. TEETH HURT INK HOLLOW KNEES	The Thirteen Colonies
1552. TEN CURB ALE	Tinker Bell
1553. TEND HURL OF INK HAIR	Tender Loving Care
1554. THAN COD DEBTS FRIED HAY	Thank God It's Friday
1555. THAN CUE FAIR REAM HUTCH	Thank You Very Much
1556. THAN CUE FOREIGN HOTS MOW KEEN	Thank You For Not Smoking
1557. THAN CUE FORK HUMMING	Thank You For Coming
1558. THAN DEGREE FIFTH SHOW	The Andy Griffith Show
1559. THAT FEELS SAND MUCK ALWAYS	The Hatfields and The McCoys

1560. THAT LAND AGO SHUN	The Atlantic Ocean
1561. THAT LAND TOUGH OWL GUNS	The Atlantic Falcons
1562. THAT LAND TUB RAVES	The Atlantic Braves
1563. THAT SUNNY TIDY YEAH	That's A Neat Idea
1564. THAW NY TEED HOLLER	The Almighty Dollar
1565. THE HATS TUBE ADD	That's Too Bad
1566. THE LOSS FAKE CUSSED RIP	The Las Vegas Strip
1567. THE RAW THUS AIM	They're All The Same
1568. THE REAM HEN HAND ABE HAY BEE	Three Men And A Baby
1569. THE REAM INN INN HAT HUB	"...Three Men In A Tub"
1570. THE SEA SIT FERN OW!	This Is It For Now
1571. THE SIS HAUL LIFE COT	This Is All I've Got
1572. THE SIS HE SEE	This Is Easy
1573. THE SIS SASS TEA CUP	This Is A Stick Up
1574. THE SIS SAW LINE HEED FERN OW!	This Is All I Need For Now
1575. THE SPECIFIC OWE SHUN	The Pacific Ocean
1576. THIEF IF THUMB END MINT	The Fifth Amendment
1577. THEIR HEAD CRAWLS	The Red Cross
1578. THEIR SNOW WEIGH HIT STREW	There's No Way It's True
1579. THEM AN HEN THIEF HAM HILLY	The Man In The Family
1580. THEM ARKS BROTH HEARSE	The Marx Brothers
1581. THEM HID DULL LEAST	The Middle East
1582. THEM OTHER OVEN FIN CHIN	The Mother Of Invention
1583. THEM RECKON WEIGH	The American Way
1584. THEM ROLLED SIT TEA	The Emerald City
1585. THERE HOCK YET SHRED DECLARE	"...The Rockets' Red Glare..."
1586. THERE HAYS SIS SEWN	The Race Is On
1587. THERE HOCKEY MILE TANS	The Rocky Mountains
1588. THERE OH! RING TWIN TEASE	The Roaring Twenties
1589. THERE SNORE HIGH MORE EASE SUN	There's No Rhyme Or Reason
1590. THESE AND SOFT I'M	The Sands Of Time
1591. THESE HANDY ECHOES WHO	The San Diego Zoo
1592. THESE HE HAREM ODD RAISE	The Sierra Madres
1593. THESE HEX ME YAWNED HOLLER MAN	The Six Million Dollar Man
1594. THESE HOUND DOVE MOO SICK	The Sound Of Music
1595. THESE IF ILL WORE	The Civil War
1596. THESE ISLAND SOLVE THEY'LL HAMS	The Silence Of The Lambs
1597. THESE MELLOW MY KNEE	The Smell Of Money
1598. THESE MYTHS ONION INSTANT HOOT	The Smithsonian Institute
1599. THESE TAKE SIR RYE	The Stakes Are High
1600. THESE TARS BANK OLD BAN HER	The Star Spangled Banner
1601. THESE TARZAN STIR EYE PSST!	The Stars And Stripes
1602. THESE TRAY TAN ARROW	The Straight And Narrow
1603. THEY BEES EASE	The ABC's
1604. THEY FEE VERSE EASE SUN	The Hay Fever Season
1605. THEY HEARSE NOPE LAY SLY COMB	"There's No Place Like Home"

1606. THEY HER SAW WAY SUCH AUNTS — There's Always a Chance
1607. THEY HOPE INNER OWED — The Open Road
1608. THEY YAWN GUNNED ARREST LESS — The Young And The Restless
1609. THEY YUM! ERA GUNNED REAM — The American Dream
1610. THEY'LL OWNS TARS DATE — The Lone Star State
1611. THEY'LL SANE JAILS — The Hell's Angels
1612. THICK ATOM HE AHH! WORDS — The Academy Awards
1613. THICK CRADLE ACHES — The Great Lakes
1614. THICK HALLS BEES HOE — The Cosby Show
1615. THICK HARD ENOUGH HEED HEN — The Garden Of Eden
1616. THICK HATS OW! TOUGH TUB HAG — The Cat's Out Of The Bag
1617. THICK HOLE DINNER WHO'LL — The Golden Rule
1618. THICK HOSE TUSK LEER — The Coast Is Clear
1619. THICK HOW WORLDLY LINE — The Cowardly Lion
1620. THICK HULL FOAM HECK SICK-O — The Gulf Of Mexico
1621. THICK HUMMING SANG OWE WINGS — The Comings And Goings
1622. THICK INN GOLF THEY JUNK HULL — The King Of The Jungle
1623. THICK REIGN BEAR HAZE — The Green Berets
1624. THICK WAITER — The Equator
1625. THICK WALLET HE SHH! OWES — The Quality Shows
1626. THICK WE ENOUGH ANGLE HAND — The Queen Of England
1627. THICK WHITE BEEF FORTIES DORM — The Quiet Before The Storm
1628. THICK YET HIS BURGERS DRESS — The Gettysburg Address
1629. THICKER HE MUFF THICKER HOP — The Cream Of The Crop
1630. THICKER HOT TEAK HID — The Karate Kid
1631. THIEF ACT HUFF THEM ADDER — The Fact Of The Matter
1632. THIEF ALLOW HER — The Final Hour
1633. THIEF AX PEEK FOURTH HYMNS ELVES — The Facts Speak For Themselves
1634. THIEF EH? SHARP HIDING — The Fish Are Biting
1635. THIEF FINE OFF RUNT EAR — The Final Frontier
1636. THIEF FORT HOPS — The Four Tops
1637. THIEF FORWARD MUST HANG — The Ford Mustang
1638. THIEF LOWER DUCK EASE — The Florida Keys
1639. THIEF LOWERED UH HEIFER GLAZE — The Florida Everglades
1640. THIEF OAKS WHACK GUN BE DULL — The Volkswagen Beetle
1641. THIEF YET NUMB WORE — The Vietnam War
1642. THIGH HUFF UH HER WRECK GAIN — The Eye Of The Hurricane
1643. THIGH OVEN HE DULL — The Eye Of The Needle
1644. THIGH SANDAL HOSE — The Highs And Lows
1645. THIGH TORE TOSS SANDY HAIR — The Tortoise And The Hare
1646. THIN ASH ANNUL LINK WIRE HER — The National Enquirer
1647. THIN BEE YEA — The N.B.A.
1648. THIN COVE MAY — Think Of Me
1649. THIN COVE THICKEN SICK WINCES — Think Of The Consequences
1650. THIN DOVE THERE ROAD — The End Of The Road
1651. THIN DOVE THROUGH HURLED — The End Of The World

1652. THIN IF AIL	The NFL
1653. THIN WORTH POLL	The North Pole
1654. THING CLASH CHANT NULL	The English Channel
1655. THING COMMON LOVE	Think I'm In Love
1656. THINKER EDIBLE HAWK	The Incredible Hulk
1657. THIS GUY YES FALL HEN	The Sky Is Falling
1658. THOROUGH CALL SHIN TOOTH WHEN	Throw Caution To The Wind
1659. THOU SIS HUFF PAR LAMENT	The Houses Of Parliament
1660. THOU SUNDIAL UNDRESS SING	Thousand Island Dressing
1661. THOUGH GLAND HAZE	The Oakland A's
1662. THOUGH TIGHT AN HICK	The Titanic
1663. THOUGH WINDY TILE	Throw In The Towel
1664. THRILL MY COY	The Real McCoy
1665. THROUGH TUB HOOK HAT	Throw The Book At
1666. THROW LINKS TONES	The Rolling Stones
1667. THROWN SIGH DOVE DETRACTS	The Wrong Side Of The Tracks
1668. THUD EH? FILM AID MEAT WHO WIT	The Devil Made Me Do It
1669. THUD HAM ITCHES STUN	The Damage Is Done
1670. THUD HEAD OVEN HEIGHT	The Dead Of The Night
1671. THUD HEN VERB WRONG GOES	The Denver Broncos
1672. THUD HER TEED US SIN	The Dirty Dozen
1673. THUD HICK FANNED HIKE SHH! HOE	The Dick Van Dyke Show
1674. THUD HOW LESS COW POISE	The Dallas Cowboys
1675. THUD HYMN OAR ERRATIC BRA SAYS	The Democratic Process
1676. THUG GLEE DUCT LEAN	The Ugly Duckling
1677. THUG GRIN CHEWS TOLL CRESS MUSS	The Grinch Who Stole Christmas
1678. THUG HIGH DANGLE HEIGHT	The Guiding Light
1679. THUG HOODS HIP LAW LEAP HOP	The Good Ship Lollypop
1680. THUMB AIR RINK OAR	The Marine Corps
1681. THUMB ENTREE AWE LEG SUPPOSE	The Montreal Expos
1682. THUMB HAH! FEE UH	The Mafia
1683. THUMB HALT EASE FOUL CON	The Maltese Falcon
1684. THUMB HAY KNEE VENT	The Main Event
1685. THUMB HIGH YAM ADOLPH HENS	The Miami Dolphins
1686. THUMB HUNT STIRS	The Munsters
1687. THUMB ILL KEY WAKE OWL LICKS HE	The Milky Way Galaxy
1688. THUMB ILL LIT HAIR REPEL LEASE	The Military Police
1689. THUMB MRS. SIP PEER EVER	The Mississippi River
1690. THUMB ODD HULL TEA	The Model T
1691. THUMB WARNING HALVED HER	The Morning After
1692. THUMB WORTH HUM HAIRIER	The More, The Merrier
1693. THUMP HIGHER ESTATE BILL DEN	The Empire State Building
1694. THUMP UNDER HOSE AHH!	The Ponderosa
1695. THUS ILL LOVE UPPER WHO FULL	The Seal Of Approval
1696. TICK SUCK HOE	Texaco
1697. TIE CURB HIGH DETAIL	Tiger By The Tail

1698. TIE MAN DUG IN	Time And Again
1699. TIE MAN HAVE DAY	Time And A Half
1700. TIE PAPER SUN OWL LIT TEA	Type "A" Personality
1701. TIE PUCKER HALF FICKLE EH? ROAR	Typographical Error
1702. TIE TENURE BUILT	Tighten Your Belt
1703. TIED AS AID RM	Tight As A Drum
1704. TIMED WHO WIT THESE HACK	Time To Hit The Sack
1705. TIMES LIP SPIES OAK WICK GLEE	Time Slips By So Quickly
1706. TO STAIN HEIGHT	Tuesday Night
1707. TOE NEEDY TYKE HER	Tony The Tiger
1708. TOE STAND GEL HE	Toast And Jelly
1709. TOMB ANKLE HONKS TOE WISH SORT	To Make A Long Story Short
1710. TON LOVE LOVE	Tunnel Of Love
1711. TOOT HURT TOLD OF SSS!	"...Two Turtle Doves..."
1712. TOOTH BUS TOUGH MONO ALLEGE	To The Best Of My Knowledge
1713. TOOTH BUS TOUGH HOUR BILLY TEA	To The Best Of Our Abilities
1714. TOOTH HUSH OR SOLVE TRIP HOLY	"... To The Shores Of Tripoli..."
1715. TOOTH VARIED HAY	To The Very Day
1716. TOOTHY RISK YOU	To The Rescue
1717. TOW MATE HOSE HOOP	Tomato Soup
1718. TREE QUARTER EAT	Trick Or Treat
1719. TRIED HINTS SHOOK HURL HISS SCUM	Trident Sugarless Gum
1720. TRY FLINGS AILS MAN	Traveling Salesman
1721. TRY HEN TOMB ACHE HAY LEAVING	Trying To Make A Living
1722. TUB ACE BAWL OLIVE AIM	The Baseball Hall Of Fame
1723. TUB ANT TALC LEAN HER	Tub And Tile Cleaner
1724. TUB PRETTY SHARK HUMMING	"The British Are Coming!"
1725. TUB RAID HEAP HUNCH	The Brady Bunch
1726. TUBE EGG FREEZE BREAD CHESS	Too Big For His Britches
1727. TUNE HIGH DEBT HAY TOGGLE HOCK	Tonight At Eight O'clock
1728. TUNE HOE HUE WHIZ TOOL OF VIEW	To Know You Is To Love You
1729. TUNE HOMEY YES TOOL OF MAY	To Know Me Is To Love Me
1730. TUNE OWE WIND	To No End
1731. TURNIP YEARN HOSE	Turn Up Your Nose
1732. TWIN TEETH SIN JURY	Twentieth Century
1733. TWO CUTE TOOTHACHE LEAN NURSE	Took You To The Cleaners
1734. TWO THREE PEAR	Tooth Repair
1735. TWO WE CHEESE SEWN	To Each His Own
1736. UH GNAWS TARP LAYER	An All-Star Player
1737. UH KNIFE READ HOUR	An Ivory Tower
1738. UH NEIGH SKIM OAK HISS	An Eskimo Kiss
1739. UH NICE BURR ACRE	An Ice Breaker
1740. UH NUNS HUG HE ROW	An Unsung Hero
1741. UH PUP PAN DAY WEIGH	Up, Up And Away
1742. UN- DARK HUNTS TRUCK SHIN	Under Construction
1743. UN HER SIRE HERE I'M	A Nursery Rhyme

1744. UN- INN YOU'RE HINT SAGE HINT	An Insurance Agent
1745. UN- INNS YOU'RE HINT SPA LESS HE	An Insurance Policy
1746. UN- WHO DISC HOLLOW KNEE	A Nudist Colony
1747. UNCLE BAY REEF IN	Huckleberry Finn
1748. UP ARK ARRANGE HER	A Park Ranger
1749. UP ARROW TIN ISSUES	A Pair Of Tennis Shoes
1750. UP ARROWS HIS HEARS	A Pair Of Scissors
1751. UP ERA SHOOT	A Parachute
1752. UP HUB LICK UP HERE RINSE	A Public Appearance
1753. UP RISEN CENTS HINTS	A Prison Sentence
1754. UP UP PEA	A Puppy
1755. UPHILL LOVE HEIGHT	A Pillow Fight
1756. UPHILL OKAY SSS!	A Pillowcase
1757. URINE HECK STONE MILE HISSED	You're Next On My List
1758. URINE HOT EVE INK LOWS	You're Not Even Close
1759. URINE TAIL EDGE HINT	You're Intelligent
1760. US CATCH BAD	A Sketch Pad
1761. US COOLED EACH HER	A School Teacher
1762. US DAY SHUN WHACK GUN	A Station Wagon
1763. US HEAVEN FOUR TEASE HEAVEN	A 747
1764. US HIGHNESS PROP PLUM	A Sinus Problem
1765. US IT EASE LIQUOR	A City Slicker
1766. US LIP PER ERODE	A Slippery Road
1767. US TAKEN PUTT HAY TOE	A Steak And Potato
1768. US WHEAT FORTH US WHEAT	A Sweet For The Sweet
1769. US WHO VENEER	A Souvenir
1770. USE HEM HE TEEN ASH ANNUL PARK	Yosemite National Park
1771. USE SEAL LAY	U.C.L.A.
1772. VAN HUSH INK REAM	Vanishing Cream
1773. VOTER GRAPH HECK MAM HURRY	Photographic Memory
1774. VOW LINT I'M STAY	Valentine's Day
1775. WAD ACRE HE PEA HISS	What A Creep He Is
1776. WAD AGE WHO HULL	What A Jewel
1777. WAD DAM ICE POSED TOOT WHO	What Am I Supposed To Do?
1778. WAD EGG HIGH	What A Guy
1779. WAD HALF HER USE HEY	Whatever You Say
1780. WAD SHORE OPEN YEN	What's Your Opinion?
1781. WAD WHO YOUTH INK	What Do You Think?
1782. WAD WOOD JEWEL HIKE FORD INNER	What Would You Like For Dinner
1783. WADDLE EIGHTY	What A Lady
1784. WADDLE UH KICK HIGH	What A Lucky Guy
1785. WADE INK VOWELS	Wedding Vows
1786. WADS FORCE UPPER	What's For Supper
1787. WAIT WHOM HUTCH	Way To Much
1788. WALL COME ISLAND MASH OOZE	Walk A Mile In My Shoes
1789. WALL CONE THE NICE	Walk On Thin Ice

1790. WALL CONE THOUGH HOWLED SIGHED — Walk On The Wild Side
1791. WALL CONE WHAT HER — Walk On Water
1792. WALL KIN THE EIGHTH HEN LINE — Walking A Thin Line
1793. WOK KING THUD HOG — Walking The Dog
1794. WANDS HIGHS FEAT SAW — One Size Fits All
1795. WANDS PAWN EIGHT I'M — Once Upon A Time
1796. WANDS TIP HAT EIGHT I'M — One Step At A Time
1797. WANT HERO FIT — Won't Hear Of It
1798. WANTS MICE SENIOR DRINK — Want Some Ice In Your Drink?
1799. WARES MOM HONEY — Where's My Money?
1800. WARES TUCK INN THUMB HID DULL — We're Stuck In The Middle
1801. WASHING TANNED EASE HE — Washington, D.C.
1802. WATER COIN SAD HINTS — What A Coincidence
1803. WATER HUE GRAY SEE — What Are You? Crazy?
1804. WATER HUE TALL KENNEL BOUT — What Are You Talking About?
1805. WATER USE TEARING CAT — What Are You Staring At?
1806. WATER YOUTH INK COVE DEBT — What Do You Think Of That?
1807. WATT EYE MISS SIT — What Time Is It?
1808. WATT HALF WEEK HOT TOOL OOZE — What Have We Got To Lose
1809. WATT SAP INNING — What's Happening?
1810. WAY COUPLE HIT HULLS OOZE HE — Wake Up, Little Suzy
1811. WAY HEARSE MIKE ARK EASE — Where's My Car Keys
1812. WAY OWL TEN FUR HUNT — Way Out In Front
1813. WAY TAME HEN HIT — Wait A Minute
1814. WAY YA'LL HALF PROP PLUMS — We All Have Problems
1815. WE ENEMA SHEEP COMB SIN — When My Ship Comes In
1816. WE GNAWS SADDENED UN- — When All Is Said And Done
1817. WE LAND ILL — Wheel And Deal
1818. WE SHH! UP HONEST ARE — Wish Upon A Star
1819. WE SHINE WHO — Wish I Knew
1820. WE SHOWER NEIGH VERB HORN — Wish I Were Never Born
1821. WE SHOWER THEY'RE — Wish You Were There
1822. WE SHOWERED HOLLER — Wish I Were Taller
1823. WE WHIR WHIR KENNEL HIKED HOGS — We Were Working Like Dogs
1824. WEAK ANT HALF FIT TALL — We Can't Have It All
1825. WEAKEN MAY KIT TAP HEN — We Can Make It Happen
1826. WEAKEN SALE THESE HEAVENS EASE — We Can Sail The Seven Seas
1827. WEAKEN WERE KEY DOUBT — We Can Work It Out
1828. WEAKEN WORKER HOUND DEBT — We Can Work Around It
1829. WEALTH HISS SCISSORS SIR PRIZE — Well, This Is A Surprise
1830. WEAN EAT HUG HIT HAY WEIGH — We Need To Get Away
1831. WEAN HEED TOOT HAWK — We Need To Talk
1832. WEAN WON FORTH EGG HIP PURR — Win One For The Gipper
1833. WEARY DECK HER HATING — We're Redecorating
1834. WEAVE COTTON HOPE ARRIVE US HE — We've Got No Privacy
1835. WEAVE OUGHT TOOTHY BIT TREND — We Fought To The Bitter End

1836. WEAVE OUGHT TWO THAN HAIL | We Fought Tooth And Nail
1837. WEAVE SCENE BED HERD HAZE | We've Seen Better Days
1838. WEDGE OAR WHIZ SILL | Wet Your Whistle
1839. WEE WOE COUPLE EIGHT | We Woke Up Late
1840. WEED HAUNT FEE LIE KIT | We Don't Feel Like It
1841. WEED HEAP HEAP HULL | We, The People
1842. WEED MILE HIPS | Read My Lips
1843. WEED ROW FRIGHT BUY YET | We Drove Right By It
1844. WEED TAN DITCH ANTS | We Don't Stand A Chance
1845. WEEDY LIVER | We Deliver
1846. WEEDY MAN TUNE HOE WIT ALL | We Demand To Know It All
1847. WEEDY SURF TWIN | We Deserve To Win
1848. WEEK AIM MOTTO "K" | We Came Out Ok
1849. WEEK CODDLE HOT UP LACES TUG HOE | We've Got A Lot Of Places To Go
1850. WEEK HAIR HUB OWL CHEW | We Care About You
1851. WEEK HOOD HINT CARELESS | We Couldn't Care Less
1852. WEENIE CHORE US HIS TENTS | We Need Your Assistance
1853. WEENIE DONE ANT SIR | We Need An Answer
1854. WEENIE DONE EGG SPURT | We Need An Expert
1855. WEENIE DONE OTHER CHANTS SAT HIT | We Need Another Chance At It
1856. WEENIE THUMB HONEY | We Nee The Money
1857. WEENIE TRAIN SIP OARS | When It Rains, It Pours
1858. WEEP HULL DEEP LUG GONE KNIT | We Pulled The Plug On It
1859. WEEP LAID GUARD SAWN HEIGHT | We Played Cards All Night
1860. WEIGH SNOT WON HOT | Waste Not, Want Not
1861. WEIRD HID WIG HOE RUNG | Where Did We Go Wrong
1862. WEIRD HISS UP POINT HIDDEN NEW | We're Disappointed In You
1863. WEIRDO WISE TART | Where Do I Start?
1864. WELCH AIM BERLIN | Wilt Chamberlain
1865. WERE KENNEL EIGHT HAT THAW FIZZ | Working Late At The Office
1866. WETTER TRY | Wet Or Dry
1867. WHALE CHESS GRR! APE CHOOSE | Welch's Grape Juice
1868. WHALE COMBS HINT HER | Welcome Center
1869. WHALE HOOK CAT HOSED IMPULSE | Well' Look At Those Dimples
1870. WHALE LODGE US DAWN KIT HIT | Well' I Just Don't Get It
1871. WHALES PEA COVE THUD EH? FULL | Well, Speak Of The Devil
1872. WHAT CHORES TAP | Watch Your Step
1873. WHAT HURT OUR | Water Tower
1874. WHAT ROVER THUD HAM | Water Over The Dam
1875. WEE WARP ART NURSE INK RHYME | We Were Partners In Crime
1876. WEE! WHARF ACED HOOF ACE | We Were Face To Face
1877. WHEEL BRAND DOOR FILLER HEIGHT | Wilbur And Orville Wright
1878. WHEEL HALVED TILL WEAKER HIDE | We Laughed Till We Cried
1879. WHEEL HOOKED EYE HANDLE OWE | We Looked High And Low
1880. WHEEL YUM! AIR REAM HE | Will You Marry Me?
1881. WHEELS HE YULE HATER | We'll See You Later

1882. WHELP LESS SHORE ART — Well, Bless Your Heart
1883. WHEN DOUBLE LINES — Window Blinds
1884. WHIM ISSUE — We Miss You
1885. WHIR HUE WINTER REST DEADEN KNIT — Were You Interested In It?"
1886. WHIR USER PRIZED — Were You Surprised?
1887. WHIRL DOVE COULD — World Of Good
1888. WHIRL DRAWER WON — World War 1
1889. WHIRRED SOLVE WHIZZED HUM — Word Of Wisdom
1890. WHIZ HULL HEN THUD ARK — Whistle In The Dark
1891. WHOLE DAWN AMEN IT — Hold On A Minute
1892. WHOLE LEAGUE HOW — Holy Cow!
1893. WHY DOPE IN — Wide Open
1894. WHY KICK HEAP EACH — Waikiki, Beach
1895. WHY SKY — Wise Guy
1896. WHY TAIL HUFF HUNT — White Elephant
1897. WHY TILES — White House
1898. WIDE HAUNT WHIM HEY CUD ILL — Why Don't We Make A Deal?
1899. WIDE HIDDEN CHEWS HAZE HOE — Why Didn't You Say So?
1900. WIDE HIDDEN JUKE ALL — Why Didn't You Call?
1901. WIDE OWN JEWEL HEAD ME ATOM — Why Don't You Let Me At Him?
1902. WIDE OWN TWIG HOSE WOMEN — Why Don't We Go Swimming?
1903. WILL SAW RIM OCEAN — Wheels Are In Motion
1904. WILLED WHO WIT FERN UH- THIN — We'll Do It For Nothing
1905. WIN NIGH THIN COVE FEW — When I Think Of You
1906. WIND LIE CLAW QUIRK — Went Like Clock Work
1907. WINDOW WHEEZE TART — When Do We Start
1908. WINDOWS HITS TAR TUG HEN — When Does It Start Again?
1909. WIRE USE SEWN HER FUSS — Why Are You So Nervous
1910. WISH SHALLOW FORK HUM — We Shall Overcome
1911. WIT BIND THEY YEARS — Wet Behind The Ears
1912. WIT BLAND KIT — Wet Blanket
1913. WITCH WEIGHED HID EGO — Which Way Did He Go?
1914. WON HEIGHTS TANNED — One Night Stand
1915. WON KNEE NUMB HILL YEN — One In A Million
1916. WON SAD DAY — Once A Day
1917. WON SAND FOE RAW — Once And For All
1918. WON SHOE KITS TAR TAD — Once You Get Started
1919. WON SIS HEN HUFF FORM HE — Once Is Enough For Me
1920. WON TOOTH REEF ARF! HIVE — One, Two, Three, Four, Five
1921. WON TUBE HUCK CALM ICE WHO — 1,2, Buckle My Shoe
1922. WON WASTE WHEAT — One-way Street
1923. WON WEIGHT HICK HIT — One-way Ticket
1924. WON WHEEL CURLIER — One Week Earlier
1925. WON'T HID DEBT ORAL HIVE — Wanted Dead Or Alive
1926. WON'T HID FORM HEARD HER — Wanted For Murder
1927. WOOD JEWEL HIKE TOAD ANTS — Would You Like To Dance

1928. WOOD CHECK AIR FORD US HURT — Would You Care For Dessert
1929. WOOL FINS HEAPS GLOW THING — Wolf In Sheep's Clothing
1930. WORE THAT SWAY TEN COLD — Worth It's Weight In Gold
1931. WOW! PILL LICK HOCK — Wild Bill Hickock
1932. WRIST HUSH HARP HIT — Rest Assured
1933. YANK EAST EIGHTY YUM — Yankee Stadium
1934. YEAR FLIES SOAP PIN — Your Fly Is Open
1935. YEAR LEECH HICCUP — Yearly Checkup
1936. YEARS GRAY SEA YES YULE HOOK — You're As Crazy As You Look
1937. YELL HOPE HAY CHESS — Yellow Pages
1938. YELL LOST OWN ASH ANNUL PARK — Yellowstone National Park
1939. YO! HER STREW LAY — Yours Truly
1940. YOLK HEAP ERA — Yogi Berra
1941. YOLK HEAP ERRAND BOOB WHO — Yogi Bear And Boo-Boo
1942. YOLK UH-OH KNOW — Yoko Ono
1943. YOU SHARK ALMONDS HINTS — Use Your Common Sense
1944. YOU SHOE RED — Use Your Head
1945. YOU'DE HAUNTS HAY — You Don't Say
1946. YUM US TOUGH BEAD REAM MEN — You Must Of Been Dreaming
1947. YUM! US BEAK HIDDEN — You Must Be Kidding
1948. ZOO PERM AN — Superman

Palindromes!

What's a PALINDROME? It can be a number that reads the same forward as it does backward – like 2,332. Or, 45,654. Or….it can be a word, phrase, verse, or sentence that reads the same backwards or forwards. They can be simple words, like MOM, or DAD. Or, complex sentences like:

Marge lets Norah see Sharon's telegram.

These words, phrases, and sentences and been around for years. New sentences continue to be created or discovered, so the list found in this book is NOT a comprehensive list.

The ***Thinklers TWIST!***

Though the palindromes are not new, the way to make you figure them out….IS! See how many of the three types of challenges you can complete on your own! Good luck!

Palindromes - Words

Each of the answers to these clues will reveal **ONE** word or an abbreviation that can be read the same way forward as back. Good luck!

CLUE	***ANSWER***
1. An expression of discovery	Aha
2. Protects a baby when eating	Bib
3. Short for Robert	Bob
4. Relating to civil affairs	Civic
5. Father	Dad
6. The title to property	Deed
7. Today I do. Yesterday I ______.	Did
8. A firecracker that doesn't blow	Dud
9. To barely manage to make a living	Eke
10. An old-fashioned word for before	Ere
11. Adam's wife	Eve
12. A female sheep	Ewe
13. What you see with	Eye
14. To choke	Gag
15. A two-wheeled horse drawn carriage	Gig
16. A short laugh	Hah
17. Name that starts with H	Hannah
18. Expression of not understanding	Huh
19. An Eskimo boat	Kayak
20. A goofy person	Kook
21. Flat or even	Level
22. Short for Liloth	Lil
23. Short for MADAM	Ma'am

24. Long for Ma'am	Madam
25. Mother	Mom
26. Mother in England	Mum
27. Midday	Noon
28. Religious woman	Nun
29. Name that starts with O	Otto
30. Soft food for babies	Pap
31. Sound of a young bird	Peep
32. Full of energy	Pep
33. Dot on dice	Pip
34. Deck above the main deck of a ship	Poop
35. Soda or sudden, sharp, explosive sound	Pop
36. A young dog	Pup
37. Tracking device used in flying	Radar
38. Add a little more red and it's ...	Redder
39. To make reference to	Refer
40. Put up the paper again	Re-paper
41. Person who revives	Reviver
42. Part of a machine that rotates	Rotor
43. Viking stories or tales	Sagas
44. Looks at	Sees
45. Male and female are the different ...	Sexes
46. Former rulers of Iran	Shahs
47. Slang sister	Sis
48. Doing the performances alone	Solos
49. Save our ship	S.O.S
50. To make lace	Tat
51. An explosive	T.N.T.
52. The sound of a train's horn	Toot
53. Small child	Tot
54. Boy Pharaoh, King________	Tut
55. Expression of amazement	Wow

Palindromes Phrases

The clues in this section will uncover two or more words that can be read backwards the same way as read forward. Read the clues to figure out what the words are. If the clue words are in quotation marks, they are actually used in the phrase.

CLUE	***ANSWER***
1. Join the first letter	Add "A"
2. Type of car from Japan	A Toyota
3. A city in NV	Adaven, Nevada
4. "A" Mr. Claus "AT" the space center	A Santa at NASA
5. A city in PA with the same name as the rockets that went to the moon	Apollo, PA
6. Sphere laboratory	Ball lab
7. Tavern crustacean	Bar crab
8. Feathered animal, connected to sternum	Bird rib
9. Type of tree, what babies sleep in	Birch crib
10. Employers cry	Bosses sob

11. Big cigarette, disastrous — Cigar: tragic
12. A certain fish physician — Cod doc
13. Genetic material, country — DNA Land
14. Canine deity — Dog God
15. Do not (contraction), move head up and down — Don't nod
16. Dull poet — Drab bard
17. Sleepy long blade — Drowsy sword
18. Stupid, wet dirt — Dumb mud
19. Pour wet dirt out of a big truck — Dump mud
20. Flightless bird, exhaust — Emu fume
21. Malicious, black pizza topping — Evil Olive
22. Remember a persons *head*, remove caffeine — Face decaf
23. It's sometimes at half mast, "ALF" — Flag Alf
24. Get out of here! Santa's helper. — Flee elf
25. Make your muscles hard, Santa's helper — Flex, elf!
26. Jester, not caring — Fool aloof
27. Gossipy paper container — Gab bag
28. Male who watches the fence door, title label — Gateman's nametag
29. Present, ____Newton — Gift fig
30. Don't stop pooch — Go dog
31. Chewing candy cup — Gum mug
32. Bully "Sarah" — Harass Sarah
33. Me like 3.14 — I prefer Pi.
34. Sews cousin, smells — Knits stink
35. Not early, related to unborn babies — Late fetal
36. A buddy that sits on you when you sit — Lap pal
37. People with "colony" disease, what magnets can do — Lepers repel
38. Feeling alone, pain reliever (brand) — Lonely Tylenol
39. Liniment for the king of beasts — Lion oil
40. What the devil wants you to do — Live evil
41. Shopping place for alpacas cousin — Llama mall
42. Upset, Eve's husband — Mad Adam
43. An upset water barrier — Mad dam
44. Reflection glass, outside edge — Mirror rim
45. Army cousin, large passenger car — Navy Van
46. The net after net nine — Net ten
47. Not ever, odd opposite — Never even
48. Snip cousin, "A", tack cousin — Nip a pin
49. What a father usually says to his boy — No son
50. 1999 pounds is __________ ___ __________ — Not a ton
51. The women in white jog — Nurses run
52. An alright knock out — Ok KO
53. Dad is tree pitch — Pa's a sap
54. Friends high five — Pals slap
55. The pots 20 minute rest — Pan nap

56. Birthday celebration, hidden snare	Party boobytrap
57. Birthday celebration, mouse catcher	Party trap
58. Coke's rival is energy	Pepsi is pep
59. A swine rip off	Pig gip
60. Top edge of a ditch	Pit tip
61. Piglet's friends hula ring	Pooh's hoop
62. Opposite of a pans bottom	Pot top
63. A fast automobile	Race car
64. Train track, fib maker	Rail liar
65. Rodents take the limelight	Rats star
66. Maroon, found opposite, army fighter	Red lost soldier
67. Maroon, Casino state, seller	Red Nevada Vender
68. Hermit's stomach sore	Recluse's ulcer
69. Gambling city's soloist	Reno loner
70. Mentally disabled reviewer	Retard rater
71. Pepper cousin, map book	Salt Atlas
72. View the game officials	See referees
73. Saw the leg joints	Seen knees
74. Intelligent horned animal	Smart rams
75. Pistols that are tight in their holsters	Snug guns
76. ____ of thread, loopty _______(plural)	Spool loops
77. Place felines on top of each other	Stack cats
78. Hollywood actor, views rodent	Star sees rat
79. Halt circles	Stop spots
80. Hay cousin, _____ & crafts	Straw arts
81. Skin bumps made from hay	Straw warts
82. Emphasized sweets at the end of a meal	Stressed desserts
83. Take legal action against you and me	Sue us!
84. Exchange animals feet	Swap paws
85. Illegal baseball stick	Taboo bat.
86. This certain president = obesity	Taft : fat
87. South Pacific island, head piece	Tahiti hat
88. Gently touch Patricia	Tap Pat
89. Men's neckwear, that thing	Tie it
90. Highest dot	Top spot
91. To get tea out of the pot you….	Tip it
92. Highest place	Top spot
93. Common canned fish, cashew	Tuna nut
94. Alien spaceship, soybean curd	U.F.O. Tofu
95. All of us use needle and thread	We sew
96. We *lost then* but, we______________	Won now
97. Sound that communicates meaning, lined up in a line	Word Row
98. Us, not many	We few
99. A side street for shouting	Yell alley
100. Scream, "OR", side street	Yell or alley

Palindromes Sentences

Okay…here's what you get to do, (or make someone else do!) with these sentences that are palindromes. We will give the ***first half*** of the sentence. How do you get last half? Read the first half backwards! Remember…these are palindromes! We will mark the mid-point of the sentence with an underline. That underlined letter will not be repeated again, though it might be the end of a word, the beginning of a word, or a letter inside a word. Sometimes we will include a few letters past the underlined word just to complete a word or make it easier to read etc. Sometimes the underlined mid-point is a space past the last letter. That means, just like before, it is time to turn around. Though, when you turn around now, you will be using that previous letter again.

For example: [NO, IT IS OP_]

The last part of the sentence is: *POSITION* Added to the OP, it becomes OP*POSITION.*
So, the whole sentence is: NO, IT IS OPPOSITION.

Remember that the punctuation marks are usually not used again when the sentence hits the mid point and starts it's palindromic ending. And, hey….it is pretty amazing that these sentences read the same both ways, so … don't expect them to make a whole lot of sense or use perfect grammar! Have fun!

1.	A berry tastes O, s	A berry tastes O, so "set", satyr – Reba.
2.	A buck cabs	A buck cabs back, Cuba.
3.	A car, a man,	A car, a man, a maraca!
4.	A Dan, a clan, a c	A Dan, a clan, a canal – Canada!
5.	A Dan acts Niagara w	A Dan acts Niagara war against Canada.
6.	A Danish custard –	A Danish custard – drat, such sin, Ada.
7.	A dim lap and I di	A dim lap and I did napalm, Ida.
8.	A dim or fond?	A dim or frond? No – from Ida.
9.	A dog! A panic	A dog! A panic in a pagoda.
10.	A dog, a pant, a panic	A dog, a pant, a panic in a Patna pagoda.
11.	A Goth saw Ad	A Goth saw Ada was toga.
12.	A man, a plan, a c	A man, a plan, a canal, Panama.
13.	A man, a plan, a canoe	A man, a plan, a canoe on a canal – Panama.
14.	A man, a plan, a cam, a yak,	A man, a plan, a cam, a yak, a yam, a canal, - Panama!
15.	A man, a pain, a m	A man, a pain, a mania – Panama.
16.	A maj, a plan, a c	A maj, a plan, a canal, pajama.
17.	A mot_ ?	A motto, Ma?
18.	A new order began; a more	A new order began; a more Roman age bred Rowena.
19.	A nut for a j ?	A nut for a jar of tuna?
20.	A poem, a carol, ?	A poem, a carol, or cameo, Pa?
21.	A pre-war dres_	A pre-war dresser drawer, Pa!
22.	A rash self-warning: I s	A rash self-warning: I sign in raw flesh, Sara!
23.	A rat stole	A rat stole lots, Tara!
24.	A Santa_	A Santa at NASA.
25.	A Santa, deif	A Santa, deified at NASA.
26.	A Santa dog lived as	A Santa dog lived as a devil god at NASA.
27.	A Santa lived as	A Santa lived as a devil at NASA.
28.	A Santa lives	A Santa lives evil at NASA.
29.	A Santa taps	A Santa taps Pat at NASA.
30.	A Santa snaps	A Santa snaps pans at NASA.
31.	A Santa snips	A Santa snips pins at NASA.
32.	A Santa spat _	A Santa spat taps at NASA.
33.	A Santa pets rats, as Pat _	A Santa pets rats, as Pat taps a star-step at NASA.
34.	A Santa spits	A Santa spits tips at NASA.
35.	A Santa spit tabo_	A Santa spit taboo bat tips at NASA.
36.	A Santa's rats top Nat, as _	A Santa's rats top Nat, as Satan pots tars at NASA.
37.	A Santa stops	A Santa stops pots at NASA.

No.	Prompt	Palindrome
38.	A Santa spots_	A Santa spots tops at NASA.
39.	A tip: Save	A tip: Save Eva's pita.
40.	A Toyota! Race fast –	A Toyota! Race fast – safe car. A Toyota.
41.	A Toyota's a Toyota.	A Toyota's a Toyota.
42.	Age? Irony,	Age? Irony, Noriega.
43.	Ah, Satan se_	Ah, Satan sees Natasha.
44.	Aid nine m	Aid nine men – India.
45.	Al lets Della c	Al lets Della call Ed…Stella.
46.	Allen's boss knocks Ed's	Allen's boss knocks Ed's desk –conks – sobs, "Nella!"
47.	Allen's simple y	Allen's simple yelp: "Miss Nella!"
48.	Are we not drawn onward, we f ?	Are we not drawn onward, we few, drawn onward to new era?
49.	Am I drawn i_ ?	Am I drawn inward, Ima?
50.	Am I loc	Am I loco, Lima?
51.	"Am I mad, eh?" Gisel_ ?	"Am I mad, eh?" Giselle sighed, "Am I, Ma?"
52.	Amen! I cal_	Amen! I call a cinema.
53.	An aid nix ?	An aid nix Indiana?
54.	An oz., I rap. –	An oz., I rap. – Arizona.
55.	Anita got a	Anita got a toga, Tina.
56.	Ana, nab a	Ana, nab a banana.
57.	Anna, did Otto Pe_ ?	Anna, did Otto Peep? Otto, did Anna?
58.	And E.T. saw _	And E.T. saw waste DNA.
59.	Anne, I snip a m	Anne, I snip a map in Sienna.
60.	Anne, I vote no_	Anne, I vote no one to Vienna!
61.	Anne, I vote more cars	Anne, I vote more cars race Rome to Vienna.
62.	As I was, I saw Isa.	As I was, I saw Isa.
63.	At sap time, r	At sap time, remit pasta.
64.	Avid Allen spots a Toy	Avid Allen spots a Toyota, stops Nell (a diva).
65.	Avon se_	Avon sees nova.
66.	A tin mug for a j ?	A tin mug for a jar of gum, Nita?
67.	Able was I ere	Able was I ere I saw Elba.
68.	Bald elf…	Bald elf….fled lab
69.	Baltimore pa	Baltimore paper: Omit Lab.
70.	Ban campus motto: "B	Ban campus motto: "Bottoms up, McNab."
71.	Barge in. Relate mere war of 19_	Barge in. Relate mere war of 1991 for a were-metal, Ernie Grab.
72.	Barge, Dave.	Barge, Dave. Evade grab!
73.	Bar an	Bar an Arab.
74.	Bar: Canoe	Bar: Canoe on a crab.
75.	"Bed stress!" a	"Bed stress!" asserts Deb.
76.	Be stil_	Be still – it's Eb!
77.	Bell: a clang is a	Bell: a clang is a signal. Call Eb.
78.	Beware…	Beware…era web!
79.	Bob, lev	Bob, level Bob.

80.	Bombard a	Bombard a drab mob.
81.	Boredom a l ?	Boredom a la mode, Rob?
82.	Borrow ?	Borrow or rob?
83.	Bosnia – p	Bosnia – pain – sob.
84.	Bosnia gasp	Bosnia gasps again – sob.
85.	Boston di	Boston did not sob.
86.	Burst! Rap _	Burst! Rap parts rub.
87.	Bush saw Sunu	Bush saw Sununu swash sub.
88.	But, a nite! Got _	But, a nite! Got to get in a tub!
89.	But, sad Eva s	But, sad Eva saved a stub.
90.	Cain, a m ?	Cain, a maniac?
91.	Cain, am I ?	Cain, am I maniac?
92.	Camelot s	Camelot stole mac.
93.	Camel in_	Camel in Nile, Mac.
94.	Can I at_ ?	Can I attain a "C"?
95.	Cleveland _ DNA:	Cleveland DNA: Level C
96.	Cigar? Toss it in a c	Cigar? Toss it in a can. It is so tragic.
97.	Cinci packs K.C.	Cinci packs K.C. a picnic.
98.	Cis, Sal called "Pul_	Cis, Sal called "Pull-up Dell" a classic!
99.	Cis, umpires (I arm	Cis, umpires (I arm raise) rip music!
100.	Code H.T –	Code H.T – the doc!
101.	Damon, a	Damon, a nomad.
102.	Deeds? I'm an Iris_	Deeds? I'm an Iris sir, in a misdeed!
103.	Dee saw_	Dee saw a seed.
104.	Del saw	Del saw a sled.
105.	Delia saw I	Delia saw I was ailed.
106.	Delia sailed. Eva w	Delia sailed. Eva waved. Elias ailed.
107.	Dennis and E	Dennis and Edna sinned.
108.	Dennis	Dennis sinned.
109.	Dennis, Nell, Edna, _	Dennis, Nell, Edna, and Ellen sinned.
110.	Dennis, Nell, Edna, Leon, _	Dennis, Nell, Edna, Leon, Noel, and Ellen sinned.
111.	Desserts, I	Desserts, I stressed!
112.	Dog, as a devil deif	Dog, as a devil deified, lived as a god.
113.	Did dean aid _	Did Dean aid Diana? Ed did.
114.	Did I do, o' God, did I, as I ?	Did I do, o' God, did I, as I said I'd do? Good, I did!
115.	Did I draw Della to_ ?	Did I draw Della too tall, Edward? I did?
116.	Did Hannah say ?	Did Hannah say as Hannah did?
117.	Did I say Amy ?	Did I say Amy may, as I did?
118.	Did Mom po	Did Mom pop? Mom did.
119.	Di, a m ?	Di, a maid!
120.	Doc, note…I dissent a f	Doc, note…I dissent a fatness. I diet on cod.
121.	Doc, note… I dissent. A fast never p	Doc, note, I dissent. A fast never prevents a fatness. I diet on cod.

122.	Do geese ?	Do geese see God?
123.	Do good deeds live on?	Do good deeds live on? No, evil deeds do o' God.
124.	Dot saw I	Dot saw I was Tod.
125.	"Do nine men interp	"Do nine men interrupt?" "Nine men," I nod.
126.	Drab as a fool, aloof	Drab as a fool, aloof as a bard.
127.	Draw, o' c	Draw, o' coward.
128.	Draw pupil's	Draw pupil's lip upward.
129.	Draw putrid _	Draw putrid dirt upward.
130.	Dumb mobs,	Dumb mobs, bomb mud.
131.	E. Borgnine drags Da	E. Borgnine drags Dad's gardening robe.
132.	Ed is on_	Ed is on no side.
133.	Ed aced a	Ed aced a decade.
134.	Ed, I h	Ed, I hide.
135.	Ed, I saw Harpo Marx	Ed, I saw Harpo Marx ram Oprah W. aside.
136.	Ed, I spotted a clam in an	Ed, I spotted a clam in an animal cadet topside.
137.	Ed is a trader; cast	Ed is a trader; cast sacred art aside.
138.	Edit pe	Edit peptide!
139.	Ed: a general,	Ed: a general, a renegade.
140.	"Eda, Emil's red roses suck!" Cal B	"Eda, Emil's red roses suck!" Cal Black cusses, orders tram.
141.	Egad, an	Egad, an adage.
142.	Egad, a base life d	Egad, a base life defiles a bad age.
143.	Egad, a base tone d	Egad, a base tone denotes a bad age.
144.	Egad! No b	Egad! No bondage!
145.	Eh, Canada h ?	Eh, Canada had an ache?
146.	Elf farm	Elf farm raffle....
147.	Emil, a sleepy ba	Emil, a sleepy baby peels a lime.
148.	Emil saw	Emil saw a slime!
149.	Emily (as Bob),	Emily (as Bob), say "LIME".
150.	Emily's sa	Emily's sassy lime.
151.	Emit a mile...	Emit a mile...Lima time.
152.	Emit no to	Emit no tot on time.
153.	Emote no t	Emote no tone to me!
154.	Enid and e	Enid and Edna dine.
155.	Enola Devil _	Enola Devil lived alone.
156.	Epic Erma has	Epic Erma has a ham recipe.
157.	Erin is	Erin is in ire.
158.	Eros saw Avi	Eros saw Aviva was sore.
159.	Eros saw I	Eros saw I was sore.
160.	Eros? Sidney, my	Eros? Sidney, my end is sore!
161.	Erupt on maiden_Ned,	Erupt on maiden Ned, I am not pure.
162.	E.T. is op_	E.T. is opposite.
163.	Euston saw I	Euston saw I was not Sue.
164.	Eva, can I stab _	Eva, can I stab bats in a cave?

165. Eva can ignite virtuosos,	Eva can ignite virtuosos, out riveting in a cave.
166. Evade m	Evade me, Dave.
167. Eve, maiden name. Both sad in Eden?	Eve, maiden name. Both sad in Eden? I dash to be manned. I am Eve.
168. Eve damned	Eve damned Eden. Mad Eve.
169. Evil in a c	Evil in a can, I live.
170. Evil is a name of a	Evil is a name of a foeman, as I live.
171. Evita Gentle, f	Evita Gentle, felt negative.
172. Feeble Tom's	Feeble Tom's motel beef.
173. Flee to me, r	Flee to me, remote elf.
174. Flesh! (Saw I) Mimi	Flesh! (Saw I) Mimi wash self.
175. Flesh – saw Mom	Flesh – saw Mom wash self!
176. Flo, gin is	Flo, gin is sin. I golf.
177. Flower Ewoks K.O.	Flower Ewoks K.O. werewolf.
178. Food, a lass,	Food, a lass, salad – oof!
179. Freshen omelet_te….?	Freshen omelette….lemon, eh, serf?
180. Gabe's on a	Gabe's on a nosebag.
181. Gagne, I made	Gagne, I made Damien gag.
182. Gary knits a	Gary knits a stinky rag.
183. Gateman, a foe	Gateman, a foe of a nametag.
184. Gateman sees name. Gar	Gateman sees name. Garage-men sees name tag.
185. Gelatin, k	Gelatin, knit a leg!
186. Gert, I saw Ron avoid a r	Gert, I saw Ron avoid a radio-van. Or, was it Reg?
187. Gnat sums	Gnat sums mustang.
188. Go deliver a d	Go deliver a dare: vile dog!
189. Go do	Go do, dog.
190. Go help Mister B	Go help Mister Bret, simple hog.
191. Go home, d	Go home, demo hog.
192. God and a ….	God and a DNA dog….
193. God, Edam _	God, Edam made a dog!
194. God lived on _	God lived on no devil dog.
195. God saw I	God saw I was dog.
196. God, a saw _	God, a saw was a dog.
197. God, a wasp	God, a wasp saw a dog!
198. Gods send a m	God sends a madness: DOG!
199. Golf? No sir, pref	Golf? No sir, prefer prison flog.
200. Gong! Get set, Ed, to n	Gong! Get set, Ed, to not detest egg-nog.
201. Go hang a salami. _	Go hang a salami. I'm a lasagna hog.
202. H: (sarcastic…) "	H: (sarcastic…) "It's a crash!"
203. Ha! One wee_	Ha! One wee ewe, Noah!
204. Harass self	Harass selfless Sarah!
205. Harass sensuousness,	Harass sensuousness, Sarah.
206. He laid on_	He laid on no dial, eh?

No.	Clue	Answer
207.	He lived as ?	He lived as a devil, eh?
208.	He di ?	He did, eh?
209.	He maps _ ?	He maps spam, eh?
210.	He or I act a ?	He or I act at Cairo, eh?
211.	He repaid a no-name Pacif ?	He repaid a no-name Pacific Ape-man on a diaper, eh?
212.	He snubs Bo ?	He snubs Bob's buns, eh?
213.	He stops_ ?	He stops spots, eh?
214.	He traded a J ?	He traded a jaded art, eh?
215.	He traded a J ?	He traded a jade dart, eh?
216.	He won a Toy ?	He won a Toyota now, eh?
217.	He won s_ ?	He won snow, eh?
218.	I am	I am A.I.
219.	I did,_ ?	I did, did I?
220.	I did see ref ?	I did see referees, did I?
221.	I did roll… ?	I did roll…or did I?
222.	I have a motel car. I'm a stif_	I have a motel car. I'm a stiff. It's a miracle! To Ma, (Eva)…"Hi!"
223.	I led a	I led a deli.
224.	I'll let Anita N	I'll let Anita Natina Tell Li.
225.	I, man, am regal:	I, man, am regal: a German am I.
226.	I madam, I made radio! S ?	I madam, I made radio! So I dared! Am I mad? Am I?
227.	I moan, "Live on, 'O	I moan, "Live on, 'O evil Naomi!"
228.	If I had	If I had a hi-fi....
229.	I made us sit_	I made us sit tissued, Ami.
230.	I, Mary, tramp ?	I, Mary, tramp martyr. Am I?
231.	I'm a lasagna. H	I'm a lasagna. Hang a salami!
232.	"I'm a lasagna!" S	"I'm a lasagna!" Sang a salami.
233.	I'm a never-ev ?	I'm a never-ever even. Am I?
234.	I'm a bony ?	I'm a bony nob, am I?
235.	I made tale!	I made tale! Elated am I.
236.	I may or I may not._	I may or I may not. Tony, am I Roy? Am I?
237.	I pref	I prefer pi.
238.	I roamed under it as	I roamed under it as a tired nude, Maori.
239.	I saw thee, Mad	I saw thee, Madame, eh? 'Twas I.
240.	I saw, tis a tie, Carter._	I saw, tis a tie, Carter. Retrace it as it was I.
241.	I tip away	I tip away a wapiti.
242.	Is Don Adams	Is Don Adams mad?" (a nod.) "Si!
243.	Is it I?_	Is it I? It is I!
244.	Is Pep a ?	Is Pep a Pepsi?
245.	I've let a name_	I've let a name emanate: Levi.
246.	I was sad – no H	I was sad – no Hondas saw I.
247.	I won, Karen. An	I won, Karen. An era know I.
248.	Kay, a red nude, pe_	Kay, a red nude, peeped under a yak.

249.	Kayak salad –	Kayak salad – Alaska yak.
250.	K.C. is Llama	K.C. is Llama mall sick.
251.	Key lime,_	Key lime, Emily? Ek!
252.	Knob red? No w	Knob red? No wonder! Bonk!
253.	"Kodak	"Kodak ad O.K.!"
254.	L.A. ocelots_	L.A. ocelots stole coal.
255.	L.A. snow-job:	L.A. snow-job: O.J. won, Sal.
256.	La renegade l	La renegade led a general.
257.	Lace me, Portia! W	Lace me, Portia! Wait, rope me, Cal!
258.	Laminate p	Laminate pet animal.
259.	Last egg	Last egg gets Al.
260.	Lager, sir,	Lager, sir, is regal.
261.	Laminated E.T…	Laminated E.T…animal.
262.	Lana, can I sit on ?	Lana, can I sit on Otis in a canal?
263.	Laptops_	Laptops spot pal.
264.	Late Bill is ill, I bet, Al.	Late Bill is ill, I bet, Al.
265.	Lay a wallaby ba	Lay a wallaby baby ball away, Al.
266.	Lee had	Lee had a heel.
267.	Lem saw I	Lem saw I was Mel.
268.	Leno located a c	Leno located a cadet: a colonel!
269.	Leon sees Noel.	Leon sees Noel.
270.	Let sap erupt,	Let sap erupt, pure pastel!
271.	Lew, Otto has	Lew, Otto has a hot towel.
272.	Lewd did I live &	Lewd did I live & evil I did dwel (l)
273.	Liar spots	Liar spots top's rail.
274.	Lisa Bonet a	Lisa Bonet ate no basil.
275.	Lion, 'O Puma, I	Lion, 'O Puma, I am upon oil.
276.	Lived as	Lived as a devil.
277.	Live not,	Live not, on evil.
278.	Live not on evil, mad	Live not on evil, madam, live not on evil.
279.	Live on evasions?	Live on evasions? No! I save no evil.
280.	Lived on decaf. _	Lived on decaf. Faced no devil.
281.	Loaded NET	Loaded NET ended AOL.
282.	Look, sire, pa	Look, sire, paper is kool!
283.	Madam, in Eden,	Madam, in Eden, I'm Adam.
284.	Mad Amadeus_	Mad Amadeus sued a madman.
285.	Mad dastard, a s	Mad dastard, a sad rat – Saddam.
286.	Ma handed	Ma handed Edna ham.
287.	Ma has	Ma has a ham.
288.	Ma is a nun,	Ma is a nun, as I am.
289.	Ma is as self	Ma is as selfless as I am.
290.	Ma! I say! Lee's a	Ma! I say! Lee's as eely as I am!
291.	Mac snubs Bo	Mac snubs Bob's bun scam.
292.	Mac spots tip at	Mac spots tip at a pit-stop scam.
293.	Mad, as it is,	Mad, as it is, it is, Adam.

294. Mad at ?	Mad at Adam?
295. Madam, I am ill. I've nine m	Madam, I am ill. I've nine men in evil Lima. I'm Adam.
296. Madam, I do get a m	Madam, I do get a mate. God, I'm Adam.
297. Madam, I help Martin.	Madam, I help Martin. I trample him ---Adam.
298. Madam, I	Madam, I'm Adam.
299. Man, Oprah's _	Man, Oprah's sharp on A.M.
300. Marg, I pen an	Marg, I pen an epigram.
301. Marge lets Norah se_	Marge lets Norah see Sharon's telegram.
302. Marge, let's send a m	Marge, let's send a madness telegram!
303. Marge, let's send a s	Marge, let's send a sadness telegram.
304. Marty, Bo got Han_	Marty, Bo got Hannah to go by tram.
305. Mary's words (in a pajama), "	Mary's words (in a pajama), "Japan is Drowsy Ram."
306. Ma's story	Ma's story rots Sam.
307. May a banan ?	May a banana nab a yam?
308. May a pal _	May a pal lap a yam.
309. May a moody ba ?	May a moody baby doom a yam?
310. Mike, can El_ ?	Mike, can Ellen ace Kim?
311. Mike Modano's	Mike Modano's on a dome.
312. Mix a m	Mix a maxim.
313. Mom's dad &	Mom's dad & Dad's mom.
314. Moor let Omani _	Moor let Omani in a motel room.
315. Mr. Owl ate my	Mr. Owl ate my metal worm!
316. Murder, for a j	Murder, for a jar of red rum.
317. Must sell at_	Must sell at tallest sum.
318. "My gym tasks are too lonely?" a Jay	"My gym tasks are too lonely?" a Jay Leno looter ask at my gym.
319. Nail a tin	Nail a tin Italian.
320. Nail a tired rotini _	Nail a tired rotini in it, order Italian.
321. Nail Li	Nail Lillian!
322. Nam, order a	Nam, order a red Roman!
323. Nam? Raw_	Nam? Raw war, man.
324. Nam was a_	Nam was a saw man.
325. Name is Orton,_	Name is Orton, not Rosie, man!
326. Name now	Name now one man.
327. Name no	Name none, man.
328. Name no _	Name no one, man.
329. Named under a ban -	Named under a ban - a bared nude man.
330. Name tabo_....	Name taboo....Bateman.
331. Naomi, di ?	Naomi, did I moan?
332. "Naomi," _	"Naomi," I moan.
333. Nate bit a	Nate bit a Tibetan.
334. Ned, I am	Ned, I am a maiden.
335. Ned, go ga	Ned, go gag Ogden.

336.	Nedra Olson is	Nedra Olson is in Oslo, Arden.
337.	Neil a. Se_	Neil a. Sees alien.
338.	Neil, an	Neil, an alien.
339.	Net forev	Net forever…often.
340.	Net for even signi	Net for even signing is never often.
341.	Networks (al_l)	Networks (all) ask row ten.
342.	Never od_	Never odd or even.
343.	Nina Ric_ci	Nina Ricci ran in.
344.	Nino's cut di	Nino's cut did Tucson in!
345.	No cab. No tuna	No cab. No tuna nut on bacon.
346.	No devil_	No devil lived on.
347.	No devils met if	No devils met if items lived on.
348.	No gnu have…never after fret far.	No gnu have…never after fret far. Even Eva hung on.
349.	Niagara, o' r	Niagara, o' roar again!
350.	No garden. O	No garden. One dragon.
351.	No, it can	No, it can action.
352.	Now do I repay -	Now do I repay - a period won.
353.	No lemon,_	No lemon, no melon.
354.	No lemons,	No lemons, no melon.
355.	No evils	No evils live on.
356.	No evil I did	No evil I did. I live on.
357.	No iron on	No iron on Orion.
358.	No misses order	No misses ordered roses, Simon.
359.	No, is iced dab a ?	No, is iced dab a bad decision?
360.	No, it is op_	No, it is opposition.
361.	No, it is open on	No, it is open on one position.
362.	No, Mel Gibson is a c	No, Mel Gibson is a casino's big lemon.
363.	No, miss. It	No, miss. It is Simon.
364.	No mists or f	No mists or frost, Simon.
365.	No pet so tragic as a	No pet so tragic as a cigar to step on.
366.	No, she stops __ ?	No, she stops spots, eh son?
367.	No side, no in u	No side, no in union, Edison.
368.	No sign in ev	No sign in evening is on.
369.	No slang is a	No slang is a signal, son.
370.	No Stetson hats. Operas	No Stetson hats. Operas are post. Ah…no Stetson.
371.	No, tie	No, tie it on.
372.	No yarn I ?	No yarn in rayon?
373.	Noel, let's eg_	Noel, let's egg Estelle on.
374.	Nora, a raft! Is	Nora, a raft! Is it far, Aaron?
375.	Norm, I'm	Norm, I'm Ron.
376.	Norma, I	Norma, I am Ron.
377.	Norma is as self	Norma is as selfless as I am, Ron.
378.	Not a bana	Not a banana baton!

379.	Not New York.	Not New York. Roy went on.
380.	Not lads simple h	Not lads simple help, Miss Dalton.
381.	Now I see, ref	Now I see, referees, I won!
382.	Now, Ned, I am a maiden nun.	Now, Ned, I am a maiden nun. Ned, I am a maiden won.
383.	Now, sir, a w	Now, sir, a war is won.
384.	Now, son, E	Now, son, Enos won.
385.	Now's evil for evil? Ah, a	Now's evil for evil? Ah, a liver of lives won!
386.	"Nurses run!" says sick	"Nurses run!" says sick Cissy as nurses run.
387.	Oh! Cameras	Oh! Cameras are macho.
388.	"Ol' Israel cunning" is a	"Ol' Israel cunning" is a sign in a nuclear silo.
389.	O' stone me!	O' stone me! Not so!
390.	O…Lisa se_	O…Lisa sees a silo.
391.	Oh, no! D	Oh, no! Don ho!
392.	Oh, who was it	Oh, who was it I saw? Oh, who?
393.	O.J. nabs Bo	O.J. nabs Bob's banjo.
394.	Older castle f	Older castle felt sacred, lo!
395.	One resort,	One resort, Rose…Reno!
396.	On Elba…Kramer saw Tim.	On Elba…Kramer saw Tim. It was remarkable, no?
397.	On a clover, if alive, erupts a v	On a clover, if alive, erupts a vast pure evil – a fire volcano!
398.	One gnome let a lime rot;	One gnome let a lime rot; or Emil ate lemon, Geno.
399.	Oozy rat in a s	Oozy rat in a sanitary zoo.
400.	O, stone, b	O, stone, be not so.
401.	Otto made N	Otto made Ned a motto.
402.	Otto saw pup -	Otto saw pup - pup was Otto.
403.	Pa stole macadamia nut_	Pa stole macadamia nut tuna. I'm Ada…Camelot sap.
404.	Pa, tall Edna _	Pa, tall Edna and Ella tap.
405.	Pa's a	Pa's a sap
406.	Paget saw an Irish to_	Paget saw an Irish tooth, Sir, in a waste gap.
407.	Pal sat in A	Pal sat in Anita's lap.
408.	Panic in a title? "To H	Panic in a title? "To Hotel Titanic I Nap!"
409.	Par that U	Par that Utah trap!
410.	Pat and e	Pat and Edna tap.
411.	Peel Sam	Peel Sam asleep.
412.	Pet's _	Pet's step.
413.	Pet's never	Pet's never even step.
414.	Pepsi _	Pepsi is pep!
415.	Play Latin o	Play Latin on Italy Alp.
416.	Poor Dan is	Poor Dan is in a droop.
417.	Poor Das i	Poor Das is a droop.
418.	Pot? No! I saw DNA_	Pot? No! I saw DNA and was I on top!

No.	Prompt	Palindrome
419.	P.U. – Erase L.A. shoe king,	P.U. – Erase L.A. shoe king, Nike. Oh…sales are up!?!
420.	Pull a bat. I h	Pull a bat. I hit a ball up.
421.	Pull up if	Pull up if I pull up.
422.	Pull up, Bo	Pull up, Bob, pull up!
423.	Pull up, Eva! We're h	Pull up, Eva! We're here! Wave. Pull up!
424.	Pupils! I say	Pupils! I say as I slip up.
425.	Put Eliot's	Put Eliot's toilet up.
426.	Put it	Put it up.
427.	Rail at	Rail at a liar.
428.	Rats drown i	Rats drown in WordStar.
429.	Rat, I say, be off fats! St. Lover _	Rat, I say, be off fats! St. Lover revolts. Staff foe? By a sitar.
430.	Rats live on _	Rats live on no evil star.
431.	Raw foe, Russia,	Raw foe, Russia, is sure of war.
432.	Raw Nixon:	Raw Nixon: Ox in War
433.	Red lost case, Ma. Jes_se	Red lost case, Ma. Jesse James acts older.
434.	Red? No. Who is it?_Tis I.	No. Who is it? Tis I. Oh wonder!
435.	Red roots	Red roots to order
436.	Redraw a	Redraw a warder.
437.	Red rum di	Red rum did murder.
438.	Red rum , sir,	Red rum , sir, is murder.
439.	Re-flog a	Re-flog a golfer.
440.	Remarkable was I, er	Remarkable was I, ere I saw Elba Kramer.
441.	Repel evil as	Repel evil as a live leper.
442.	Reviled did I live _:_	Reviled did I live : evil I did deliver.
443.	Revered now I live on. O' did	Revered now I live on. O' did I do no evil, I wonder, ever?
444.	Rise to v	Rise to vote, sir.
445.	Rob a loneliness?	Rob a loneliness? Senile, no labor.
446.	Rot can rob a	Rot can rob a born actor.
447.	Roy, am I	Roy, am I mayor?
448.	Sad I'm _	Sad I'm Midas.
449.	Sages u	Sages use gas.
450.	Salt an	Salt an atlas.
451.	Same nice	Same nice cinemas.
452.	Satan, oscillate my m	Satan, oscillate my metallic sonatas.
453.	Sela Ward di	Sela Ward did draw ales.
454.	Saw tide rose?	Saw tide rose? So red it was.
455.	Selma, I	Selma, I am Les.
456.	Seniles revert at	Seniles revert at reverse lines.
457.	Sir I'm	Sir, I'm iris.
458.	Sh! Tom se_	Sh! Tom sees moths.
459.	Sis, ask Costner to N	Sis, ask Costner to NOT rent socks "as is"!
460.	Sit on a pota	Sit on a potato pan, Otis!

No.	Clue	Answer
461.	Six ate nin	Six ate nine taxis.
462.	Six attack	Six attack cat taxis.
463.	Slap my g	Slap my gym pals.
464.	Sleep on_	Sleep on no peels.
465.	So, Ida..	So, Ida….Adios!
466.	Snug all L.A.	Snug all L.A. guns!
467.	So, camera sol	So, camera solos are Mac OS?
468.	So I dare to Ned, "__	So I dare to Ned, "Denote Radios!"
469.	So, Mama, I won _	So, Mama, I won now. I am Amos.
470.	"Some deer fees?" I say	"Some deer fees?" I say as I see free demos.
471.	Some men interpret	Some men interpret nine memos.
472.	Son, I sack	Son, I sack casinos!
473.	Sonar posses_	Sonar possesses sopranos.
474.	Spay dogs, a	Spay dogs, as God yaps.
475.	Star? Come Donna Melba, I'm an	Star? Come Donna Melba, I'm an amiable man. No Democrats!
476.	Star Wars awe	Star Wars awe was raw rats.
477.	Star comedy b	Star comedy by democrats.
478.	Star-red rum and E	Star-red rum and Edna murder rats.
479.	Stella won _	Stella won no wallets.
480.	Step on _	Step on no pets.
481.	Story a waste: gram _	Story a waste: grammar gets away, rots.
482.	Straw? No. Too stupid a f	Straw? No. Too stupid a fad. I put soot on warts.
483.	Stunts is, niece	Stunts is, niece insists, nuts!
484.	Sub's knob _	Sub's knob bonks bus.
485.	Sue, yes, God's	Sue, yes, God's dogs eye us.
486.	Sums are not set as	Sums are not set as a test on Erasmus.
487.	Sue, sue us._	Sue, sue us. Sue, uses us!
488.	Sununu's tonsil	Sununu's tonsil is not Sununu's.
489.	Swen, on gnus, __	Swen, on gnus, sung no news.
490.	Tarzan raised a_	Tarzan raised a Desi Arnaz rat.
491.	Ted? A c ?	Ted? A cadet?
492.	Tel Aviv erases	Tel Aviv erases a revival: E.T.
493.	Tell a b	Tell a ballet.
494.	Tell Abe to v	Tell Abe to vote ballet
495.	Tell a body –	Tell a body – do ballet!
496.	Ten animals I_	Ten animals I slam in a net.
497.	Ten animals di	Ten animals did slam in a net.
498.	Tennis: Tip s	Tennis: Tip spits in net.
499.	Tie us, sir, or	Tie us, sir, or issue it.
500.	Tim, aim it. _	Tim, aim it. Tim, I am it.
501.	Tim Arch, to be sure , p	Tim Arch, to be sure , peruse both…cram it!
502.	Timid as Ma, I	Timid as Ma, I am sad I'm it.
503.	Tin mad Ron s	Tin mad Ron snore, damn it!

504.	Tina, Emil...	Tina, Emil...I mean it!
505.	Title fit…I	Title fit…I felt it!
506.	Todd erases	Todd erases a red dot.
507.	Toni Tenille f	Toni Tenille fell in net. I, not.
508.	Tonya m	Tonya may not!
509.	Too bad, I h	Too bad, I hid a boot.
510.	Too hot _	Too hot to hoot.
511.	Toot, ot_	Toot, Otto, toot!
512.	Trash Tim S	Trash Tim Smith's art.
513.	Trays simple h	Trays simple help, missy art!
514.	Tug at	Tug at a gut.
515.	Tut tut. Star comedy b	Tut tut. Star comedy by democrats. Tut tut.
516.	Un-gate me, Vic,	Un-gate me, Vic, I've met a gnu.
517.	Un-glad, I tar	Un-glad, I tar a tidal gnu.
518.	Vanna w	Vanna wanna a "V"?
519.	Vote to not slip up. Ref	Vote to not slip up. Refer pupils to note TOV.
520.	Wanna t	Wanna tan? Naw.
521.	War-distend	War-distended nets I draw.
522.	Warsaw _	Warsaw, was raw.
523.	Wary alpine z	Wary alpine zen – I play raw!
524.	Was it a b ?	Was it a bat I saw?
525.	Was it a bar o ?	Was it a bar or a bat I saw?
526.	Was it a car o ?	Was it a car or a cat I saw?
527.	Was it a c ?	Was it a cat I saw?
528.	Was it a r ?	Was it a rat I saw?
529.	Was it Eliot's ?	Was it Eliot's toilet I saw?
530.	Was it felt? I had	Was it felt? I had a hit left, I saw.
531.	We freed venison._	We freed venison. No sin, even if deer few.
532.	We few erase cares. Al,_ ?	We few erase cares. Al, laser aces, are we few?
533.	We panic	We panic in a pew.
534.	We passed Odessa…pew!	We passed Odessa…pew!
535.	We placed a	We placed a decal pew.
536.	We'll let da	We'll let dad tell Lew.
537.	Wo, Nemo, toss a lasso	I, man, am regal: a German am I.
538.	Wonder if Sununu's ?	Wonder if Sununu's fired now?
539.	Wonton?_	Wonton? Not now.
540.	Won't lovers ?	Won't lovers revolt now?
541.	Ya, Rob Marc, I mimic	Ya, Rob Marc, I mimic I mimic Rambo Ray.
542.	Ya! (A sleep apnoea.)_	Ya! (A sleep apnoea.) A eon, Pa peels away.
543.	Ya, Dot traded	Ya, Dot traded art today.
544.	Yawn a more	Yawn a more Roman way.
545.	Yawn…Madonna fan?	Yawn…Madonna fan? No damn way!
546.	Yen: Omega-	Yen: Omega-age money.
547.	Yer Duane ?	Yer Duane 'n Audrey?

548. Yo! Bana	Yo! Banana boy!
549. Yo, Bob, mug a	Yo, Bob, mug a gumbo boy.
550. Yo! Boz	Yo! Bozo boy!
551. Yo! Bottom's up	Yo! Bottom's up - us motto boy!
552. Yo, bad anaconda h	Yo, bad anaconda had no Canada boy.
553. You bat one in, resign in ev ?	You bat one in, resign in evening. Is Ernie not a buoy?
554. Young Ada h	Young Ada had a gnu. Oy!
555. Zeus se_	Zeus sees Suez.
556. Zeus, was deif	Zeus, was deified, saw Suez.
557. Zeus" "Nile macaroni, ma is a nitrate-	Zeus" "Nile macaroni, ma is a nitrate-tart, in Asia Minor, a camel in Suez!"

Palindromes Sentences

Word by Word

Here are some sentences that read the same forward as back, but NOT by the letter…by the WORD! Nothing to figure out - we just wanted to include them for your enjoyment!

King, are you glad you are king?
Fall leaves after leaves fall.
Says Mom, "What do you do?" – You do what Mom says.
You know, I did little for you, for little did I know you.
First Ladies rule the State, and state the rule: "ladies first."
Please me by standing by me please.
Blessed are they that believe that they are blessed.
Escher, drawing hands, drew hands drawing Escher.
You can cage a swallow, can't you, but you can't swallow a cage, can you?
Did I say you never say "never say never"? You say I did.
What? So he is hanged, is he? So what?

Other Products from **Missing Piece Press** & **FUNaddicts Games:**

Missing Piece Press and ***FUNaddicts Games*** are publishers of educational books and games. Our products have won numerous awards and are being used and enjoyed in thousands of homes & schools.

Parents' Choice Award
Museum Tour Product of the Year

Have you been looking for something intriguing to start off your meetings? Have you been looking for something that gets people thinking while having fun? Do your students want a puzzle or riddle to figure out? Does your family need something else to think about in the car? Here it is! This comprehensive book has enough riddles, puzzles, and other challenges to keep those minds spinning for months. Our BEST seller!

$16.95

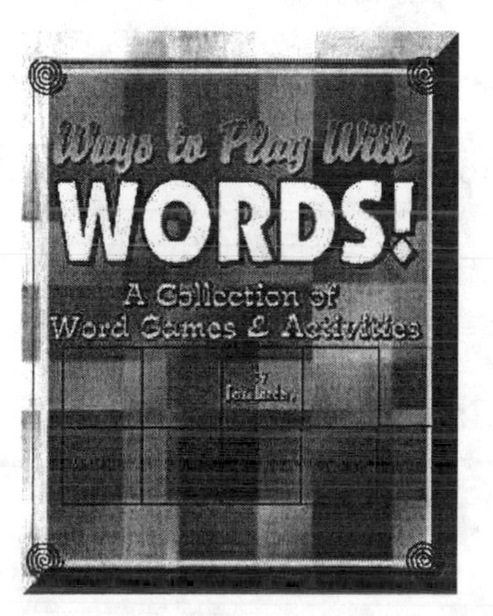

Ways to Play with WORDS!

Pages and pages of intriguing little word activities! This 256-page book has something for everyone. Perfect for the classroom. Great for rainy days at home. And be sure to take it along on the family camping trip!

$15.95

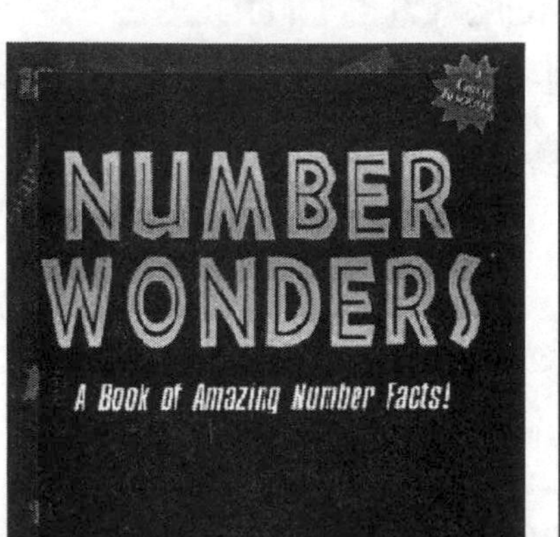

Number Wonders

Do you enjoy learning fun and interesting facts? This collection of number facts will absolutely astound you! Categorized into subjects such as Space, Animals, Human Body, etc., this book has hours of mind boggling facts--all of which include numbers. Have fun playing a "higher/lower" game, or just watch the mouths drop as you share an amazing fact!

"Number Wonders is a book that will satisfy the most demanding minds. An excellent resource for teachers wishing to interact with their classroom on an educational but laid back manner..."
Family Review Center

$16.95

State Debate: Book & Card Set

This is an engaging & intriguing card game about the states. But...there is more. The book that comes with the 50 fact-filled state cards has instructions and rules for **49** MORE games!!! There are reasoning games, trivia games, math games, matching games, and spelling games! Good for ages 8 on up. State Debate makes a great family, home, or travel game, plus it works perfectly in a classroom setting, too. It's a GREAT value!

Card sets can be purchased separately.

....

* ***National Parenting Seal of Approval Award Winner***

$16.95 Cards Only = $6.95

Dreams, Screams, & JellyBeans

Thoughtful, wild, & silly verse, created by a Middle School teacher and illustrated by a kindergarten teacher, will have young and old entertained for hours! There's a poem for every occasion.

$9.95

ShanJari

WINNER of the '**Parents' Choice Gold Award**' '**Children's Magazine Excellence Award**' and the '**Parent's Guide to Media Award**'. This award winning game is full of intriguing fun, is endlessly challenging, and a must for all game-loving families.

'The rules are so simple and the strategy so open ended, that this game should earn a permanent place in the family's game collection.'

Ruth B Roufberg
Parent's Choice Foundation
Game Analyst

$24.95

Frazzle!

Want to get loud? Want to get crazy? This award-winning word game will have players screaming with delight as they compete to be the first to find a winning word! A great adult party game, but watch out….the kids like to snatch it and play too!

Games 100 Award Winner

$19.95

Purchasing

Please ask your local book, toy, game, or educational store for our products. There are also many online retailers that carry them. Please call or email us if you are having trouble finding our products or would like to place an order. We appreciate your interest and would be happy to assist you with any further questions that you may have.

MissingPiecePress.com
Questions@MissingPiecePress.com
Ph. 253-813-2303
Toll Free 1-877-56-THINK! (84465)

"Minds are like parachutes – they only function when open!"

\- *Thomas Dewey*

MissingPiecePress.com
Questions@MissingPiecePress.com
Ph. 253-813-2303
Toll Free 1-877-56-THINK! (84465)

MissingPiecePress.com
Questions@MissingPiecePress.com
Ph. 253-813-2303
Toll Free 1-877-56-THINK! (84465)